MAGIC FIRE

RICHARD WAGNER

Magic Fire

SCENES AROUND RICHARD WAGNER

by

BERTITA HARDING

THE BOBBS-MERRILL COMPANY • INC.

INDIANAPOLIS   *Publishers*   NEW YORK

First Edition

To

CHARLOTTE AND WILLIAM DIETERLE

*whose wide knowledge
of theater gave dramatic
shape to this work. . . .*

*"He gave so much—dear God, how much!
—to the world."*—Rosalind Ivan

FOREWORD

SERIOUS scholars will be able to list, triumphantly, a thousand
facets in the career of Richard Wagner which have been left
out of this book. Readers unwilling to do without the fullest
possible detail are earnestly referred to the voluminous Wagner literature and the composer's own *Mein Leben (My Life)*
which lie piled up and sadly unread on the world's library
shelves.

BERTITA HARDING

CONTENTS

LIST OF ILLUSTRATIONS

PART I

Minna

CHAPTER 1

THE year 1812 was pregnant with adventure and calamity that would ravage the map of Europe and splash its history with lurid colors. It was the prologue year of the great Napoleonic setbacks.

Life had moved steadily forward and upward for the obscure Corsican artillery corporal who had risen to Emperor of the French and conqueror of a continent. Holland, Italy, Egypt, Austria, Germany, Spain and a part of Portugal had fallen successively before him. He had married a general's widow, divorced her and taken to wife a Hapsburg archduchess who bore him a longed-for son. And he was now setting out at the head of an army of 600,000 men to climax his career with one final triumph—the invasion of Russia. No sibyl was at hand to inform him that, with this bold and foolhardy step, the turning point in his fortunes would begin.

No one in Europe knew very much about Russians or their tactics of warfare. As the confident Bonaparte pushed across the Elbe, Vistula and Niemen rivers, he saw no reason for alarm. Subdued Germans and Poles could not hinder his progress, while, once on Muscovite soil, the French invaders looked in vain for a chance to prove their mettle. They were in full battle dress, bristling with arms and ammunition, but nowhere did an opposing Cossack show his face. Quietly, tantalizingly, the Russian "horde" rolled back, sucking the unbidden visitors ever deeper into a yawning trap.

On June 24 Napoleon entered Vilna, which was evacuated simultaneously by its obliging garrison. Proudly he moved on over damaged roads, abandoned villages, burned fields, unaware of the grim significance of "scorched earth" both in the event of prolonged occupation and sudden retreat. With great fanfare he took Moscow on September 14, or believed he did. Actually the trap was at last ready to be sprung. Seemingly defenseless, the ancient city had been carefully prepared with hundreds of concealed fagots that awaited a secret signal. Once the French troops joyously laid down their packs and settled themselves for a night of long-missed urban comforts, the invisible enemy came to life. Simultaneously, all over town, the incendiary fires sprang up into a ghastly conflagration. By dawn only the shell of a once resplendent capital was left.

Napoleon's talents did not include a proper grasp of fire fighting. His armies carried muskets and cannon, but no sprinklers, pumping gear or hose. And, in any case, the Russians had seen to it that Moscow was without water; both banks of the Moskva River were a solid wall of flame.

For four days the French battalions struggled to stave off disaster. Their food stores, clothes and equipment burned, they dug through the smoldering ruins for living quarters and provender. In a ghostlike city they hung on like ghosts, awaiting a decision from their fearfully perplexed commander. While they waited, nature joined forces against them in the form of an early Russian winter.

On October 18, 1812, Napoleon began his retreat from Moscow. He plowed through the white-blanketed steppes that were like silent seas of snow, and the loss of his legions—reduced to a ragtag band of 120,000 starved and freezing men— taught him the meaning of that undefeatable Asiatic strategy: scorched earth. Nowhere along that horrible return route was there a tree stump or brush for the building of campfires, nor a cattle barn, goatpen, pigsty, grain bin or potato patch to furnish sustenance for ravenous bellies that grew bloated with hunger toxins.

Christmas of that bitter year saw the last straggling legionaires of the *Grande Armée* limping through Germany. A fifteen-year-old poet, Heinrich Heine, witnessed their passing and enshrined it in his verses *"Die Beiden Grenadiere"* ("The Two Grenadiers"). But it was not yet the end. The Bonaparte dream was still a long time dying, as, after a short rest in Paris, Napoleon decided on a second Russian campaign to wipe out the shameful defeat. He raised new levies in France and her conquered territories, particularly in Saxony and Prussia.

The busy industrial city of Leipzig was a favorite recruiting target, as its educational institutions and factories attracted bright and brawny young men from provincial towns and farms. Daily the Leipzig chief of police was pressed by French occupation authorities for information regarding reluctant youths whose unquestioned physical fitness was equalled only by their aptitude for wriggling past military dragnets.

"We'll have to do better," confided the *Polizei-Rat* to his underpaid assistant, "or there will be sanctions imposed on all of Saxony!"

The assistant, Karl Friedrich Wilhelm Wagner, hardly knew what to answer. He was himself concealing a young man in his house, an aspiring actor named Ludwig Heinrich Christian Geyer. Humanitarian considerations were not the only reason for sheltering a reluctant draft candidate: Geyer helped pay his benefactor's rent.

This was no small factor in the Wagner household, with six growing children and a seventh on the way. Actually there had been eight little Wagners: Albert, Rosalie, Julius, Luise, Klara, Ottilie, and the two who died in babyhood, Gustav and Therese. Frau Johanna's current pregnancy was therefore her ninth and, like the Napoleonic era attending it, big in portent.

On the afternoon of May 22, 1813, familiar preparations were afoot at the rooming house of the "Red and White Lion," located on Brühl Street (Auf Dem Brühl). Two flights up, in the Wagner flat, a midwife had put water on to boil, while Papa Wagner rounded up his noisy brood for a walk in the park.

"I'll take them off your hands," Geyer proposed. "There's a Punch-and-Judy show, left over from the Easter Fair."

It was a good suggestion, gratefully accepted. With the lively sextet out of the way, the ordeal at home could follow its course under a minimum of clatter and confusion. By seven that night, when the puppet show was over, the children returned to find a new infant brother in the well-worn cradle. Two days later, at the Evangelical Church of St. Thomas, the baby was baptized with the names of Wilhelm Richard, of which only the second would ever be used.

Papa Wagner's joy was mingled with economic worries. Another mouth to feed in these times of political unrest and high prices! More than ever the loyalty and freehanded help of Geyer was appreciated; filling occasional engagements in the provinces, the actor contributed not only his rent but many a trussed duck or fine sausage for the family larder. Without his help, medical bills and even the most urgent daily necessities would certainly have gone upaid.

The second Bonaparte campaign against Russia had meanwhile gained momentum. New legions, less confident and eager this time, plodded across Europe by late summer, picking up forced levies as they went. But a will to revolt had sprouted among the conquered nations. Austrians and Prussians in particular took courage from the previous year's Moscow debacle, which had disclosed Napoleon as no superman but only a badly beaten general on the run. Surely what had happened once could be made to happen again! Fiercely the rebel elements girded themselves for effective opposition. And now, having displayed their reawakened grit, they found support from rallying allies. Sweden and Russia quickly joined in a pact to meet the French steamroller head on and put an end to Bonaparte vainglory.

The site chosen for battle turned out to be Leipzig, and the date was October 16 through 18, 1813. Napoleon numbered some 400,000 motley conscripts, while the Allies—under the fiery leadership of Sweden's Bernadotte, Austria's Schwarzenberg, Prussia's Blücher and Russia's handsome Emperor Alexander I—commanded half a million fervent volunteers who saw theirs as a holy cause.

The *Völkerschlacht*, or Battle of Nations, echoed around the world, heralding the finish of the Bonaparte legend. On horseback, hatless, Napoleon galloped through Leipzig's rubble-strewn streets, followed by a remnant of his army in full rout. Behind a curtained window the older Wagner children and their parents beheld the mighty warrior's flight. For Napoleon there remained Elba, a further trouncing by Wellington at

Waterloo and the final eclipse on lonely St. Helena. For Europe came the burials, the binding of wounds, the sorting of debris, the rebuilding of ruins and the general sweeping-up that is called peace.

It was a process that, long after war's close, continued taking its toll of casualties. Too many dead horses and men awaited removal from city streets and outlying districts. Before the task was halfway accomplished a pestilence broke out, ravaging the civilian population. One of the first to be struck down, on November 22, was Johanna Wagner's husband, exactly six months after the baby Richard's birth.

For the young widow this was disaster indeed. Apart from her personal sorrow, she faced the added loss of the family's financial mainstay—the paying roomer. No longer could the bachelor, Ludwig Geyer, continue under the same roof without causing neighbors' tongues to wag. His departure, on the other hand, meant that Johanna must seek smaller quarters so as to cut down on rent. She made the choice, stretching her small widow's pension as far as it would go and doing seamstress chores to eke out the budget.

The children grieved for their dead father, but it was Geyer whom they truly missed. At forty-three, Papa Wagner had represented adult authority, while the much younger *Onkel Ludwig* was their idolized playmate and friend. What games Geyer knew, what tales of wonder and adventure he could tell! Johanna would have found it difficult to fill the void left by the children's adored companion. As it happened, she never tried. She was simply too overworked and too tired.

Geyer, to be sure, remained in touch with his young friends. He joined a touring company which played a theatrical circuit extending through Saxony, Bavaria and the Rhineland, but periodically he returned to Leipzig and looked in on Johanna and her brood. These visits, one or two months apart, became highlights in the family's otherwise drab existence. With shining eyes the children, and Johanna too, heard about *Onkel Ludwig's* latest stage roles: Hamlet, Macbeth, Iago, of one William Shakespeare. Also Goethe's Duke of Alba (in *Egmont*), Friedrich von Schiller's Don Carlos, or any one of the leading male parts in *Kabale Und Liebe.* In addition, he disclosed himself now as a budding playwright, sketching the plots for two comedies, *The Girl From Afar* and *Harvest Festival,* as well as a Biblical drama entitled *The Slaughter of the Innocents.*

All this, of course, did not affect the baby Richard in his cradle. Placidly gurgling or sleeping away the hours, the youngest Wagner nestling lived through the portentous first year of his existence as untouched by its personal and historic impact as any sprouting vegetable. The thunder of Napoleonic cannon faded out unheard, just as for him a father's love must be counted lost without having ever been consciously possessed. The whole climactic year 1813, marking a crisis and a turning point in modern civilization, was to the newborn infant nothing more than a cycle of feedings and other animal functions as monotonously comforting as they are biologically timeless.

Contemporaneously, in an obscure provincial hamlet called Bayreuth, a graying man of letters expounded some ideas on musical and literary criticism. He was the Franconian novelist Jean Paul Richter, and the essence of his analytical plaint ran: "Up into our era Apollo has bestowed the gift of poetic invention with his right hand, and that of melody with his left, to widely disparate individuals. We still await the artist in whom these godlike endowments are *combined.* ..."

Finally, the same clamorous and resounding year of 1813 chronicled another noteworthy birth—in Italy—of a lad in penurious circumstance. At Roncole, Duchy of Parma, a peasant couple named Verdi forgot the burdens of national vassalage under the same Napoleon who had been the scourge of Leipzig. Was there time to argue about high taxes and attendant vicissitudes when one could look with joy on a bouncing, blackhaired, small Giuseppe? ...

CHAPTER 2

A YEAR after her husband's death Johanna Wagner gave prying neighbors something to talk about. She accepted Ludwig Geyer's offer of marriage. Already, for some months past, there had been whispers and raised eyebrows regarding the young man's frequent calls, his uncommon good looks and the shocking nature of his profession. It was a day when theatrical artists might be applauded extravagantly behind the footlights, yet must count on being snubbed in drawing rooms of both an elite and a middle-class society. Stage people were simply a breed apart.

Gossip did not subside when, with scandalous promptness (six months, to be exact), a baby daughter, Cecilie Geyer, was born. With little Richard still a toddler who could have no memory whatever of his own father, wagging tongues indulged in cynical arithmetic. Richard Geyer, they began calling the lad, pointing out the gap in years between him and the older children. What looked like sudden romance between the widowed Johanna and her new groom had been a long time brewing! The gossips, at least, would not have it otherwise.

Additional tattle concerned itself with the proposition that Ludwig was a Jew. The cognomen Geyer meant Hawk. Descriptive names, particularly those involving towns, animals and flowers, were greatly preferred in German-Jewish circles. But research extending as far back as 1700, by Otto Bournot for his book *The Step-Father of Richard Wagner*, discloses an unbroken line of Protestant Geyers, many of whom served as organists in evangelical churches but could be linked in no manner to a synagogue. This does not, of course, preclude a possibility that prior to 1700 there is evidence of Semitic origin.

However, if so, the strain and genes still surviving in Ludwig must have been faint indeed.

For Johanna and the children this matter had no importance whatever. They all loved Geyer for his greatness of heart, his goodness, his gaiety and charm and the extraordinary brilliance of his mind. Now that he was head of the household these intellectual gifts in particular came into bolder relief. Not only was Geyer a promising actor and playwright, but he proved a singer and portrait painter as well. And he was a born teacher. Within a few months of becoming their new parent he was training the older children in voice culture, recitation and stagecraft. In no time Albert, Rosalie and Klara were inspired to take up theatrical careers, first in child roles, then as full-fledged adult thespians.

Richard was too young to reap the full benefit of his stepfather's wise tutelage. By the time the boy was eight years old and capable of responding to artistic guidance, Ludwig Geyer's incandescent nature had burned itself out. The tireless trouper returned from one of his acting tours flushed with fever. Pleurisy developed, then pneumonia, against which medical resources of that day could not prevail.

The children hovered in an adjoining room, ready for a call from the sick man who had their fierce devotion. Strangely, in his dying hours, Ludwig had the boy Richard on his mind. He had not given this lad enough of himself. Was it too late now?

"I think Richard has musical talent," Geyer gasped with labored breath to Johanna. "Let him play something for me on the piano."

Up to that moment Richard had never received an hour's instruction in harmony or instrumental techniques. But he had heard his stepfather sing popular tunes, as well as light arias from his operatic idol, Karl Maria von Weber. With no difficulty at all the boy made it a habit to pick out such melodies on the old square piano that filled one end of the family's cramped living room.

At Geyer's request Richard now rushed to the keyboard and promptly drummed out a little folk song: *"Üb' immer Treu' und Redlichkeit . . ."* ("Forever practice loyalty and truth . . ."). This behind him, with matter-of-fact thoroughness and dispatch he plunged into the bridal number from *Der Freischütz: "Wir winden Dir den Jungfernkranz aus veilchenblauer Seide . . ."* ("We weave for thee a maiden's wreath of violet-blue silk . . .").

Ludwig Geyer listened from his bed. Here was no child prodigy, or *Wunderkind,* no budding virtuoso. Mozart, at six, had concertized all over Europe, playing his own compositions, while currently a ten-year-old Hungarian lad named Liszt was the pianistic sensation of the day. No, Richard's painstaking and determined thumpings hardly gave promise of similar prowess. He would make no performer. Still, there was something . . .

"I don't know what it is," Geyer was heard to murmur almost in a whisper, "I don't know—but his place, his whole life, will be music. . . ." These were the last words Johanna caught from the expiring lips.

In the immediate future this prophecy fell rather short of realization. A brother of the generous Ludwig Geyer offered to take the younger children under his wing until Johanna was economically adjusted to a second widowhood. Thus Richard lived for a time at the "uncle's" home in Eisleben, and thence was sent to the Kreutz School in Dresden. Shakespeare held an astonishing prominence in the study plan for minor children in the Germany of that day. At the age of ten Richard was conversant with the British dramatist's greatest tragedies, though his mind lacked the maturity to grasp more than surface plot and bloodcurdling action. Indeed, a year later the boy tackled a drama of his own, freely based on a blend of *Hamlet* and *King Lear,* with plagiarized tidbits from lesser shockers in the Bard's pen. No fewer than forty-two characters were done to death in this first Wagner opus, a toll that handicapped matters as the action progressed since, presently, there were not enough living people around to wind up the tale. Richard was forced to bring back an array of ghosts from the Beyond for further dealings with his few survivors, or there would have been no second or third act. In all, he spent two years laboring on this masterpiece, then cast it aside because he could not think of a fittingly grandiose title.

In 1827, as the older children had one by one become self-supporting, Johanna summoned Richard back to Leipzig. He now was enrolled, successively, in the Nikolai and Thomas schools, both of which counted music among curricular requirements. Students attended concerts in the famous Gewandhaus, where Richard now heard Mozart's *Requiem* and the Beethoven score to Goethe's *Egmont*. Instantly, with adolescent *élan*, he caught fire and decided on a composer's career. There was no other instrument available save Johanna's old square piano, hence this must be his medium. The question of music-writing technique appeared negligible: after you thought up a melody, all that was needed would be a bass that went *oom*pah, *oom*pah. Richard borrowed a textbook by Johann Bernhard Logier, entitled *Practical Thoroughbass*, which seemed to cover the subject. Promptly thereafter he composed a sonata, a quartet for strings (of which he had not the faintest idea) and an aria. Each of these efforts used up much paper and amounted to exactly nothing.

When he was sixteen Richard underwent a tremendous experience. He saw the glorious Wilhelmine Schröder-Devrient starring in Beethoven's *Fidelio*, a vocal performance justly renowned in musical annals. Given the special susceptibility of his years, it is difficult to ascertain whether Madame Schröder-Devrient's rare artistry or her luscious beauty made the deeper impression on young Wagner. Certain it is that, after the final curtain, he raced to the home of a fellow student where, on borrowed stationery, he addressed himself to the goddess in an uneven, albeit bold, schoolboy script:

Today my life has acquired meaning. . . . Should you ever hear my name honorably pronounced in the world of the arts, be assured and reminded that this evening you have made of me what, herewith, I swear to become!

Beyond a doubt the singer found both scrawl and syntax somewhat obscure. At all events, though Richard carried the letter in person to her hotel, he received no reply.

This in no wise cooled his ardor, for he now plunged into the writing of an overture for full orchestra which might crowd

Beethoven's Ninth Symphony straight into oblivion. Technic-
ally Richard had made considerable progress under an expert
harmony teacher, Kantor Theodor Weinlig. His self-confidence
knew no bounds.

As the overture took shape a clarifying feature occurred to
him. Why not employ different colored inks to distinguish his
instrumentation? Painstakingly he carried out the idea, writing
string passages in red, brasses in black, woods in green, percussion in purple. Also, for zest and excitement there was a crash
of kettledrum and cymbals recurring with mathematical precision after every fourth measure. In fortissimo, no less.

Inexplicably, this monstrosity was accepted for a trial performance at the Leipziger Theater on December 24, 1830. During the playing of it Richard hovered offstage, his eyes glued
to a slit in the scenery from which he could observe the audience. At first there was a perceptible shock evinced by listeners
who no sooner tried to relax in their seats than they were
snapped upright with a jolt as drummer and cymbalist went
into action. Angry faces were turned toward the percussion
section, where skulduggery was at first suspected. Only when
it became unmistakable that the orchestra was adhering scru-
pulously to the composer's text did a wave of merriment spread
over the assemblage. Progressively, thereafter, each earsplitting detonation was greeted with soft titters, then laughter,
and finally ungovernable howls.

By the end of the First Movement there was movement in
the audience too—toward the exits.

Behind a curtain, in the wings, Richard smarted with the
pain of it. Disdainfully the conductor handed back the score
and added a sad but fitting admonition: "Take it home, my
boy, for kindling. It ought to make a snappy fire."

For the rest of that winter Richard's muse retired in a pout.
No more flights of fancy to the summits where melody and lyric
inspiration dwelled. More realistic, down-to-earth matters were
to enlist the young man's attention. Two of his sisters, Luise
and Ottilie, had married into the respected Brockhaus family,
publishers of a widely circulated encyclopedia. Ottilie's husband, Hermann Brockhaus, was inactive in the firm, as he en-

joyed a professorship in Oriental languages at the University of Leipzig. But Friedrich, wedded to Luise, carried on the business established by his namesake and father, currently launching a new edition (the ninth) of Wilhelm Adolph Becker's *World History*. In the preparation of this enterprise Richard's services had been enlisted as proofreader. For each corrected galley page he received ten groschen, a sum then equivalent to about two cents.

It was Richard's first earned cash and he derived enormous satisfaction from the task, since in addition to collecting a "wage" he soon found himself engrossed in Becker's scholarly work. A new concept of humanity, different from the lifeless parade of dust-dry schoolroom accounts, sparked his imagination. And suddenly he began to see history not merely as a recording of things past but active and urgently living in the present. In fact, he was in the midst of it. The year 1830 accounted for one of the more lurid pages in the story of mankind.

After Napoleon's death France had been ruled by the last Bourbon kings—Louis XVIII and Charles X—whose incompetence led to the "July Revolution" and a trial replacement by another dynast, Louis Philippe of Orléans. To balance himself on his shaky throne, Louis Philippe made numerous liberal concessions, including a pronouncement that his royal name was synonymous with republicanism.

Reports of these ideological changes reached Europe's more conservative and reactionary areas, particularly the loosely joined German states, each of which supported a minor princeling or sovereign at its head. Concepts of "constitutional government" began to be bruited about as youthful hotheads studied political developments in the West and aligned themselves with the new trend.

University students were the most ardent apostles of the democratic creed, and Richard Wagner, freshly steeped in Becker's analysis of Ancient Greece, counted himself eagerly among them. His patriotic activities did not amount to much. In the first blush of enthusiasm, Richard considered composing another overture—a song for revolutionaries, as it were—forming a counterpart to the rousing "Marseillaise." But the German liberal movement was as yet only in its experimental stage and had no need for marching tunes. Also, Richard's earlier musical fiasco was still a vivid memory. No self-respecting music firm would be likely to sponsor another effort from his pen, at least not very soon. In short, whatever warm and heroic sentiments he harbored in his breast on the subject of political progress, these promptings must remain dormant for some years to come. Richard contented himself with faithful attendance at student gatherings and fervent absorption of high-flown oratory, preachments and catchwords freely expounded there. "Every halfway educated and forward-looking person," he confided to his diary, "must occupy his mind with politics."

On February 23, 1831, Richard entered the University of Leipzig. He still had not decided on a future profession; but, to be on the safe side, one of his subjects remained harmony and composition. The following summer—it was the year of Goethe's death—Richard made a walking tour to Vienna and Prague, where his imagination was fed by hoary sagas, abandoned castles and chivalric lore. The dramatist in him awoke again and he sketched a hair-raising melodrama entitled *The Wedding*. It was his hope to provide this opus with an eventual music score, but on returning home he showed the manuscript to his favorite sister, Rosalie, who promptly pronounced its doom.

There was no gainsaying Rosalie's judgment, for this elder sister had already made a name for herself as an actress. Together with Albert and Klara she toured the provinces, occasionally making guest appearances in Austria and Bohemia. Yes, Rosalie knew what she was about.

On her sadly urgent advice Richard consigned his third major effort to the trash pile.

CHAPTER 3

AGAIN he realized that he did not know enough. To supplement his academic studies Richard frequented a Leipzig lending library run by Friedrich Wieck, whose thirteen-year-old daughter Clara (later the wife of Robert Schumann) ranked already as a noteworthy pianist. Herr Wieck, himself a musical pedagogue, recommended numerous tomes on harmony and composition as well as on subjects of wider cultural range. He introduced Richard to the currently discussed work of Arthur Schopenhauer, the great philosopher living in near-by Frankfurt. Thus a profound passage from *The World, Manifested in Will and Imagination* impressed itself on the young man. He brooded on it endlessly and transferred a portion of the Schopenhauer text to his journal:

Nature is engaged in a constant evolutionary process, from simple chemical action in inorganic spheres to vegetable life with its dim self-absorption—and thence to the animal kingdom, in which intelligence and consciousness dawn, rising gradually from feeble stirrings toward the last and greatest step, which is Man. Here Nature reaches the zenith and goal of her productions, the most elaborate and difficult feat of which she is capable. Yet even so, within the human species there occur notable gradations of intellect, so that a superior or *highest* intelligence is only rarely encountered. This, then, remains Nature's masterpiece, priceless and perhaps unique in the Cosmos. . . . Within such an intelligence a grasp of life's meanings can be approximated and may even be ultimately attained. Certainly the possessor of it has at his command the noblest and most precious treasure on earth, an eternal fountainhead of delight dwarfing all else, so that he

requires nothing from outer surroundings save quietude in
which to rejoice and, undisturbed, polish his diamond. . . .
For, all other, non-intellectual pleasures are of inferior category. They arise from will-promptings, in the form of hopes,
fears and cupidities which, regardless of their object, reach
no fulfillment save through pain. In addition, these wish-
demands as a rule find realization tempered by traces of
faintly bitter disappointment whereas the joys of the intellect
are unadulterated and true. The intelligence suffers no ache;
it rules by purest insight. . . .

Richard was not entirely sure that he understood all this,
particularly the matter of nonintellectual pleasures being inferior in category. At nineteen he recognized a variety of
appetites stirring within him which had not the remotest con-
nection with the mind. But the image conjured up by the
philosopher's words regarding that quietude wherein to polish
one's diamond became for him an obsession. He read the passage over and over, neglecting in the end to return the book.
Repeatedly Herr Wieck found it necessary to write crusty letters and to charge an added fee, which at times all but entitled
Richard to ownership of this and other borrowed volumes. To
a voracious reader who lacked a sense of time the respectable and low-priced circulating library could become a den of
iniquity.

Mama Wagner unquestionably found it so. She objected to
her youngest son's inroads on the slim family purse no less than
to his membership in the Saxonia Corps, a student fraternity
that mixed beer-drinking contests with gory dueling bouts.
Richard was not given to drink, but he wished to be rated a
hero and master swordsman, hence he seldom dodged any
provocation to test his prowess with a blade.

It took almost no effort in those days to find oneself summoned to a duel. A chance remark, a witty but unflattering
phrase, a depreciating glance, or no glance at all but an oversight that might be taken for a snub—all served as a prelude to
combat. This was especially true among freshly baked initi-
ates, eager to prove their mettle. As a new cap-wearing mem-

ber, Richard set up something of a record: he left his first
fraternity meeting with six jousts lined up for the following
dawn. Only the most extraordinary interplay of circumstances
saved him from meeting these staggering commitments. That
is, by morning three of his challengers had been arrested for
a gambling-table brawl, a fourth was stabbed in a previous
fencing engagement, while the remaining two appeared to
have overslept. For Richard this meant six uncontested vic-
tories without having actually crossed arms. But the anxious
night spent by his family earned him no medals. Before the
end of that semester his mother put down a firm foot. Tossing
the would-be swordsman's paraphernalia out the window, she
issued a different kind of challenge to her son: Richard must
forgo the university and find himself a job.

He did so willingly and with satisfactory results, at least
from an economic standpoint. By budgeting his time he was
able to coach several backward lyceum students and to give
evening lessons in harmony as well. But the earnings so obtained led to new temptations. Late hours and a ready opportunity for mingling with shady companions brought the youth
in touch with gambling circles, where the thought of doubling
his funds quickly took shape. For some months the anxious
family watched Richard's comings and goings, taking note of
his irregular bedtimes and indeed of the fact that some nights
he did not come home at all. But, happily, this too would pass.
Just when Mama despaired of her ungovernable boy's future,
and after Richard's favorite sister, Rosalie, would no longer
speak to him, a wholesome stroke of fate intervened. For two
straight weeks the gaming tables turned against him. He lost
at cards, dice, dominoes and roulette. Dame Fortune, it was
plain, did not choose him for her elect. Abruptly this realization dawned on him, as well as the plain mathematics involved.
With no funds to show for half a month's labors, not to mention
loss of sleep, he was promptly cured of his passion.

Redemption came too late, however, for local rehabilitation.
Word had got about of Richard's frivolous habits and the bad
company he kept. Respectable parents withdrew their offspring
from his tutelage, and even the number of his adult harmony

MINNA WAGNER   MATHILDE WESENDONK

students fell to half. Obviously he had wrecked his chances for
success at home. He must go elsewhere and make a new start.

It so chanced that his old friend and teacher, Kantor Weinlig, knew of a vacant conductor's post at the Magdeburg Opera
Company, an organization currently touring the provinces with
a summer repertoire.

"You are no orchestra conductor," said Weinlig soberly, "not
by a far stretch. But there's always a time to start. Here's a
letter to Herr Stegmayer, the company's business representative. See what you can do."

Richard hopped on a stagecoach to Magdeburg, where he
presented the Weinlig credentials to an absent-minded and
overworked impresario who, this being midsummer, had been
unable to find a nameworthy replacement and was glad to sign
anyone he could get.

"The company plays Lauchstaedt next week," Stegmayer
pressed, without bothering to check the young man's qualifications. "It's only a day's journey from here. If you hurry you
can get in a few rehearsals."

Richard hurried. Again by post chaise, he set out for the
small spa that lay nestled in the Thuringian forest and arrived
there on a hot August day of 1834. In the quaint Gothic town
square he motioned to the driver to stop. "Could you show me
the way to the Provincial Theater?"

The coachman pointed. "You are practically there, sir. Just
across the square."

The youth picked up his single piece of luggage and, with
head erect, strode along the cobbled pavement. He held himself consciously straight because he was small in build and unhappily aware of it. Yet his face could be called fair—striking
in profile and framed by wavy blond hair. His clothes were, of
course, modest, poor in cut and material, and altogether there
was about the spare figure a look of undernourishment.

Behind the theater's box-office grille an old porter could be
seen dozing. It was the hour of the *Mittags-Schläfchen,* or
afternoon nap. Richard knocked and the porter's eyelids lifted.
"Performance sold out. Box office closed." The voice trailed
off to complete an interrupted snore.

"But I don't want any tickets," the young visitor protested firmly. "I wish to see Herr Bethmann, the manager."

The porter was wide awake now, his pupils blinking suspiciously through the aperture. "Your name, sir?"

"Wagner—Richard Wagner."

"And what is it you want from the manager?" The veteran attendant was obviously unimpressed.

An eager smile spread over Richard's face. "I am the new orchestra conductor!"

The porter looked startled. He shook his head in disbelief, then shrugged his shoulders and stepped off his stool to open an adjacent door. "This way, please."

He led the way down an inner corridor, still doubtful regarding the stranger's identity. Baton wielders, everybody knew, were professorial gentlemen with ample beards and graying temples, like Herr Harsch, who had just been taken ill. But a mere boy like this, presumably a half-baked conservatory student—?

They had reached another door that opened into an unbelievably cramped and untidy office where Manager Bethmann sat at a desk piled high with programs and music scores.

"Herr Richard Wagner," announced the porter before making his retreat.

Bethmann, his nose buried in papers, gave no sign of having heard, which afforded Richard a chance to survey the scene. The so-called manager's office appeared to be part of Herr Bethmann's living quarters as well as the theater's administrative center. A partially draped opening in the opposite wall revealed another room no less crowded with domestic and theatrical appurtenances, all piled in mad confusion. Ashes and cigar stubs on saucers, used coffee cups, soiled cutlery, cake crumbs and music scores covered the nondescript furniture, in addition to a venerable accumulation of dust. Herr Bethmann himself did not look so proper either, in sloppy dressing gown and slippers, with unshaved cheeks that denoted a less than casual approach to the social niceties.

Still waiting, Richard risked a glimpse into the next chamber, where a table and sofa could be seen, in addition to a fat and frowzy female figure—obviously that of Frau Bethmann, her husband's fitting better half—moving ponderously about. On the sofa, unless the curtained light deceived him, he further distinguished a swarthy gentleman with sideburns, easily fitting the description of a typical Latin tenor (though later revealed as the company's basso profundo), whom Frau Bethmann seemed to be entertaining with an intimate *Kaffeeklatsch.*

Richard thought it time to clear his throat. "I beg your pardon," he said, addressing himself to the paper pyramid piled on the desk.

The head behind it stirred. "Who are you?"

"The new conductor, engaged by your associate, Herr Stegmayer, in Magdeburg."

Bethmann jerked forward in his chair. "Well, it's about time! I've been waiting——" He interrupted himself, jaws dropping, eyes staring in disbelief at his visitor's extreme youth. "*Who* did you say you were?"

"The substitute orchestra conductor. Herr Stegmayer sent me——"

"Bah! Stegmayer is a fool!" Bethmann exploded. "I told him to hire me an experienced musician, not a schoolboy." He had risen to pace nervously up and down the room, the dressing gown trailing behind him as he stopped by an open window where the heavy-laden branches of a cherry tree were within reach. He helped himself to some cherries, spitting the stones into space while barking his next question. "How old are you?"

The youth braced himself. "Twenty-one."

Bethmann choked on his next cherry. "Worse than I thought! An infant, that's what you are!" He winced as if in pain. "You won't do, young man. You won't do at all!"

From the adjoining room an authoritative voice became audible. "Oh, I don't know. Herr Wagner may surprise us." The curtain moved aside a few inches and Frau Bethmann appeared in full view. She studied the caller, then murmured approvingly, "Hmm. Twenty-one!"

"That's what I was saying—a greenhorn." Bethmann bowed apologetically to Richard. "Musically speaking, you understand."

Frau Bethmann brushed this comment aside. "Nonsense! We need some new blood around here." She smiled benignly at the visitor, then turned on her husband. "Besides, we have a performance scheduled for tonight and no conductor. With a sold-out house you can't just call the whole thing off."

"I wasn't intending to, my dear." The manager tried to maintain his authority. "I ordered the concertmaster to take over. He's been rehearsing the company since yesterday." He thought of Stegmayer again and groaned, clenching his fists. "When I get hold of that idiot of an agent I'll . . ."

Richard stepped forward politely. "I don't think you should speak that way about your business partner. I consider Herr Stegmayer a man of sound judgment."

Bethmann flushed, and there was sarcasm tinged with irritation in his reply. "You don't say? At twenty-one, I take it, you have very profound opinions."

"No. But I am a composer myself."

At this undaunted announcement both the Bethmanns and the basso in the next room laughed out loud. Between guffaws the manager managed to gasp, "A composer, no less! I suppose you'll be telling me next that you are writing an opera."

"Not at the moment, sir," Richard answered in dead earnest. He snapped open his travel case. "But here are two that I've already finished—*Die Feen* and *Das Liebesverbot*. The second is really much better. It's based on Shakespeare's play *Measure for Measure*. Would you like to hear it?"

Bethmann threw up his arms, then pointed to the shelf-lined walls. "Look! I've got operas by the ton, mountains of operas. What I need is *one* conductor!"

The young man nodded brightly. "I know. Why not try *me?*"

Exasperated, Bethmann beat his forehead with the flat of his hand. "You are wasting my time and your own," he cried desperately as he tossed a coin on the table. "Here's your fare back to Magdeburg. The stagecoach leaves at six. Good day."

Richard shook his head. "I don't live in Magdeburg. My home is in Leipzig."

"Leipzig, then." Bethmann picked up his coin and put down a smaller amount. "Now, get out!"

The applicant was nothing if not persistent. "You're quite sure you can't use me?" he wanted to reascertain. "I mean, what can you lose?"

"My job and my reputation!" Bethmann roared, his patience plainly at an end. He was about to show Richard the door when rapid footsteps approached from the corridor and a rotund gentleman with thick eyeglasses bounced across the threshold. He was stage director Schmale, and with him the chill air of high tragedy blew into the room.

"It's happened," called Schmale, shaking the few remaining wisps of hair that graced his polished pate. "It's happened, just as I said it would—and we might just as well pack and leave town right now!"

Frau Bethmann, who had retired again to her private domain, lifted the curtain. "Don't be so dramatic, Schmale. Sit down and have some coffee. There! Now, what is it that's happened? Did your landlady catch you again smuggling in your dog?"

Schmale accepted the proffered cup with thanks, then made vigorous denials. "Oh, no. My Mops, he's a clever little beast. He waits outside till the whole house is dark before he comes scratching at my window. Then, one flip and he's in my bed."

Richard's eyes glistened sympathetically. The name *Mops* went with pug dogs as automatically as did *Jock* with a Scotch terrier. "You have a pug dog?" he asked the animal-loving little man.

Schmale beamed. "Yes, and an exceptionally intelligent one. Why—would you believe it?—he knows opera. He barks to Weber's *Freischütz* in rhythm!"

Beyond doubt other canine accomplishments would have come under discussion had not Bethmann pounded his desk at this point. "Let's not get sidetracked, Schmale, with a recitation of your beast's virtues," he commanded. "What was it you came tearing in here about?"

Schmale bethought himself, his face darkening with gloom.

"You won't like this, Herr Bethmann. That concertmaster in whom you put so much faith—he won't do. Half the orchestra has walked out on him."

"What!"

"He doesn't study his scores, he uses the wrong tempi—in short, the third drummer could do as well or better on the podium."

Bethmann jumped to his feet. "But that's impossible! Do you realize, man, that the curtain must go up on *Don Giovanni* tonight or we are ruined?" Beating his fists together, he stared disconsolately into space.

At this point young Wagner, who had delayed his exit as long as he dared, stepped forward. "I know the score of *Don Giovanni*," he said quietly.

The words struck like a cannon charge. In a body, Schmale, the Bethmanns and the Italian basso (who spoke enough German to grasp that something vital was afoot) surrounded the youth.

"Wonderful!" cried Schmale. Then, with less assurance, he noticed the lad's beardless face. "Who is this boy? What is his name?"

Bethmann did not bother with introductions. "Take him backstage," he urged breathlessly. "Put him to work. There's no time to lose!" Then, turning to Richard, he added wryly, "You may be a genius, at that." An edge crept into his voice. "For your own sake, and mine, you'd better be."

CHAPTER 4

BEFORE leading the new conductor to the practice hall at the back of the theater, Schmale took him to an upstairs office that lay directly above the Bethmann rooms. An upper branch of the same cherry tree which Richard had observed earlier bobbed invitingly outside the window, a circumstance of which Herr Schmale made full use. While taking down data regarding the young man's personal history the stage director paused intermittently to harvest a mouthful of succulent fruit, spitting out pits with no less virtuosity than did his colleague below.

"The matter of salary," said Herr Schmale, "is not handled by my department. I assume you have talked with Herr Bethmann about that?"

Richard had not, but he nodded all the same.

"Good." Schmale closed his files and pointed the way downstairs. "Let's get to work."

They wandered down a passage crammed with trunks, costume racks and stage props and came at last to a door marked ORCHESTRA, behind which pandemonium appeared to have broken loose. Gingerly, Schmale opened a crack and peered inside. But he withdrew his head almost instantly as the door flew open and a frantic figure rushed past, broken baton in hand.

"Ah," Herr Schmale observed needlessly, "there goes the concertmaster. Well, my lad, good luck!" With this he pushed his companion gently inside while withdrawing himself from the scene of battle.

Richard stood alone, confronted by a grumbling, stamping and gesticulating pack of musicians. For what seemed an eternity no one took the slightest notice of him. He did not mind. Quietly he waited in the shadows for the turmoil to calm down before he stepped onto the podium. Once there— he had never done this before in his life—he raised his hands in a sweeping command.

"Gentlemen, Prologue, Act I, of *Don Giovanni,* please."

He had no score before him and was by no means sure of minor nuances in the Mozart text. But his training at Leipzig's illustrious Conservatory had been sound; it stood him now in good stead. He knew the sequence of the opera, its high spots, its major breaks. For the rest, his own nerve and youthful self-confidence must see him through.

Miraculously, that was just what happened. After only a moment of confusion, during which the baffled orchestra members looked at one another in bewilderment and doubt, individual instruments were lifted and held poised for action. Almost imperceptibly the ensemble, disrupted and chaotic a few minutes earlier, sensed that it faced a leader.

In the theater wings Bethmann and Schmale listened and exchanged delighted nods. They knew they had a winner through whom the Lauchstaedt engagement was saved.

Two hours later the rehearsal ended and Richard again found himself in the manager's office. This time he was offered a chair.

"Young man," said Bethmann, for once forgetful of the bobbing cherry branches, "that was very fine, very fine indeed!"

"Thank you, sir."

"Now regarding your pay . . . " He paused to clear his throat, then pursed his lips in grave meditation. "You realize that for a post such as this you are definitely underage. We can regard you only as a substitute conductor, at half salary."

"I understand."

Bethmann relaxed in obvious relief. "Excellent!" The subject of money was readily dismissed. "Are you all set for lodgings?"

"Not yet."

"Nothing better around here than Frau Danner's rooming house, just back of the theater. Cheap but clean. Caters to show people. All but the top stars in our company stay there."

"Thanks."

Richard rose to depart. He needed a rest and a chance to clean up before the evening's performance, which loomed ahead as a frightening test. Carrying his small valise, he followed Bethmann's directions.

Frau Danner's rooming house was a gabled baroque structure identified by a gilt cherub suspended over the door, with a swinging sign that read ZUM GOLDENEN ENGEL. Frau Danner herself presided in well-corseted dignity over the reception desk at which the newcomer made known his wishes.

"A room? But certainly. We have just the right thing, on the top floor, with a view over the Thuringian forest. Follow me, please."

Jangling a bunch of keys, she led the way up narrow stairs to what seemed interminable heights, stopping at length before a stiflingly hot and cramped garret chamber through which daylight filtered from an infinitesimal dormer window. The promised view of the forest of Thuringia reduced itself to a patch of greenish outline beyond row upon row of slate-covered roofs.

"Our last available space," Frau Danner purred, "and only one gulden per week. Will you be moving in today?"

Richard gulped, feeling the wet band of his shirt collar. He visualized himself asphyxiating in the closeness of that dingy attic chamber, which no economic consideration could persuade him to accept. But the landlady had fixed a gimlet eye on him, which froze his words of protest and caused him instead to seek an evasive phrase. After all, she need not be told that he was in town to stay.

"I must check my travel schedule," he murmured. "The next stagecoach to Dresden——"

"The next stagecoach to Dresden leaves the day after tomorrow," Frau Danner said helpfully.

"All the same, my plans are somewhat uncertain."

He managed to steer himself downstairs again, followed by the nettled landlady who obviously could make no sense out of so vague and irresolute a traveler. Back in the lobby, she replaced her key ring on its customary hook, responding to the visitor's farewell with a curt nod.

At this point it happened.

As Richard hastened through the front entrance, he observed that part of the "Golden Angel's" ground floor had been let to a pastry and confectioner's firm, just under the sign of the gilt figurine. Inside this shop, pointing daintily at a selection of *petits fours,* stood a pretty young creature whose brown locks and frilly dress were made to captivate even the most casual and jaded eye.

Richard's was neither. As he watched, entranced, through the shop window, the lady in question finished her purchases and emerged into the street. In full daylight she was even more enchanting than he had at first supposed. The dimpled cheeks, the full and sweetly shaped mouth, the retroussé nose, the sparkling eyes, the tantalizingly rounded figure—all combined to leave him stricken with delight. Before he could recover from the happy shock, however, the vision vanished. It disappeared straight through the front door of Frau Danner's hostelry.

Losing no time, Richard retraced his steps. Inside the lobby he managed to catch sight of the last flipping ruffle of a crisp tarlatan skirt and of a feather boa above it, as the unknown damsel turned the first landing of the stairs.

Ah, she was not just a caller but obviously a resident here; that much seemed clear. But what was her name? He considered inquiring at the desk, yet, at sight of Frau Danner's unsmiling countenance, thought better of it.

"I've come to a decision," he addressed the landlady, manfully mastering his excitement. "Er . . . about that room—I'll take it."

The sharp eyes measured him anew. Then, business being business, Frau Danner handed him the register and pen. While he signed she detached a key from the jangling brass ring. "Number nineteen, *mein Herr.* Here you are." Her eyes narrowed. "You remember the way?"

"Oh, yes!"

She watched him hasten up the stairs, two steps at a time. A smirk of understanding twitched across her dry lips.

As for Richard's rapid ascent, it culminated in disillusion, for his dream vision was nowhere to be found. On tiptoes he retraced his steps down to the first landing above the lobby, where he made sure of remaining out of Frau Danner's sight. But spy as he might, the object of his quest had vanished beyond call.

Dejectedly he crawled back under the eaves and threw himself on the narrow cot that passed for a bed. A second later he was up again, unpacking his meager belongings. Regretfully he noted the wrinkles in his best suit. Perhaps the sticky summer air that filled the room was good for something after all; it might smooth out his coat and breeches. One thing was certain: on the salary offered by Bethmann, Richard could not afford the services of a tailor.

Mildly irked by these reflections, he dropped back on the pillows and closed his eyes. A half-hour's slumber refreshed him. He awoke with a clear head and a more rational appraisal of his situation. What, after all, was eating him? He was a budding composer, with a job—however tentative!—on the side, and he lived in a garret cubbyhole atop a house that harbored somewhere in its dark recesses a slim and ravishingly attractive young woman. Well, her tracks were bound to cross his, tomorrow if not today. Meanwhile it was true that he could not count a soul in town his friend, yet he felt anything but friendless. No one wedded to art, as was he to music, could ever be truly forsaken. *Don Giovanni* played tonight under his baton at the Provincial Theater. His spirits took a bounding leap. Could anyone be downcast who had Mozart for a friend?

An hour before curtaintime he was dressed and impatient to be off. A walk through the broad Kurpark Avenue would do him good, besides shortening the way to the theater. He wanted to be in the pit well ahead of the others so as to get his bearings. Again taking two steps at a time, Richard sped downstairs. From her desk Frau Danner saw him pass like a streak. She saw also the collision outside her front door, where a small dog was romping on the sidewalk. To avoid stumbling over the animal, Richard leaped aside and all but knocked down a passer-by loaded with bundles. On recovering his balance, he recognized the young woman of the candy shop. She was fighting mad.

"You clumsy peasant!" she cried in fury. "Look what you've done!"

He looked. A hatbox lay open in the street, its beribboned contents spilling forth, while sundry smaller parcels were scattered near by.

"Oh, I am so sorry!" He doffed his hat, then stopped to retrieve the articles, at the same time pausing to pat the frisky pup who had been the cause of it all. "There, there, little fellow."

The young woman stamped her foot indignantly. "Well! I should think that *I* deserve your apologies, rather than a stray dog!"

Richard flushed with confusion. "Yes, of course. Please believe me, I am very sorry."

Their eyes met. There was a pause during which each appraised the other, seemingly with some pleasure. Richard had picked up the damaged hatbox and managed to replace its lid.

"Permit me." He offered to carry it. "I hope the bonnet is in better shape than the box. Have you far to go?"

"No." She relented enough to accord him a faint smile. "But you—are you always in such a hurry to smash into other people?"

He shook his head. "As a matter of fact, I'm in no hurry at all. I'm much too early for the theater."

"The theater?"

He bowed. "Allow me to introduce myself. I am the new conductor, Richard Wagner."

It was her turn to flush. "Oh," she gasped, dropping a curtsy, "I've already heard about you, Herr Wagner."

"You have?"

"The musicians—they all live at Frau Danner's—they've

talked the whole afternoon about the rehearsal. They think you're wonderful!"

Richard was less interested at the moment in what went on in the minds of the orchestra members. He wanted to know the pretty stranger's name. "You are at Frau Danner's too, I believe," he prodded gently. "You also belong . . . er . . . to the theater?"

"Yes, in a way."

"In a way? What does that mean?"

"Well, I'm no opera singer."

He laughed. "I can see that at a glance. You don't look like a hippopotamus." He stepped closer. "In fact, you're very lovely. But you still haven't told me your name."

"Wilhelmine Planer. They call me Minna for short."

"They?"

"The other actors. You see, I belong to the Magdeburg Company's theater troupe. One week there's opera, the next a straight play." Her lashes fluttered modestly. "I've just done bit parts so far. But Herr Schmale says I'm soon to have the second lead."

Richard was delighted. "An actress! That means we're colleagues, in a way, and shall be seeing a lot of each other."

She smiled noncommittally, then headed for the inn. "I must go now." There was a roguish twinkle in her eye. "I'm sure we'll run into each other again some time."

He sprang to the door and held it open, allowing her to pass. In the narrow space her bright curls brushed against his face, while the mauled hatbox and parcels were crushed still further.

This latter fact was something neither of them noticed.

CHAPTER 5

I N AN ERA that had barely begun outgrowing candlelight,
the Magdeburg Company was considered highly progressive. It employed oil footlights, trimmed at curtaintime by
a liveried attendant, thus offering evening performances when
most theaters played only afternoons.

Richard had allowed himself more than an hour to spare on
leaving his chamber, but the encounter with Fräulein Planer
and her parcels must have taken longer than he realized. As
he now entered the stage door the lamplighter had already
completed his chore and the theater was packed with a Bieder-
meier-dressed audience.

A nervous Bethmann chewed his nails outside the orchestra
pit. "This won't do, young man," he blustered excitedly. "It
won't do at all! You'll have to be more punctual."

"Yes, Herr Bethmann." Abashed, Richard improvised a lame
excuse. "I walked through the park and misjudged the distance."

"All right, all right. Get started with the overture!"

A second later Richard had mounted the podium and signaled the orchestra to attention. Before the first bars of music
opened, a gasp rippled through the audience, indicative of
general surprise—and some skepticism—at sight of the conductor's youth. Some measures farther on the doubtful tension
relaxed, as eyebrows rose appreciatively. Then, at the height
of the richly melodious prologue, the listeners sat up, electri-
fied. He had them now, he knew it. He had them in the palm
of his untried but altogether sure hand. And now the curtain
parted on the First Act. . . .

Outside in the foyer, Frau Bethmann sat in the box office,
checking the accounts. She had just finished adding up a col-

umn of figures when her husband stuck his round head through
the door.

"Well, Rosina?" he queried. "How much did we make?"

Frau Bethmann answered without interrupting her pencil
work. "Plenty. Only a few soreheads objected to the program
change and turned back their tickets."

Bethmann beamed. "That boy saved our necks." He opened
the cubicle door a fraction. "Just listen!"

A wave of music could be heard, followed presently by a
wild burst of applause. Frau Bethmann nodded approvingly.
"Good. Good."

"Is that all you can say?" her spouse challenged. "It's wonderful! Tremendous!" He rubbed his hands and licked his
lips in delighted anticipation. "I was thinking, Mama, such
success calls for a celebration. I could take maybe some cash,
eh? Champagne for the whole company?"

She rewarded him with a stony stare, daring him to touch
the money box.

His exuberance wilted somewhat. "Well, maybe not for the
chorus. But Herr Wagner and the principal singers—how about
them?"

Frau Bethmann's expression did not change.

"It doesn't have to be champagne, Mama. A round of nice
schnapps, domestic, will do."

By now his wife's formidable gaze had reduced Bethmann
to his true henpecked size. He said no more as she lifted the
lid of the till and from it took a tiny snap purse, which she
opened. With extended index finger and thumb she extracted
one lone coin. She waved it before his nose. "Here. This is
for you, Papa. The singers and musicians, they get their pay,
no?" She surrendered the copper. "Go buy yourself one beer.
And sip it, Papa, sip it! That way you make it last all evening."

Crestfallen, Bethmann accepted the donation, then turned
to slink away.

In the lobby he was met head on by an avalanche of people
pouring forth for the first intermission. Their voices resounded
with enthusiasm, even jubilation. There was no doubt about
it: the Magdeburg Opera Company was chalking up a triumph

with its initial performance of *Don Giovanni* at Lauchstaedt's Provincial Theater.

It was the same after the next act and on through the final curtain. Hovering amid the crowd, Bethmann listened with growing joy to the praise heaped unstintingly on the substitute conductor. A mere schoolboy, people called the fair-haired slender lad who summoned up such ardor and authority in handling Mozart. Others stepped up and congratulated Bethmann on pumping fresh blood into his moribund organization, for the Magdeburg troupe—despite its progressive spirit—had tottered for years under the threat of bankruptcy, all because of a superannuated orchestral setup. With the acquisition of so promising a talent as this young unknown Wagner, the organization's future was assured.

No one knew this better than Bethmann himself. His main concern now was to hold onto the gifted youth who had proved such a find. Directly after the performance he summoned Richard to his office.

"I owe you an apology, my lad," he opened uneasily. "When you came to us earlier today, I . . . er . . . did not at once recognize your capabilities."

Richard raised a protesting hand as, for a moment, the blood left his cheeks. He realized only too keenly how well founded the manager's doubts had been, since, except for a few Leipzig Conservatory tryouts with student musicians, he had never conducted an orchestra. The fact that the *Don Giovanni* score happened to be etched in his mind was sheer luck. It was the last opera he had studied before leaving the tutelage of Professor (Kantor) Theodor Weinlig.

"Herr Schmale and I engaged you," Bethmann went on, "as a temporary replacement. But I am now asking you to finish the summer tour with us and to return to Magdeburg as our permanent conductor."

Again Richard's heart missed a beat. Acceptance would mean days and nights of frantic cramming to build up a repertoire before his scanty knowledge was exposed. He was twenty-one, untried, undaunted, and he had just tasted his first applause. A chance like this might not soon come again. He couldn't afford to turn it down.

"I accept," he said quickly. "Thank you very much!"

Bethmann held up a paper with closely spaced writing. "Your contract. Sign here. And now let us join the cast for a celebration."

The night, already far advanced, wound up with toasts and speeches at a near-by tavern where Bethmann nursed his single beer while the rest of the company pooled their funds for a round of Waldmeister punch. It was around two o'clock in the morning when Richard, escorted by sundry new colleagues and drinking partners, returned to the rooming house of Frau Pauline Danner. That worthy lady, to be sure, had long since retired. All lights were extinguished. The front door was securely locked.

Richard had no key.

"*Povero* Riccardo!" chanted the Magdeburg Company's Italian basso whom Frau Bethmann had entertained earlier in her parlor; a somewhat raucous chorus joined in the improvised doggerel, "He does not have a key!"

The basso scanned the hotel's windows. "Which is your room, *Signore?*"

Richard pointed. "Up there, not quite under the eaves."

"*Avanti!* That is where you shall go!"

At a signal several stalwarts stepped forward and lifted the startled conductor on their shoulders, aiding him in climbing a trellis that supported an old pear tree all the way to the roof. It would have been a hazardous ascent but for two balconies, one above the other, spaced between the ground floor and the top. On reaching the second of these havens, Richard paused to rest.

From below, Bethmann's anxious voice warned, "Careful, careful—don't break your neck!"

Someone laughed, shouting in Italian, "This new conductor, he is a valuable property, eh, *amici?*"

Richard descended a few steps and held out his hand toward Bethmann. "That reminds me—I haven't been paid yet."

"Paid?" The manager looked shocked. "Look here, you are supposed to be an artist . . . er . . . artists don't haggle for money in the streets."

"They don't expect to wash the landlady's dishes in return

for breakfast, either. But that's what *I'll* have to do," Richard retorted with urgency, "unless I get some cash."

Bethmann sighed wistfully. "Ah, cash! How I would like some myself! But my wife Rosina, she holds the purse strings. I'm afraid you'll have to deal with her in person."

With a shrug Richard started his climb once more, cheered on by the shouting onlookers. He turned to admonish them. "Stop that infernal racket, or you'll get me thrown out!"

At the same instant a mansard window above him opened and a female figure clad in a filmy dressing gown leaned out. It was not Frau Danner; even in the shadows the outline of face and figure were too delectable for that.

"What goes on here?" asked a soft but distinctly disapproving voice. "Where do you think you're going?"

Now Richard recognized her, and the realization almost threw him off balance. Clinging precariously to tree and wall, he tried to doff his hat. "Fräulein Planer! I beg your pardon . . . er . . . that's my room there, next to yours."

His explanation must have struck her as nonsensical. "In that case, couldn't you think of a less unusual way to reach it?" she replied.

Meanwhile they had identified her from the street. There were cries of "Hey, Minna, meet the new conductor, Herr Wagner."

"Thank you," she called back, "but I don't think I like his manners."

Richard was too enchanted by her presence to hear this. On a sudden impulse he tried to pull himself up a little nearer to where her hand lay on the window ledge, only to find her withdrawing abruptly as the shutters slammed in his face. Sobered, he negotiated his own room and disappeared momentarily to light a candle. Then he returned to wave away the merrymakers below, who had begun scattering in the darkness. As the last footsteps faded down the street, he lingered there in a happy trance, rejoicing in his luck. To think that the beauteous creature he had met only this afternoon was his immediate neighbor! Morning and night he would thrill to the patter of her dainty feet. Ah, it was too much to bear.

Overwhelmed with emotion, he stepped back from the window and opened a portfolio on his desk. He pulled out an envelope and addressed it *Frau Johanna Wagner, Markt Platz,
Leipzig*. Then, by the light of the candle, he scrawled across
a sheet of paper: *Dearest Mother—I have a job, and I am in
love*.

Having delivered himself of this earth-shaking news, he
dropped into bed and was swept into the untroubled sleep of
youth.

The following day might have brought words with a ruffled
Frau Danner over the night's unseemly disturbance. But the
Magdeburg Company came to town only once a year and hotelkeepers vied with one another for the resultant business. Frau
Danner was far too eager to retain her boarders, whom she
hoped to count on for next season. She preferred to make no
issue of the matter.

Nor did Fräulein Minna. Indeed, after the night's encounter
the young lady had given some thought to the irrepressible
blond newcomer who was at the orchestra's helm. She had
not attended the performance of *Don Giovanni* nor bothered
to read the next day's ecstatic reviews. Not being a singer, she
would not be dependent on Herr Wagner's favor. Still, he was
bound to exercise some influence on the company's repertory,
including the choice of nonmusical plays. It behooved her,
therefore, to be on friendly terms with him. Nor would this
be too difficult, since she found his person attractive and his
youthful fervor rather flattering.

For his part, Richard wasted little time in fruitless mooning
over his elusive yet utterly delightful neighbor. It was his firm
purpose to know her better; therefore, between periods of in-
tensive dedication to his orchestral job, he kept an eye on the
theater bulletin board where impending productions and their
casts were listed. To his joyous surprise Minna's name soon
appeared, not on the drama playbill but in the opera column.
Then she was a singer after all? The role in which she had
been cast was that of Fenella in Daniel François Auber's *La
Muette de Portici*, a work of which Richard had never heard.
Of course, as he promptly began learning the score it dawned

on him that *The Mute Girl of Portici* called for a heroine who needed only to look alluring, while never once opening her mouth. The dumb Fenella expressed herself through mimicry, not sound.

During rehearsals this factor proved somewhat thwarting, as Fräulein Planer's activities came under Stage Director Schmale's department rather than the music conductor's. Aside from a few ardent glances cast in her direction, Richard had practically no chance for a moment alone with the young actress since, long after nonsinging members of the company knocked off work, he remained on the job drilling vocalists and musicians, including the always weak choral ensemble.

At last, however, the night of the performance arrived and Richard thrilled at sight of his adored one in her first major role. Looking up from his vantage point on the podium, he found her even more exquisite, if this were possible, than he already knew her to be. The footlights, reinforced by a few tallow candles within metal shields, shot golden highlights through her hair and gave a starry sparkle to the large china-blue eyes. As for her figure, revealed rather than concealed by the flowing folds of her costume, Richard hardly dared take notice of it for fear of being distracted from the more urgent business at hand. As it was, he twice lost his place and had difficulty covering up while the violin section doggedly sawed away at a fortunately extended cadenza, all because Fenella—in diaphanous veils—had approached the pit far too close for any halfway perceptive male's equilibrium.

During the first intermission, while seat holders stepped outside for exercise, Richard retired to his backstage cubicle and dropped into a chair. There was no doubt about it: he was smitten to the depths of his soul. The successful unfolding of the opera (Auber wasn't a very good composer in the first place) did not concern him half so much as the location of Fräulein Planer's dressing room. He spent the full interval before Act II weighing the propriety of roaming, as ranking conductor that he was, through the wings in search of some minor soubrette's retreat where, temporarily, Minna had alighted with her make-up kit. During the next two intermissions he still wavered between dignity and brash abandon, but when the fourth and last pause came his powers of restraint were spent. Careless of criticism, he asked a wardrobe mistress for the way. A second later he stood outside Fräulein Planer's door.

Now that he was so near his goal he felt himself suddenly struck dumb, while the supposedly voiceless Fenella could be heard chatting gaily with a group of admirers inside. As he still tarried, trying to summon up his nerve, the signal bell backstage announced the start of the last act. Even as he raced back to his post the breathless Minna scurried by, ready for her lava death in an eruption of Mount Vesuvius on stage.

How he got through the rest of the performance he would never know. By the time the "mute" heroine had taken her final bow, however, his own speech returned. "Magnificent!" he cried across the footlights, joining in the applause that rang generously through the house. She gave him a sweet nod which he interpreted, somewhat extravagantly, as an invitation. Practically on her heels, he gained the door to her dressing room, certain that this time he was ahead of all others.

Alas, he couldn't have been more wrong. Crowding the tiny chamber were at least a dozen gentlemen of every age, rivals all and equally on homage bent. Richard's elation suffered a hard blow. To think that he must share this sublime moment with a coterie of bores, none of whom could possibly match the ardor that burned in his breast! A further disadvantage accrued to him from the circumstance that these other cavaliers appeared to have considerable experience in matters of gallantry. Each carried a floral offering, a box of bonbons or some other present to lay at the adored one's feet. Poor Richard had nothing save the starting point for a conversation.

"I hope you haven't forgotten," he told her, "that we live under the same roof."

She laughed gaily. "How could I?" She spoke to the circle around her. "This gentleman chooses the most unconventional approach to his quarters. He climbs up the wall!"

The remark drew huge guffaws from the listeners. Rather more, in fact, than the recent nocturnal incident merited. Also, it was becoming evident that Fräulein Planer inclined ever so slightly toward coquetry. At least, her gaiety and friendliness toward all who sauntered into the dressing room struck Richard as unnecessary. He found himself resenting it. She ought to show a preference for someone. She might, for example, consider *him*. Could she not see that his feelings for her were deeper than those of all the others combined?

They were. And Wilhelmine Planer knew it. She had already grasped that in this blond youth with the clear brow and intense gaze there burned fires that might be worth nourishing. But experience—she was twenty-five and had been on the stage since the age of sixteen—had taught her a few lessons. One of these was the value of withholding favors. With tantalizing grace she kept admirers at a safe distance, knowing well the pitfalls that beset the path of a young actress. Among her colleagues of the Magdeburg Company she was held in high esteem for her seemingly irreproachable conduct. She was the drama section's favorite juvenile, affectionately called "Minel" by young and old, yet none could boast of further familiarity.

It came, therefore, as a complete surprise to the present gathering when Fräulein Planer singled out the new conductor as an escort to see her home.

"We *do* live at the same address," she confirmed sweetly to the others, while handing Richard a dress carton and her make-up kit. Above these she tossed a frilly evening wrap and shawl.

He was beside himself with pride. Bearing the treasured burden, his nostrils caressed by the perfume of her garments, Richard accompanied the doll-like creature to the theater's back exit. A lovely walk, albeit a short one, lay before them. The long European dusk had faded into deep night, leaving the tree-lined streets and the winding Kurpark paths eerily silent. Richard was about to suggest a charming detour when he felt a jerk on his coattail.

"Herr Wagner! Herr Wagner!" cried a squeaky, asthmatic voice. It belonged to old Kröge, the theater doorman whom Richard had approached at the box office on his first day in Lauchstaedt.

"Yes?"

"Director Schmale wishes to see you in Herr Bethmann's office."

Richard hesitated. He was tempted, in Minna's presence, to make a show of independence. Was he not, after all, the *Herr Orchesterdirigent?* A personage, surely, of estimable weight. Still, prudence dictated compliance with the demands of a job in which he was not yet firmly grounded. He had been hired. But he could be fired.

"Thank you, Kröge," he said resolutely, tossing Minna's clothes and cosmetic box into the doorman's arms. With an apologetic bow to the young woman, Richard followed the summons.

"Well!" Minna gasped, dumbfounded. "I suppose I'm to stand here and wait!"

"Please do," the ingenuous Richard called back. "I'll return as quickly as I can."

But she did not hear him. Her soft mouth pursed in a pout, she snatched her belongings from the tottering Kröge and flounced off.

T HE conference in Bethmann's office lasted no more than five minutes. It concerned the following week's program, rehearsals for which were to start on the morrow. Pocketing the outlined schedule, Richard made haste to rejoin Minna, of whose impatient departure he had no idea. But again he was delayed. In passing the orchestra's practice hall he heard the clash of angry voices. Peering inside, he saw a group of musicians and actors, the latter still in stage make-up, engaged in heated debate.

"It's not as if there wasn't any money," a supernumerary complained. "The house sold out tonight!"

Several singers flailed their arms excitedly. "The choral section has gone without salary for two months. If that old goat Bethmann didn't drink so much, maybe we'd get paid once in a while."

A fretful cellist seemed to know the answer. "It's his wife, I tell you, who is robbing us to pamper her boy friends. That fat Niccolo Pava hangs around Her Ladyship night and day. You don't think *he* goes without salary, do you?"

Various expletives and scurrilous outcries greeted this remark, leaving no doubt in Richard's mind that outbursts of this nature appeared to be the order of the day. A sense of delicacy prompted him to cough and make his presence known. But this in no wise changed the tenor of the protest meeting. Gatherings of this sort had evidently taken place before, with tonight marking a particular crisis.

"I say we put an end to it!" an elderly stagehand now announced. He appeared to be an accepted spokesman for the group, whose word carried. "Tomorrow no one shows up for rehearsals. Instead, we camp on Bethmann's doorstep and threaten police action unless we get our due."

"*Jawohl! Jawohl!*" echoed the listeners with fervor. A few, catching sight of the conductor, pressed him for an expression of loyalty. "You are with us, *Herr Kapellmeister?*"

Richard nodded. He too, after all, expected to draw his pay without having to join Frau Bethmann's boudoir guard to earn preferment. But the thought of being drawn, involuntarily, into a conspiratorial action left him vaguely uncomfortable. A feeling of guilt hung over him as he slipped away from the theater and hurried home. Minna and her stage finery had been blotted completely from his mind.

The following morning, as foreseen, the demonstrators were gathered outside Bethmann's lodgings, with a small cordon of police in attendance. As Richard arrived, the old stagehand—Alois Zettl—was pounding on the door. Some seconds later Bethmann appeared on the threshold, slightly rumpled and ill at ease. He obviously knew what the demonstration was about.

"Now just be patient, everybody," he burbled, with hands upraised.

"We want our money! We want our money!" chorused the restive crowd.

Bethmann cleared his throat. "You all know, my colleagues and friends, that the theater everywhere is going through a crisis and that our own company has had to carry a deficit over from last year——"

Zettl's voice cut him short. "We don't care about last year's deficit. We have rent to pay and food to buy *today!*"

Suddenly Richard knew himself to be part of the common cause. He pushed his way through the demonstrators and faced Bethmann head on. "That's right," he backed Zettl's challenge. "Either everyone here gets paid in full, or I don't conduct rehearsals."

Bethmann stared at him in glassy-eyed consternation. Then, quickly conciliatory, he murmured, "Ah, but of course, Herr Wagner, by all means. If you will come to my office around noon—" he lowered his voice to keep the others from hearing—"you shall have a month's salary in advance."

"I don't want any advance," Richard shouted. "I want my fellow workers here to get their back wages. Is that clear?"

Again the mob stirred and growled. "Yes—what about *us?*"

Bethmann knew he was cornered. "All right, all right," he temporized. "There'll be something for everybody, I'm sure, if you'll all go now and get to work. Just let me run through the bills and see which are the most pressing." He edged his way back through the door with a parting dodge. "Come back at noon."

As the lock clicked shut there was a general grumble of incredulity and despair. But under Zettl's quiet urging the more ruffled tempers calmed down. One by one the complainants started for the rehearsal hall. It was now that, among them, Richard caught sight of Minna. She smiled at him over the heads of several younger choristers. Then, as if on a sudden impulse, she came running toward him. Her anger at yesterday's slight appeared to be forgotten.

"That was a fine thing to do," she said, and he noted the warmth in her voice. "I mean, taking up our battle with Bethmann."

He loved her praise, but courtesy demanded that he belittle it. "Isn't it my battle too?" he countered nobly.

"Not in the same measure. The rest of us, except for three or four headliners, can easily be replaced, so we're left dangling. But you're important. Bethmann knows better than to mistreat you."

Richard's sense of justice rebelled, so that he could not savor the personal flattery inherent in her words.

"This is terrible—people working and not getting paid!" he snapped. "How long have these abuses been going on?"

Minna shrugged. "Oh, weeks, months. It's nothing unusual for stage people to wonder where their next meal is coming from."

"But you yourself, how can you live this way? Have you no family?"

"Sure—my parents and . . . a small sister. But they look to *me* for help, not I to them."

He was moved by her answer, and silenced. What point was there in bringing her personal problems to light when there

was so little he could do about them? Gently he took her arm
and escorted her to the theater, where she had an appointment
to keep with the wardrobe mistress while he must run through
the score of next week's opera. Before parting he remembered
his defection of the night before.

"Whenever I see you," he blurted, "it seems I've something
to apologize for. First we collide on a wide and empty street,
then I come crawling up, Romeo-fashion, to your balcony——"

She frowned in mock disapproval. "At a scandalous hour,
too!"

"Then last night——"

"You stood me up. I really shouldn't ever speak to you
again."

"But you've forgiven me?"

She gave him a candid look. "Yes. You are an important
person, with important responsibilities."

"I hope that doesn't mean you think me willfully discour-
teous."

"Of course not." Her tone changed to genuine admiration.
"You are much too modest, considering how everybody has
been raving about *Don Giovanni*. You were a great success!"

His eyes fixed on some point beyond her. "No, not a *great*
success—yet. Not the kind of success I hope one day to be."

A faint smile played on her lips. "I used to talk like that."

"What do you mean, 'used to'? You're by far the prettiest
girl in the company, and I'm sure you're as talented as you are
lovely."

Carried away by his own words, he seized her arms with
ardor, almost clasping her to him. She side-stepped this deftly,
remaining composed and matter-of-fact.

"There are lots of pretty faces," she said, "and younger ones
coming along each year. And if you're no singer there aren't
many parts to count on with an opera company."

"I suppose not."

Her tone changed to a note of defiance. "Well, I'm fed up.
I've been thinking of making a change."

"A change?" Richard made no effort to conceal his alarm.
"You mean you want to leave the company?"

"Yes, why not? I'd like to try for a job in Dresden or Berlin."

Richard was incoherent with sudden despair. "You can't do that. You can't——" he began to stammer.

"You mean no one will have me?" She frowned.

He shook his head vehemently. Of course that wasn't what he had meant. But there was no time now to explain the feelings that lay choked within him. Rehearsals had started; the orchestra was waiting. "Don't do anything till I see you at Frau Danner's this noon," he begged. He would try to get a chair next to hers at the long dining-room table. But now he must be off or he would find himself without his fine job.

The rest of the morning went by with a first reading of Giacomo Meyerbeer's *Robert le Diable,* a pastiche of the facile and often hackneyed Italian school for which Richard had little veneration. Since the score lacked both originality and depth, it made no demand on the imagination. Measure on measure unfolded while artists and musicians were able to pursue their private thoughts, as did the visibly distraught conductor.

Three hours later Richard entered Frau Danner's well-polished hall off which the clatter of luncheon dishes could be heard. Minna was already there, plainly on the lookout for him. Punctuality, he noted with satisfaction, was another of her virtues. He was rushing across the room, hat in hand and a greeting on his lips, when a tall, thin gentleman in travel tweeds intercepted him.

"Hello, Richard," cried a distinctly familiar voice. "At last I've caught up with you! Remember me? Theodor Apel, your classmate of two years ago."

There was a pause, then recognition. "Theo, but of course! Only it's nearer three years, I should say. What are *you* doing here?"

"Taking the mineral baths." Apel tapped his left knee. "My old hunting injury—that's never stopped bothering me. As for you, I don't need to ask. Heard about your success last night, so I was just on my way to the theater to look you up. You're a sensation, my friend. The whole town is buzzing!"

Embarrassed, Richard turned to indicate the dining room. "Have you eaten?" It was now that he again saw Minna and realized that she and Apel had not met. He beckoned them both and furnished quick introductions. "Herr Apel, a Leipzig schoolmate of mine, and the only person I know who doesn't have to work. His father is rich. Theo, meet Fräulein Planer, a fellow artist."

Apel bowed gallantly. "Oh, I know the popular Minna Planer. I mean, I've seen you on the stage."

Minna's eyes lighted up. "You have?"

"There!" Richard nudged her fondly. "You see how you underrate yourself? When the sophisticated and bored Theodor Apel notices your work you are a celebrity."

Amused, and possibly because he felt that it might please Richard, Theo underlined his chivalry by kissing Minna's hand. But it soon became clear that this gesture was part of his habitual polish and that the girl held no further claim to his attention. It was Richard who interested him.

"Tell me, how long have you been with the Magdeburg outfit?"

"Less than a week."

Apel's eyebrows arched. "And got hired on the spot to direct Mozart? Quite a feat, my boy."

"Not on the spot, exactly," Richard admitted. "The truth is— I wasn't wanted. But old Bethmann had no one else. Even his concertmaster walked out, so I won the job by default."

"Well, you kept it, didn't you? And Bethmann's the winner, I say. With *you* in the pit, I'll attend operas again. There hasn't been much lately that's worth listening to, either in opera or on the speaking stage."

Minna rallied to the last remark. "What can you expect—" she spoke up courageously—"when theater people are underpaid—and sometimes dropped with no back wages at all?"

Richard admired her spunk. "Minna is right. Conditions here are shocking."

Minna broke in with growing intensity. "Not just here. It's true of every theater in the country. I've been around enough of them to know."

Apel appeared only mildly concerned. "I should think that's a matter for the authorities." His tone was vague and a trifle smug.

"Spoken like a true German!" Richard flared up. "No one

wants to take on personal responsibilities, everything is left to
that impersonal but venerated deity the Authorities and nothing ever gets done."

Apel raised a protesting hand, but Richard had not finished.
Indeed, he was just warming to his subject.

"The whole world knows how our officialdom works. In our
kind of society you lick the boots of the fellow above you and
kick the teeth out of the one below."

Minna supported him earnestly. "As for us, artists and theater
folk, we have no rating whatever, nor any chance of a fair
hearing. We'd starve to death before your precious authorities
took any notice."

Now Richard launched a tirade against complacent power.
Pacing back and forth, he spoke of social injustice and the
stifling influence of rank and position. Suddenly he paused.
"What I am saying only amuses you," he said bitterly.

"Well, you *are* playing from an old score" was Apel's comment. "Words and music are both familiar."

Theo was right, of course. What Richard proclaimed today
had been said thousands of times, throughout history and in
all languages. He himself, in student discussions, had often
enough mouthed the same noble phrases. Now there was a
difference, however. Richard felt it through every muscle, every
cell. If such thoughts were trite, they had the terrible triteness
of truth. From being an academic social reformer, he felt himself now turned into an activist, knowing he would always remain one.

He glanced at the impeccably dressed Apel, in whose eyes
could be read only kindly tolerance without conviction. For a
moment all the fire went out of Richard. How to convince
such a pampered individual, to whom missing even one meal
was an unknown experience? He laid a hand on his friend's
shoulder.

"Theo, you were born rich. You have position. You couldn't
possibly understand what it's like to start at the bottom, fighting for everything one gets. But, take my word, your own class
is setting loose a tremendous upheaval in Europe, and there'll
be no stopping the trend. Look at America, where every man

has a chance at success, regardless of origin or station. That will come here too. It must, it *shall* come!"

"Ah, the American experiment, Freedom's Torch and all that." Apel's expression was quizzical. "Are you idealist enough to hold that all men are equal?"

"In ability or intelligence? Of course not." Richard shook his head impatiently. "I'm talking about the God-given right to equality of opportunity, and of treatment before the law." He softened. "But don't think I'm blaming you personally for the sins of the selfish rich. At least you never shirk when approached for support of a worthy cause."

"Thanks."

"And furthermore—" Richard tried to direct the conversation into lighter channels—"you do have the most commendable taste in music."

Apel was quickly mollified. He had long been accustomed to his friend's "democratic rantings" without grasping more than a fraction of their meaning. But as long as Richard found words of praise for him, however moderate, he deemed himself not wholly unfit. For it was Theodor Apel's secret dread to be despised because of his wealth and to be accused of leading a misspent life.

"Show me another issue that deserves support and I'm with you all the way," he rallied eagerly. An idea struck him. "See here! All these grievances you've been talking about, why don't you put them on paper for the whole country, for all of Europe, to learn? Write a play or an opera on the subject, and I'll subsidize you while you're doing it!" He paused for a worried afterthought. "But no flaming political tract, mind you. I don't want to risk arrest or exile for backing some socialist mischief."

Richard smiled bitterly. "Generosity with strings attached, eh? You ask me to speak out on crass abuses, but the truth must be sugar-coated and served up as entertainment, so people will miss it altogether." He shrugged, resigned. "Well, even so, I'm going to accept your offer."

Apel beamed. "Splendid!"

Richard turned to Fräulein Planer, who all this time had

stood by in silence. "What would you say, Minna, to a play about social injustice—with you in the star role?"

The girl gasped in thrilled surprise. "Oh, that would be marvelous!"

"Then it's settled. I shall tackle it." Richard paused, then frowned. "Of course, I must warn you that, with me, music may gain the upper hand, and what starts out to be a speaking part could well end as an operatic aria."

Minna agreed humbly. "That would be all right." Her admiration for him was growing by the minute. "It will be a great work, whatever it is."

While they talked the adjoining dining room had filled with hungry lodgers, and Frau Danner waited impatiently, hand on table bell, to give the order to serve. Her sharp gaze was fixed on the dilatory trio near the doorway, until at last its compelling insistence pierced Apel's consciousness.

"Psst—" he signaled Richard with a nod—"I think we are upsetting the house routine."

Frau Danner shook the bell and almost instantly a serving girl came through the kitchen entrance bearing a steaming soup tureen. In single file the three late-comers trailed toward their seats.

CHAPTER 7

RICHARD was much too preoccupied to eat. His thoughts were on the happy prospect opened up by Apel's promise and the intoxicating hope aroused within him by Minna's praise. Throughout the meal, of which he scarcely partook, his mind weighed and discarded half a dozen schemes that were to bring about a reformation not only on the German stage but in the theatrical world at large. Before Frau Danner's dessert course—a somewhat watery bread pudding—made its appearance he had already dragged his companions outside.

"I've thought it all out," he told them with determination. "You, Theo, and Minna here, offer me a challenge. But playwriting or composing both take time, while there's a line of needy actors, stagehands and musicians pounding on Bethmann's door right now. They can't wait for some poet or composer to come up with an inspiration. They need help quickly, and I intend to give it to them. Are you really with me?"

Apel nodded, inflamed with Richard's earnestness. "Certainly. What can I do?"

"You can set up a cash fund to keep my orchestra and all the Magdeburg Company's personnel housed and fed while we are bleeding the turnip. And bleed it we shall, I promise. Once we catch up with Bethmann, that is."

"Agreed!" said Apel, pulling out a jingling purse and pressing it into his friend's hands. "I've always told you to call on me for anything you need."

Richard smiled. "Thanks."

"Don't thank me. I'm just a useless citizen of means, with no talent except for spending money."

He paused openmouthed, for Richard had just turned the

purse over to Minna with the admonition, "Here, my dear. You shall be in charge of the fund. Put it away under lock and key. I'll see you later at the theater."

Enthralled, Minna tucked the money into her reticule and, with a nod, hastened for the stairs leading up to her room. Apel looked after her in astonishment, then turned questioning eyes on Wagner. "That girl," he murmured under his breath, "she means something to you?"

"A great deal," Richard replied. "Why?"

"That was a great deal of money."

Richard gave him a long, steady look. "I would trust her with my life. In fact, I intend to."

Apel was too shocked to answer. Despite his profound love of music and related arts, he drew a sharp line between the theater and its performers. In this he shared an attitude common throughout the Europe of that day. Stage people, with their reputation for unconventionality and loose living, were not considered *comme il faut*. Admittedly there had been nothing about this Fräulein Planer at which Theodor Apel could take offense. She was an appetizing creature, fresh and rosy as a peach, to whom he himself would not have minded paying playful court. But on any less frivolous terms she was of course not acceptable. Yet here was Richard, talking like an unmitigated fool.

"I mean, Theo," he was saying, "that I am going to marry her."

Apel had recovered his speech. "Are you out of your mind? Take the girl for your mistress, show her a good time, buy her some trinkets, and then good-by. As for marriage—that's impossible, and you know it!"

Richard flushed with anger, but he mastered himself quickly and made light of his friend's words. "You've traveled and seen a lot of the world, Theo, but you know little about the human heart. I can tell you that Minna is different. She is respected by her fellow workers, all of whom marvel at her virtue and decorum."

"I suppose you expect me to believe that you've never had your arms around her?"

"That's right. The nearest thing to a caress that she will tolerate is to let me kiss her finger tips."

"Stop it, stop it," Apel cried with a mock shudder, "you'll have me in tears!" He took Richard's arm. "Come, I'll walk with you to the theater. Since you won't take my advice in your love life, let me do some dilettante tampering with your rehearsals."

Laughing, the two friends walked off arm in arm.

For the following weeks Apel remained in Lauchstaedt, attending all the Magdeburg Company's offerings, which had been made possible by his financial support of the workers in their fight against the Bethmann management. Their wages paid up at last, the artists exerted themselves with special fervor to give their best in return. By late September the Lauchstaedt season ended and trunks were packed as the company made ready to continue its tour. Theodor Apel too resumed his travels, for he customarily spent the autumn in Paris and on the French Riviera. In parting he pressed Richard's hand.

"You have my address. Remember to call me when you need me." He made no mention of Minna, knowing that the lovesick young man was not to be swayed from his purpose.

"Thanks, Theo, you've done a lot. I don't think old Bethmann will give us further trouble."

Through the fall of the year the Magdeburg Company toured such music-loving cities as Rudolstadt, Halle and the queen of German baroque towns, Würzburg. Everywhere audience acclaim was warmly enthusiastic, with special kudos heaped on the heretofore unknown conductor. Soon the name Richard Wagner began to be featured on programs and theatrical bulletin boards in larger type, even above featured singers or stage stars. As the tour progressed through Stettin, Danzig and Königsberg, the youthful conductor's self-confidence had gained in strength, with regard both to professional aptitude and to his prospects as a lover. Listeners of both sexes clamored for curtain calls when he stepped from the podium, but feminine admirers waited outside Richard's dressing room, giving him to understand that his favors would not be spurned. However, his yearning was for Minna alone.

There was some speculation now among Minna's colleagues as to her "involvement" with the popular conductor. Before leaving Lauchstaedt, Richard had suffered an attack of facial inflammation, a form of erysipelas to which his extremely fair skin would be subject throughout his life. During this illness Minna had been seen entering his room at Frau Danner's pension with a basin of medicated compresses to ease his fevered brow. Raised eyebrows met word of that discovery, and there were cynical tongues ready to question the Samaritan nature of the visits. However, such gossip missed the truth by a wide margin. To Richard's own aching distress, Minna remained obdurate against the smallest caress. When, in an access of gratitude for her tender ministrations, he ventured a chaste embrace she disengaged herself primly and with ladylike poise. She appeared indeed to be a rare phenomenon in the backstage world of that day—a virtuous maid. This discovery, of course, only intensified Richard's passion.

Back in Leipzig his mother viewed the matter more quizzically. Of her eight children, five had chosen stage careers, influenced by their Thespian stepfather, Ludwig Geyer. Thus the seamier aspects of a grease-paint existence had been frequently discussed in the family circle. Without ever setting eyes on her, Mama sensed that the coy and cautious Fräulein Planer was probably no ingénue. In his next letter from home Richard found an admonition against the siren's deceptive lure.

Before he could compose a fittingly outraged protest, a new cloud darkened his horizon. Shortly after opening in Königsberg the Magdeburg Opera Company was again in hot water, this time beyond salvage. While temporarily meeting the weekly pay roll, the management had obviously fallen behind with theater rentals, hauling costs and other operating commitments. In Königsberg, matters came to a head. Arriving at the stage entrance for morning rehearsals, Richard found the door padlocked, with signs plastered across it reading PERFORMANCE CANCELED and CLOSED BY ORDER OF TOWN MARSHAL FOR NON-PAYMENT OF DEBTS.

Promptly he rushed to the front of the theater, only to be met by a flock of excited colleagues, the old stagehand Zettl among them.

"The Bethmanns, and Schmale too, have flown the roost," Zettl shouted, "and they've taken the cashbox with them!"

Other voices mingled in a general uproar. "A bunch of creditors brought suit in Police Court to impound all company property. That means our costumes!" the women wailed.

"And our instruments!" echoed the musicians. Several orchestra members furtively tucked flutes, pipes and piccolos inside their clothing, while others could only stare disconsolately at their unwieldy cellos and bass fiddles.

Richard, tremendously aroused, stepped forward with a proposal. "I have it!" he cried above the hullabaloo. "We'll give a benefit performance and pay off the most pressing claims. Then we'll form our own company and——"

Harsh laughter cut him off as Zettl, again in the role of spokesman, made a taunting gesture. "Rubbish! What will you use for a score? All the music has been seized, and in any case we've no authority——"

"*I* give you authority," Richard announced stubbornly.

"You!" With mockery in his voice Zettl turned to the others. "Herr Wagner, one gathers, is speaking for Rossini, Berlioz and Meyerbeer." Shouts and guffaws greeted this pronouncement.

"No," Richard said with composure. "I speak for myself."

Doubt, mingled with hope, began to be mirrored in the faces of his listeners as Wagner now climbed a parapet along the theater frontage. From this vantage point he addressed himself to Zettl.

"You say we can give no performance because the music is impounded? Well, I'll furnish the music. I'll give you a *fresh* opera, never before heard!" He reached into the leather brief case under his arm and pulled forth a manuscript which he waved high in the air. Now he was facing the crowd. "Here you have it, my friends! *Das Liebesverbot*—by Richard Wagner. I am counting on you to give it a resounding *première*."

Ready to grasp at any straw, the stranded troupers burst into cheers. At least Richard offered a means of saving their livelihood. "Are you with me?" he asked one last time, certain already that they were on his side. "Then, off to the town marshal for the theater keys!" In a body they all marched into town.

The following week was spent in strenuous labor as the somewhat trite and inept *Liebesverbot* took form. It was a conventional opera set in the most conventional of operatic backgrounds: Italy. The plot dealt with a cruel governor of ancient Palermo, under whose iron rule all customary joys of the Carnival season were to be forbidden. In a suitably lurid denouement this same heartless tyrant, cold to the charms of wine, women and song, was himself hopelessly smitten with desire for the unattainable Isabella, a novice in a strict Sicilian convent.

Fortunately the action-packed story unfolded itself in two longish episodes, with only a single intermission. This kept down costs and shortened the period of rehearsal. Königsberg audiences, already disappointed at the change in program, would at least not have long to wait.

The ticket sale was going fairly well, even before dress rehearsal, and on opening night there was a surprising rush at the box office. For the first time in his embryonic professional career Richard experienced true elation. This was it. Not merely as conductor but as composer he had arrived.

Well, not quite. There was still the performance to be got through, and here the Fates had a shattering surprise in store. Inside the theater a gala audience was settling into place, rapt and eager with anticipation. It wasn't every day that Königsberg found itself singled out as the setting for a world *première*. The townspeople were of one mind about returning the compliment thus paid their city. Quelling whatever doubts might lurk among a few musical connoisseurs, they intended to give the new opera and its performers a rousing reception. For once no singer on stage would have to purchase private applause. The whole audience could be counted on for a claque.

It was almost curtaintime. Richard stood in the wings, ready to step on the podium, when he was suddenly pulled back by a costumed member of the chorus.

"Herr Wagner—there's a fight on in one of the dressing rooms! The prima donna and her husband—it's because of that Signor Cimbellini."

Richard threw up his hands. "Those confounded Italians! Not one of them but thinks he's another Casanova."

In haste he followed the shrieks and shouts that came from backstage. Outside the prima donna's dressing room he was halted by the scrimmage there in progress. Husband, wife and interloping tenor appeared to be exchanging blows. Make-up jars, combs, brushes, shoes and corsets came flying through the air, short of their respective targets but adding to the general hysteria. In the melee the signal bell went unheeded and the curtain rose with neither orchestra nor stage personnel in place. Astonishment, then displeasure, seized the audience. People whistled and stamped their feet. Some rose and started up the aisles, plainly in search of the nearest exit.

Backstage, Richard was doing his utmost to calm the tempest, but all in vain. By now the prima donna's face was puffed and garnished with two black eyes where her own starry blue orbs were wont to be, while the great Cimbellini leaned over a chair, arms folded over his groin, for he had suffered a low and decidedly illegal punch. The irate husband, himself only a mediocre baritone, was still on his feet. But it was obvious that he alone could not carry the show. With two stellar artists *hors de combat,* the opera would have to be called off.

Heavy of heart, Richard gave the order. On stage the prompter climbed gingerly from his box and made an announcement: "Ladies and gentlemen, it is with the greatest regret that, due to unforeseen circumstances, the performance of *Das Liebes-verbot* must be canceled." With diffidence he retired once more to the depths, as the audience angrily marched from the theater.

Following this fiasco, the Magdeburg Opera Company disbanded. Like frightened pigeons the singers, musicians, actors and stagehands scattered to seek employment elsewhere. Among the first to leave was Minna. She had set her sights on Berlin.

"I have friends there," she explained to the dismayed Richard. "I'm sure they can get me a new engagement." It was rather obvious that Herr Wagner, the unemployed orchestra conductor, no longer interested her very much.

With no means of holding her, Richard forced himself to say good-by. But he was disconsolate. In long letters to Theodor Apel he unburdened his heart, chiding himself for not having married Minna forthwith. Apel, a confirmed bachelor, replied with callous cynicism. He reminded his lovesick friend of the fascinating discussions they had engaged in, during student days, on the subject of "modernism" and a new code of ethical values. Marriage was old-hat. The dull Philistine proprieties were passé. Mankind had entered upon the era of free thought, free worship, free politics, free love.

It all sounded extremely mature, so unencumbered and convenient, until Richard visualized Minna living in far-off Berlin by the same principles, or the lack of them. Suddenly the thought of all that freedom, so prized in oratorical exchange, made him a trifle bilious. Minna belonging to anyone but himself—that would be unbearable. Yet how was he to prevent it save by choosing that most stodgy and timeworn expedient—matrimony? "Monogamy, monopoly, monotony!" warned Theodor's acrid pen. Still, what other way was there to take a pretty girl out of circulation?

From a practical angle there were difficulties too. Without a job, what right had Richard to engage in dreams of wedlock? His savings were barely sufficient to tide him over another fortnight, provided he tightened his belt. No matter. He could bear his agony no longer. Before sober reflection checked the mad impulse, he hopped a stagecoach and set out for Berlin.

He had no idea where Minna lived or how he would pick up her trail. But he intended to tramp over every inch of the sprawling capital until he found her.

CHAPTER 8

THE search proved less difficult than Richard had expected. Minna's Berlin "friends" were evidently people of some influence, for she had found employment almost immediately in one of the Prussian city's more fashionable music halls. Here, though she was no singer, her voice sufficed for the recital—to musical accompaniment—of dubiously spiced couplets and monologues. The chances for professional advancement in the field of serious drama could hardly be furthered by this type of job. But the pay was good. Also, for the first time, Minna saw herself billed as a headliner. Her name, together with an enticing charcoal sketch of her face and figure, appeared on street placards and kiosks. It was thus that Richard had been able to locate her.

Again he waited outside her dressing-room door. Also again, on being admitted, he found Minna surrounded by admirers toward whom she showed her usual and disconcertingly impartial friendliness. Nor did her manner change at sight of him. Richard was greeted with the same courtesy—no more, no less—accorded the others. He enjoyed equal privileges with all who came, limited privileges that permitted the staking of no claim. The issue was plain. If he would eliminate competition and be the sole captor of her fancy, he must offer something more than Bohemian camaraderie or romantic adoration: he must propose marriage.

For this he had first to catch Minna alone, in itself a difficult maneuver. Berlin dandies appreciated her fresh bloom even more, if possible, than Lauchstaedt swains had done. At all times there appeared at her beck and call a covey of gentlemen, some youthful, others of distinctly and distinguished mature years, eager to serve as escorts or protectors against the pitfalls of the metropolitan jungle. To beat these rivals, most of whom came early and stayed late, Richard befriended a member of the cabaret's gypsy band, who signaled him when Minna's act was due for a short intermission. It was thus that he intercepted her before the others closed in, like bees on honeysuckle.

"What are you doing here?" he challenged her, almost savagely. "I never dreamed you would throw yourself away in a place like this!"

She brushed off his hands that had gripped her shoulders. "It's a living," she said calmly, "and a better one than I've been offered lately."

"But it's not good enough. You should be looked after."

"I can take care of myself."

"No. You ought to be married and have a home. *I want to take care of you!*"

There. He had done it. In a garbled and utterly incoherent way he had proposed. And he was certain that the clumsiness with which he had blurted out his feelings would draw from Minna's lips a mocking laugh. But he was mistaken. Her face showed neither scorn nor jest, only bewildered and complete astonishment which, presently, turned to unvarnished joy. Now it was his turn to be flabbergasted, for she had thrown her arms around his neck and—unspeakable delight!—their faces touched in shy prelude to a kiss.

"Minna, Minna, my darling!" he cried ecstatically, crushing her to him. "I'll work for you. I'll do everything to make you happy. You won't be sorry, I promise—I promise!"

She seemed to have no doubts at all, and even fewer regrets, about leaving Berlin. On short notice she walked off her job and joined Richard on the next stagecoach to Königsberg. Once there, the pair went straight to the marriage clerk's office and, without fuss or feathers, became man and wife. Only a seedy old magistrate, who issued the license and witnessed the signatures, congratulated them.

Richard pressed Minna's hand in his. "This isn't the way I would have planned it—without any celebration at all."

"Don't worry, dear." She was radiant. "We have each other. And there's all of life before us for celebration!"

They walked arm in arm down the street, heading for his bachelor quarters, a modest abode several degrees below Frau Danner's in quality. But here, on the rickety doorstep, a surprise awaited them. Seemingly notified by a fleet messenger from the city hall, a scattered group of former Magdeburg players had assembled to greet the newlyweds. Not only that. The pastor of a near-by parish waited in cap and ceremonial robes, offering to seal the marriage vows with an ecclesiastic blessing.

"A church wedding after all!" Minna exulted.

To the sound of an ancient wheezing organ the bride and groom entered the House of God, followed by the impromptu wedding party. A more elaborate ritual was now pronounced, and the good preacher even produced a pair of borrowed rings.

"You can bring them back tomorrow," he whispered in Richard's ear, "after you've bought your own."

While the church ceremony was in progress some furtive activity went on at Richard's unfestive lodgings. Thoughtful colleagues had hastened there to sweep up and set things in order, not forgetting to assemble some pretzels and beer for an impromptu spread. Also, with a lone cello and a flute, a musical reception was quickly rehearsed. This included a solo by the prima donna with the blackened eyes, who had remained at liberty since her recent beating. Crushingly aware that her romantic dalliance had thrown so many fellow workers out of their jobs, the good lady was bent on making amends. She had a tremolo in her upper register, and in any case she did not sing very well when emotionally upset, but none could stop her from rendering, in paraphrase, the wedding song from Weber's *Der Freischütz (The Free Huntsman)*:

> *"Wir winden Euch den Hochzeitskranz*
> *aus veilchenblauer Sei-ei-ei-de!"*

The tune was emitted in such strident screeches that listeners disrespectfully transposed the operatic title to *"Der Schreifritz"* ("Fritz the Screamer").

All the same, Richard and Minna were overjoyed. The ecclesiastic blessing of their union had already left them with a

warm glow, but the gaiety that was to follow would exceed
their boldest wishes. Not only did the refreshments whip up
spirits; there was even a spontaneous sprinkling of presents, including a magnificent elongated rye bread, two pewter spoons,
an Edam cheese and—from the prima donna—a silver-plated,
highly rococo sugar bowl.

In presenting her gift the disillusioned diva blubbered, "I
hope—*ach*—this brings you greater happiness than it gave me."

On overhearing that remark, her husband, newly enraged,
stepped forward to remonstrate, whereupon Signor Cimbellini
—also among those present—clipped him across the jaw. In no
time the feud had started up again and the hair was flying. In
pell-mell abandon the principals went to it, but wedding guests,
crockery and furniture were soon equally involved, the latter
taking quite a lot of punishment.

Quick-witted Minna braved the skirmish, skittering here and
there to save her wedding presents. She clutched what she
could under one arm, and, with the prized sugar bowl held
aloft in the other hand, retired to the bedroom. Richard meanwhile enlisted the aid of a few sober-headed colleagues who put
an end to the fracas by running the whole kit and caboodle out
of the house.

Outside a chill autumn rain had started, which served to cool
raging tempers. Considerably dampened, the guests went their
separate ways, not altogether displeased with the day's achievement. After all, they had done their bit in getting Richard and
Minna thoroughly married. The date—November 24, 1836—
would have otherwise faded into dreary insignificance. An improvised celebration, and a bout of fisticuffs too, lifted any
occasion well out of the commonplace.

For a honeymoon the bride and groom went job hunting.
The prospects of forming a new theatrical company looked unfavorable indeed. But again, as in Lauchstaedt, a suddenly
vacated orchestral post provided Richard with a temporary
niche. The Königsberg Symphony needed an arranger and
substitute conductor.

"The hours are long and the pay is short," he told Minna,
"but it may be a step leading to something better."

Minna nodded absently, her mind engrossed by something else. She had received a letter that morning from her parents in Leisnig. The letter posed a problem.

"My father and mother," Minna began breezily, "are so sorry to have missed our wedding."

He took her in his arms. "I'm sorry too. As soon as I can possibly afford it we'll go to see them."

"Meanwhile—" Minna proceeded with some caution—"they have sent my little ten-year-old sister Natalie to pay us a visit."

"What?"

"She arrives on the afternoon stagecoach. It's almost time to meet her now."

This was quite a surprise. Richard harbored only the most amicable feelings toward his wife's relatives, but he was in no immediate hurry to make their acquaintance. Surely a bride and groom ought to be allowed some time alone. Well, maybe the little girl would stay a week. He would take her to the St. Nicholas Fair and the Christmas booths, showing her a good time before dispatching her back home again.

"Natalie is to live with us," Minna added casually, as if she had just recalled an oversight. "I've always taken care of her, you know."

This disclosure came as something of a shock. To find himself suddenly in possession of a family was more than Richard had bargained for. He struggled to cover his dismay, for he could read anxiety and distress on Minna's face.

"That's fine," he managed to blurt in reply. "Come on, let's meet the coach."

An hour later Richard encountered yet another jolt. The young sister-in-law with whom he was being so abruptly presented was a singularly unprepossessing child, devoid of even a trace of Minna's prettiness and charm. She was forthright, however, and trusting.

"My full name is Ernestina Natalie," she informed Richard, giving him a quick hug. "But everybody says that's too long."

He agreed, after recovering from the disappointment of finding her so plain. And now that she was here his heart opened, for his great love of pets extended also to children. Throughout his life he would never be without a dog, cat, parrot or other assorted beasts, so why not Natalie? He accepted the child, praising Minna the more for her daughterly solicitude in relieving her needy parents. Their small living quarters, already inadequate for two, might burst at the seams with addition of a sleeping sofa for their guest. But if Minna was bighearted and generous enough to put up with the situation, he, Richard, must match her fine spirit.

Oddly, it was precisely Minna's fine spirit which presently would undergo a change. Once her mind was relieved regarding the possibility of Natalie's rejection by Richard, her attitude of diffident concern gave way to something approaching querulousness. She began making observations on the unsuitability of the bachelor lodgings in which they were confined, a fact which no one could dispute. But instead of recognizing that the arrival of a house guest had considerably cramped their living space, she put the blame on Richard. That is, in veiled remarks she managed to convey that, if his earning powers were only better, the situation could be easily relieved.

He was too much in love to feel the stab, and too masculine in any case to return it in kind. The plan of bringing Natalie to live with them had certainly not been his. He might have said so. He might also have pointed out that a husband ought to be consulted about any such plan. But his whole being was too happily perturbed by the wonder of marriage, the newness of intimacy, the pride of possession. This was a time of bliss. He had no thought of blighting the fair hymeneal sky with clouds of bitterness.

Professionally, it so happened, he was doing rather well. Under his baton the Königsberg Symphony Orchestra attracted favorable notice among critics, both locally and in music journals from near-by cities. He was even approached with an offer to take his string section on a short concert tour of the provinces, a proposition which, of course, he was not free to accept. But the satisfaction of having been asked at all contributed greatly to his sense of security.

It was a false security, at least on the domestic side, for all was not well with Minna. Unknown to Richard, and perhaps to herself, she was but sparingly endowed with wifely virtues. Housekeeping, with its daily round of repetitious chores, revealed itself to her as unutterably dull. It was not long before she saw her white hands roughened by kitchen tasks to which they were unaccustomed. Soon the first traces of boredom, distaste and resentment made themselves felt. She could not help looking back to a past that was glorified in retrospect. She missed the fluff and excitement of her actress days, which her imagination now reconstructed as a whirl of gay parties, adulation and applause. The pursuit of such fancies was naturally not conducive to contentment or the next best mental state, resignation. Minna soon gave way to fits of moping and to secret tears.

Decidedly, wedlock was not the haven of delight she had expected it to be.

CHAPTER 6

CARPENTER LAUERMANN walked down the Manken-
strasse at a leisurely pace, checking house numbers until
he found a door that agreed with the address scribbled
on a paper in his hand. Ah, there was the knocker, and under-
neath it a hand-printed card reading RICHARD WAGNER, *Kapellmeister*. He tapped discreetly and waited. Surely Frau Wagner
was inside. The greengrocer had mentioned seeing her pass
an hour ago on her way home from marketing. Lauermann
knocked again. Then, trying the knob, he found the door unlocked. He entered the small vestibule and stood about awkwardly, not knowing whether to venture farther, when he heard
a rustling sound in the next room.

"Good day, Frau Wagner!" He stopped in the narrow arch-
way to the parlor, where Minna appeared engrossed in rummaging through the contents of a battered trunk. She must
not have heard him, for her hands were smoothing out the folds
of a frilly garment, which she held tentatively against her figure. Now she ran into the next room, trailing a hat and scarf
to be tried on before a dressing-table mirror. Lauermann saw
her reflection in the glass. It was not the radiant face one might
expect in a bride of less than three weeks, he mused briefly.
Then, with a guilty feeling, he cleared his throat and set down
his bag of tools.

Now Minna turned about and stepped through the bedroom
door. "Oh, it's you, Herr Lauermann."

"Yes, ma'am. I knocked, but I guess you were too busy to
hear me, so I just walked in. Your husband says you got some
carpentering for me today." Before she could answer he gave

vent to a personal opinion. "Quite a man, the *Herr Kapell-meister*, if I may say so—quite a man! He crosses in front of my workshop every morning on his way to the theater. Sometimes I am sitting out in the square, by the fountain. No matter what the weather is, always he stops for a chat." He paused long enough to scratch his head and take another breath. "Yes, a wonderful person, the *Herr Kapellmeister*—always interested in others, even in common people like myself. Why, one day last week he asked me to sing him a *Schnadahüpfl*, just a plain ditty from my native village, would you believe it? And then he said, 'My good Lauermann,' he said, 'that's a remarkable voice you have there, a remarkable voice.'"

Minna stifled a yawn. "Fascinating," she said with deadly indifference. Then her hand pointed listlessly across the room. "That armchair you fixed a fortnight ago broke down again."

"The one got busted at your wedding?" Lauermann smirked delightedly. "Must've had a circus at that party!" His manner grew confidential. "Me and my wife do like a bang-up celebration like that, with plenty to eat and drink and——"

There was impatience in Minna's tone. "I'm afraid, Herr Lauermann, the chair won't hold together with just a few nails. It needs a whole new leg."

He nodded. "Yup, that's what my wife said the other time. 'Anything worth doing, August,' she said, 'is worth doing well.'"

Minna came to the point. "Will it cost much? You'll have to buy new wood, I suppose."

He pondered the matter. "Well, there's the wood, and a stain to match, not counting the carving. But seeing as how the *Herr Kapellmeister* is interested in my voice—" he cleared his throat in happy confusion—"I could make it real cheap for you, yup, practically for nothing!"

Minna disregarded this. "I think you had better name a price," she said.

Lauermann appeared obsessed with his subject. "There's talk all over town about your husband making a big change in the policies of the Königsberg Symphony. He has introduced grand opera in concert version, and with local talent, too—in the face of the notion that only foreigners, like them slick

French and Italians, can sing. Why, he's hired a working girl right here, out of the poorest neighborhood, to try out something by—by——"

"Beethoven, the *Fidelio* part—I know." Minna's brows met in a frown. A sensitive nerve had evidently been touched.

"That's it! And he wants more 'home-grown' voices in the chorus, people say." Lauermann went on, stressing the native-soil angle by aiming his index finger at the floor, and then exclaiming with admiration, "Who ever dared such a thing!"

"Oh, there's never been a lack of German singers."

"But they don't make up a majority in our theaters. Me, I perch up in the cheapest seats—the Student Roost, they call it—but I'm a music lover and I know. Your husband, he's what they call a pioneer, he is."

Minna's voice grew suddenly petulant. "I wouldn't know. I'm not in the theater any more."

This brought forth a new flood of approval from the irrepressible carpenter. "Well, that's as it should be, now. A married lady you are, with a husband to support you. Me, I don't hold with respectable wives up there behind the footlights, hugging and smooching with some grease-paint Romeo. No indeed."

Minna's patience was at an end. "You'd better take the chair with you, Herr Lauermann, to get the right measurements. If you'll excuse me, I have some things to do."

"Oh . . . er . . . yes, ma'am."

While Minna retreated once more to the bedroom, Lauermann bent over the chair in question and examined it. He hammered tentatively at the damaged leg, still reluctant to abandon the absorbing discussion. But soon, in happy extrovert fashion, his spirits rose again and he started singing in a frightful off-key voice. His repertoire appeared to be a blend of folkloric trills and alpine yodels, in which he excelled through long and stubborn practice. After some minutes of accompanying himself with plane and hammer, he picked up the chair, inverted it over his head and stalked toward the hall door, calling back to Minna from the threshold, "I got good news for you, Frau Wagner."

Minna came back into the parlor. "Yes? What is it?"

"You don't need a new leg, ma'am, just a special kind of joint. I got one over in my shop."

"That's fine, Herr Lauermann. Then it won't cost so much, will it?"

Instantly he found the opening wedge again. "It wouldn't cost you anything at all if you could persuade . . . er . . . I mean, if the *Herr Kapellmeister* would let me try for——"

With a shudder Minna recalled his vocalizing of a moment ago. "You want an audition, is that it?"

"I am a lover of music!"

"So you said. But I still think you had better figure out a price."

Lauermann gave her a scornful look. "As you wish, Frau Wagner. Good day." Still with the chair resting pagoda-fashion on his square head, he marched off.

Minna closed the door behind him, then turned to survey the room. She did so joylessly and with profound ennui. Observing a fluff of dust in the corner where the armchair had stood, she went to fetch a broom, but dropped it again midway in her purpose. It was no use. She was not domestically inclined, and household chores were loathsome to her.

Now her eyes fixed idly on Richard's bookshelves along the wall. Reading matter, other than scripts from which she had studied her short stage roles, was alien to Minna's life. Richard, on the other hand, whom she knew only in his vehemently amorous aspect, began disclosing the earmarks of a scholar. Yes, there was no denying the awful fact: she had tied herself, of all things, to a bookworm. Between rehearsals with the orchestra, and evening performances, her husband was to be found at home with his nose buried in volume on volume of what appeared to be quite tedious prose. Once or twice Minna had flipped her soft, short fingers through the pages of a Voltaire essay, a biography of Christopher Columbus, or Part One of Goethe's *Faust*, but these subjects struck her as hopelessly tiresome since she could make neither head nor tail of them.

Today in pausing before the bookcase she shook her head as usual while scanning the various titles and picking up a volume or two, then putting them back with distaste. She passed

Richard's shabby rented piano and ran her fingers over the keyboard, suddenly banging down her hand on a burst of dissonance. Her lips quivered and she was on the point of tears as she returned to the open trunk and resumed her earlier absorption in its contents. Fondly she delved into its depths, now bringing forth a box of letters and photographs which arrested her attention. She was perusing these with rapt concentration when the hall door opened and, unnoticed by her, Richard entered. He tiptoed up to embrace Minna, but jumped back apologetically at her scream.

"Oh," she gasped, "it's you!"

"Yes, darling. Whom did you expect?" He kissed her. "I'm sorry. I didn't mean to frighten you."

She rose in confusion, covering the papers and photographs with one of her *bouffant* costumes. With rather uncommon solicitude she ran toward the kitchen. "Goodness! You did give me a start. What time is it? Nothing's on the stove yet."

He caught her in his arms. "Of course not. It's shortly past eleven. But you've got an absent-minded professor for a husband. I left the Bellini text behind, after having carefully gone over it last night and laid it out. I'm sure it was right here on the table." Only now did he notice the outspread crinolines and flitter. His face darkened momentarily, then brightened at a sudden thought. "Oh—I see you've been rummaging through your stage finery again. Frau Moericke, the wardrobe mistress at the theater, was asking only this morning whether you'd care to sell the stuff."

Minna drew back outraged. "No!" She was too shocked for further words.

"Everything here in Königsberg is pretty skimpy, you know," Richard went on, unaware of a gathering storm. "The symphony department is only the stepchild of the opera, with almost no costumes or props." He paused to appraise a silk bodice and skirt. "Still, the budget will stretch and we could get a decent price——"

Now she could contain herself no longer. "*We!* What do you mean by *we?* This stuff, as you call it, it's mine, *mine!*" She snatched the garment from him and laid it beside a cartwheel hat with satin bow and roses. "It suits me better than coarse kitchen aprons and a dust cloth tied around my head. Sell it? I should say not! I won't give up a single ribbon or shoelace— I won't, I *won't!*"

He tried to soothe her. "Darling, darling, nobody is going to force you. I just thought that, well, since you wouldn't be using any of it . . ."

She pulled away from him. "That's just it! You blandly assume that I'll never *want* to use my pretty things. You expect me to sacrifice a career and a future—for poverty and the life of a drudge."

"Wait a minute, dear," he checked her. "Let's not exaggerate. We are poor, but not for want of my earning power."

"Earning power! What good is that when the cash all goes back into the next production, and the next?"

"Things will be better soon, when my innovations begin to show a profit. I've been promised a bonus, once the overhead has been cleared. And that's not all. Look!" He opened a brief case on the table. "I've finished an outline for a new opera. No royalties to pay. Here are parts of the text." He held up some pages for her to see. "I'm basing it on a story called *Rienzi,* by Baron Lytton, the Englishman. You know, Bulwer-Lytton, who wrote *The Last Days of Pompeii.*"

She didn't know. And she didn't care. Her doll features were blank, as when she had earlier scanned the bookcase. Her mind had drifted far away. She sighed petulantly. "I could be in Berlin or Paris. I could have flowers and applause, instead of sweeping out this back-stairs hide-out and eating potato soup."

A grim look came into his face. He reached out and shook her vehemently. "Stop that, do you hear? You were no triumphant leading lady when I met you. You never had top billing in your life!"

She broke away from him and brushed past the trunk, dragging one of the costumes so that the packet of letters and photographs dropped to the floor. Before she could recover them Richard had stooped and picked up a batch, including some visitors' cards and a large picture.

He glanced at the cards and tossed them one by one on the

table after reading off the names: "Mueller, Dietrich, Piefke—
the prima donna's admirers, I suppose."

She flared up. "Give me those! At least they prove that even
without leading parts I had my public." Fondly she sorted the
cards. "Mueller, he was stage manager for a Viennese theater,
and he wanted to star me in an operetta. Said I could sing, too.
Then there's Herr Dietrich, a rich merchant from Berlin—he
sent a carriage full of roses, with this card, asking me to be his
protegée."

Richard did not appear to be listening. His eyes were riveted
on some photographs in his hand. One larger portrait was
signed in a bold scrawl.

"And this pompous Saxon guardsman?" he asked, reading
the name. "Ernst Rudolph von Einsiedel. Who is he—another
flower fancier?"

Minna flushed to the roots of her hair as she reached out to
clutch the picture. "You needn't be comical about my—my
friends. I counted for something when I was alone, making my
own way."

Roughly he seized her wrist. "Just another stage-door dandy,
eh?" His grip tightened. "My dear, chorus girls don't keep
pictures of men unless something more than a posy has been
involved."

Less sure of herself, she gave him a sidelong glance. What
deductions were taking form in his suspicious mind? Anyone
less sensitive than Richard, and less subject to fits of jealousy,
might have dismissed that collection of photographs as harmless mementoes out of a professional woman's strictly professional past. But that one picture and the name "Ernst" hit
Richard between the eyes. Was not the child Natalie called
"Ernestina"?

He was reading the full signature again, then studying the
portrait more closely. "That face has something familiar. Where
have I seen it before?"

"Nowhere. You're being absurd!" Minna's voice had grown
high-pitched and frantic.

His searching inquiry confirmed what was so easy to guess.
"I have it!" he gasped. "The eyes, the tilt of the nose—they

are the same as Ernestina's, aren't they? Your little sister, indeed! I married a ready-made family, didn't I? Well? Answer me!"

Minna tried to cover her face, but he forced down her hands. Fiercely he looked her up and down, scrutinizing each feature.

"Let me look at you. What's your true age?" He laughed harshly. "Such innocence, such coy touch-me-not ways when we first met in Lauchstaedt, and all the while I underestimated your acting ability!"

Minna turned suddenly defiant. "All right, I lied to you. I'm six years older than you thought, and the child is mine. My parents took her so I could keep on working."

He was shattered. "No, it can't be true! You're making sport of me."

"Why should I? Believe me, my life's been no joke."

Yes, he believed her. Too well he recalled her sly girlish maneuvers, her carefully noncommittal flirtations, her price for complete surrender: a wedding ring. But he could not keep from exacerbating his torment by demanding further facts.

"This man—he wasn't your husband, or you wouldn't have needed to marry me, nor passed off the girl as your sister. What happened?"

Minna's sullenness gave way to a voluble outburst. "I wasn't good enough for his high-and-mighty family, that's what happened. He had to marry some baggage with a title to help him break into a diplomatic career. They sent him off to a post in England." She broke down, weeping softly.

Richard was moved to reach out for her, but he overcame the impulse. "Go on."

"What happened to *me* didn't matter. A little money came for a time, till they realized I wasn't going to give them any trouble. After a while they forgot about me altogether."

Well, there he had the whole sorry story, and what was to be gained by airing it still further? At sixteen Minna had been seduced by a worldly cavalier whose family would not condone the *mésalliance*. The callous lover had skipped off, leaving the girl to bear her shame. Was this so unique, so unheard of an occurrence that he, Richard, could view it without a faint stirring of pity? He paced the floor. Superfluous tears, superfluous confession! How could she, all this time, have lived such a lie? How could he have been fooled so easily?

There were no answers to these desperate reflections, for by this stage Minna's contrition was heartbreaking to behold. Her whole frame shook with sobs that cut through Richard's anger and drove him to distraction. Quite involuntarily he stepped forward and touched her shoulders with compassion.

"I know it's been terrible for you," he murmured in spite of himself, "an ugly and cruel experience. But why, *why* couldn't you trust me enough to tell me, instead of letting me find that picture?"

He paused, resentment flaring up and searing him anew. All of it he was generous enough to understand and forgive. What rankled was the child's first name and the fact that—ten years later!—Einsiedel's photograph had not yet been destroyed.

"The picture," he challenged again—"you've kept it all these years. It's here even now, within the walls of our home!"

He ought to pack up and leave. Self-respect demanded that he clear out of this disorderly mess, this compromise with a woman older than himself, whose past would lie like a dead weight on his future. He must break off, now, while there was still time.

But he knew better. There was no time. He was swamped by the flames of his own passion. Too young, too poor, too rapt in the brooding forces of his musical destiny, he had as yet only an adolescent's knowledge of women. The experienced Minna found it an easy task to chain, if not his soul, at least—no, by no means least—his flesh.

She was looking up at him helplessly now, with melting pupils that pleaded forgiveness. Her soft, full lips opened, but she did not speak. He struggled to master himself, and failed.

"I shouldn't have said that, dear." He was on his knees. "It's not for me to hold judgment over you. What's past, Minna, is past, and I'm willing to forget."

She could hardly believe her ears. "You—you are?"

"Of course!" He was all tenderness now. "It could happen to any girl as pretty and trusting as you."

Smiling through her tears, which came so copiously and easily, Minna made a dramatic gesture. She picked up the photograph from the table, tore it twice across and let the pieces trickle through her fingers. Then she flung her arms about Richard's neck.

"You angel," she whispered. "You strange, incredible angel!"

CHAPTER 10

THE moment of elation did not last, for there came almost at the same instant a loud knock on the door. Reluctantly Richard disengaged himself from Minna's embrace. On the threshold stood a policeman accompanied by two strangers. It was the officer who spoke.

"Is this the home of an orchestra conductor, name of Richard Wagner?"

One of the other men shook a finger in the air. "That's him, that's him! And this is the furniture, including that piano, on which he owes me two months' payments." Only now did he perceive the absence of the armchair taken by Lauermann. With heightened umbrage he turned to the third visitor. "Mister Court Clerk, I want you to check your books. There's a chair missing in this corner, a valuable chair which undoubtedly has been pawned to pay for some Bohemian carousal." He sneered. "Stage folk, bah!"

"Just a moment, Herr Gruber," Minna broke in. "None of your property was pawned. The chair is at Carpenter Lauermann's for repairs."

"Repairs, eh?" Gruber exploded anew. "Breaking up furniture before it's even paid for—I knew it!" He nodded to the policeman. "Officer, I want all these things removed at once, back to my shop."

Instinctively Richard stepped back a few paces to shield the piano. "You can't, you mustn't! My work, my new opera would be jeopardized."

Gruber held out his hand. "Then how about some coin, on the line?"

Richard went through his pockets. "I have only a few gulden. But next week, I promise for sure——"

"Promises are cheap. I want hard cash. What happens to your take at the box office? I hear it's quite substantial."

There was no persuasive way to answer this. The musicians' pay roll must be met, to be sure. But there were the added costs of experimentation with opera in concert version. Already Richard had attempted an explanation of this to Minna, without success. Gruber was even less likely to understand; in fact, he was no longer listening. For the third time he buttonholed the policeman.

"Officer, I see no chance or prospect of collecting what is due me. I want this property attached."

While the representative of the law still hesitated, Gruber walked about the room, examining various articles of furniture, tapping the piano, feeling the nap of the rug, to make sure that nothing further was damaged or missing.

The policeman looked uncomfortable. He turned to Richard. "Your answer, sir?"

"I have told you. I am sure I can do better next week."

Now the court clerk spoke up. "The City of Königsberg does not operate on promises, my good man. Do you or do you not wish to satisfy the claimant here with a token payment? As of this minute."

"As of this minute!" Richard went through his pockets again and halted, feeling his watch. "Here—here is my gold watch. It was my grandfather's. Also the chain—it's particularly heavy." He offered both. "Perhaps these will do?"

An appraising gleam came into Gruber's eyes as he snatched the articles. "Very well. They will do as security—till next week, mind you."

Wagner nodded, not fully aware of the costly sacrifice. He laid one hand tenderly on the piano. "Yes, yes, till next week."

Appeased, Gruber and his companions turned to go. In the hallway, however, they collided with the child Natalie, who came on the run, with schoolbooks and a slate under one arm, a wriggling puppy under the other.

"Look, Minna," she cried exultantly. "Frau Sieber's Poldi, next door, has puppies! Can I keep one, please, can I?"

Richard was instantly moved to pet the animal. But Minna,

a silent and resentful witness to the earlier scene with Gruber, was at the end of her tether. "I should say not!" she snapped at the startled child. "We're having enough trouble making ends meet."

Natalie turned to Richard. "Only one small puppy . . ."

He smiled regretfully. "Your moth—uh, sister is right, dear. We've quite a lot of bills just now." He kissed the child to comfort her. "Run along and take the little fellow back. I'm sure Poldi will give us another chance."

Not without tears, Natalie departed. There was a long silence, during which Richard waited for a conciliatory word from Minna. As none was forthcoming, he stepped to the piano and picked up some music. Then, without looking back, he closed the front door behind him.

Minna was alone, free to surrender to her anger. How easy it was for a man to dispose of a problem: he simply walked out and lost himself in his work! For the rest of the morning Richard's thoughts would be taken up with Bellini, while the afternoon was devoted to revisions of the *Rienzi* outline. Of course she, Minna, had no such escape. Like most wives, she was caught in the treadmill of domestic duties, with never a prospect of relief or change. A half hour ago she had perceived, in a passing glimmer, that she was married to a man of tolerance and vast generosity. But this realization had quickly paled beside the Gruber episode, which laid bare that most unforgivable of husbandly failings—a lack of a knack for piling up coin. Richard's high-minded acceptance of Natalie had been forgotten. What Minna remembered was the anemic state of his finances.

With drooping spirits and dejected gait she wandered into the bedroom and sat down before her dressing table. She studied her face in the mirror, then rose to get a view of her figure. What she saw was not bad, not bad at all. In somewhat better mood she returned to the front room just as a clock in the near-by church tower struck noon. This roused her from her reveries and she hurried into the kitchen, emerging presently in an apron and with a cooking pot of potatoes. She sat beside the table and began to peel, letting the potato skins fall

into her lap. The task was visibly distasteful to her. She paused
drearily, letting her mind wander, while her eyes rested now
and again on the visiting cards Richard had left strewn on the
sideboard. She could just make out the names of some of her
former beaux, dwelling on them as if mesmerized. Now she put
down her paring knife and reached for one particular card,
deciphering the faded script, reading in a half whisper:

"In humble homage to one so talented!
P.S. *If you are ever in Berlin do not hesitate to call on me at
Löwenstrasse 18.*
                                    R. DIETRICH."

She remembered Herr Dietrich rather well, for he had been
one of her more persistent admirers. He lacked hair and he
had a paunch—two reasons why in her younger days she had
turned him down. But, she now recalled, he also had a factory
in Dresden or Berlin—a furniture factory, or was it sausages?
. . . Richard's stacked manuscripts and biographical tomes in-
truded on her vision. At least she had never seen Herr Dietrich
with a book, that was certain. Chewing meditatively on the
card, she began to ponder. Did he still have all that money?
And had he not forgotten her?
    With an impatient gesture she set down the potatoes and
took off her apron, then opened the buffet drawer and took out
paper and pen. Almost without thinking she wrote down that
last question and a few things more. Now the address—it was
Berlin after all—and a bit of wax to make sure her billet-doux
was well sealed before tossing it in the mail. The post chaise
left shortly after twelve. She could catch it and be back in a
trice if she ran.
    The Mankenstrasse was deserted as Minna darted out her
door, hatless, and with the envelope clutched in her hand. No
one saw her. Almost no one, that is. For around the corner,
without puppy and very subdued, the small figure of Natalie
came into view. The child's eyes took in Minna's purposeful
stride without registering particular surprise. Now Natalie
opened the narrow garden gate and entered the house. Find-

ing no one at home, the child automatically picked up the
crumpled apron and tied it twice around her middle before
starting to set the noonday table. Then, as though quite accustomed to taking over when the lazy Minna walked out on her
job, Natalie sat down and with grave concentration finished
peeling the potatoes.

It was scarcely a week later, by return post according to the
standards of those days, that an answer arrived from Berlin.
Both Richard and Natalie were gone when the mail carrier
stopped, leaving Minna alone with her secret. She trembled
as she held the letter, for it was not difficult to guess its contents. Obviously the aging Lothario had not, or pretended that
he had not, forgotten, else there would have been no response
at all. In breathless eagerness Minna tore the envelope and
skimmed through the message. Yes, here was balm for her
starved vanity. Herr Dietrich's somewhat flowery prose gave
testimony of a startling sort: either he was a man of noblest
loyalty, or else he had reached a time in life when amatory
dalliance was less readily available. In the latter case even a
warmed-up former romance might present a prospect over
which, figuratively, he smacked his lips. Possibly too he was
a stickler for thoroughness who hated to leave anything unfinished. In any event, Herr Dietrich seemed eager to consummate the postponed rendezvous to which, in earlier years,
Minna had not acceded. In beseeching terms he urged her now
to fly to his arms.

Her senses reeled. With deliberate intent she had banished
the memory of the letter writer's true person. Wishfully her
mind's eye envisioned the corpulent, bare-pated Dietrich in a
new and more acceptable format—young, blond, appealing. Almost like Richard, actually. That is, Richard with money.

The thought of money brought her up short. She was back
in reality, surveying the modest flat, the unpaid furnishings,
the makeshift kitchen. What gall of Richard's to presume that
she deserved no better than this!

"I fail to see," he had told her only that morning in one of
their increasingly frequent quarrels, "why it's such a sacrifice
for you to be a wife and homemaker."

Wife and homemaker indeed! A servant drudge, that's what she was, thanks to a husband who did not know how to provide even the barest necessities. Why did she put up with it? Was not Herr Dietrich's gallant summons the open-sesame she had been yearning for, the easy passport to freedom?

She folded the letter lovingly and tucked it into her bodice. Then, with a furtive look about her, she hurried into the bedroom and fetched a small satchel from the cupboard. Feverishly she began packing a few clothes, selecting only her prettiest frocks and daintiest shoes. When this was done she put on a cloak and the most becoming of her theatrical hats, making sure that the streamers were tied in a fetching bow.

Now she was ready. Her reticule bulged with cosmetics, gloves and some carefully hoarded cash. She checked it over again and took another look at the address on Dietrich's printed card, recalling as she did so that this innocuous keepsake had precipitated her first serious matrimonial rift. Her lip curled in defiance. "Löwenstrasse Eighteen," she repeated several times, etching the street number on her mind. Then, before replacing the card, she gazed with satisfaction at its long-memorized yet ever-refreshing penciled message.

"In humble homage to one so talented!" her lips whispered, lingering on each delicious syllable.

Wife and homemaker?

She had stepped outside and closed the door behind her. "Poor Richard," she tossed back under her breath, "don't be funny. I don't play character parts—not at these prices!"

CHAPTER 11

RICHARD put down his baton and motioned his players to break off the rehearsal. Herr Bonsel, the manager of the Königsberg Royal Theater, wished to have a word with the symphony director. When Herr Bonsel appeared in person the matter was serious.

"Herr Wagner, one moment please!" Bonsel approached the podium, waving a paper in his hand.

"Yes?" Richard stepped down politely.

"We had better cut next Sunday's concert and the operatic experiments. I have here a letter from the Comédie Française——"

"The Comédie Française?"

"That's right. They have started early on their annual tour. That means you must vacate the theater so we can get ready for them. You know, trapeze equipment and that sort of thing."

Richard could not contain himself. "But that's outrageous!" he cried with a gesture toward the musicians. "My people here, they've rehearsed for weeks, and the ticket sales are good. You will lose no money!"

Bonsel raised an eyebrow. "My dear man, what you call a 'good' ticket sale is laughable compared to the admission I can charge for some lively French entertainment."

"But you promised, sir, that my artists and I might use the theater till the start of the new season."

"So I promised. 'If nothing turns up,' I promised. But you have no contract." Bonsel waved the letter in Richard's face. "The stage is to be cleared as of tomorrow morning, *basta!*"

"The stage is cleared," Richard exploded, "as of this moment!" He gave the orchestra a sign of dismissal, then gathered up his music and stormed offstage. A moment later he was

94

on the street, heading down the theater steps, when a well-dressed man halted in his path.

"Hello there—whoa—no time to greet a friend?"

"Theo!" Richard came to a stop, struggling to regain his composure. "Where did you drop from, another planet?"

Theodor Apel smiled. "Almost. I've been halfway around the world since I last saw you—a year ago, wasn't it?"

"More than that."

"Much too long, anyway, without news from each other. How are things? What have you been doing?"

"Oh, nothing unusual." There was bitterness in Richard's voice. "I've been fired, with boring regularity, from a whole string of jobs."

"Sorry, old man." Apel was shocked. He reached automatically for his wallet, but Richard waved him off.

"No, thanks. I had a hard enough time paying back your last loan. I don't want a new load of debts."

"Can't I make you understand that I never expect you to pay me back? I've got more useless money that I'll never spend——"

He broke off, for Richard was not listening. They walked silently down the street, coming eventually to a big open square that appeared overrun with people.

"What's this," Apel asked, "a county fair during Lent?"

"No. A far bigger attraction. Take another look."

Richard pointed to one end of the square where the populace was thickest. Over the heads of the crowd a gallows was being raised for a public execution.

Apel buttonholed a stranger. "What's going on here?"

The man shrugged. "Some poor devil, a thief they say, is 'meeting justice' at high noon."

Richard drew back with a shudder. "Horrible! When will civilization do away with such spectacles?" His fists clenched. "*There's* your greatest audience attraction—a display of cruelty. Even the Comédie Française can't draw a crowd like that."

Repelled yet fascinated, the two friends moved closer to where they could make out a wretched creature hunched between a pair of guards. The condemned man seemed to be taking leave of his dog, a huge Newfoundland. Now one of the executioner's assistants shoved the animal away. On seeing this, Richard pushed through the crowd to the prisoner's side. Without a word he seized the dog's collar and drew the beast to him.

A trace of a smile lighted up the condemned man's face as he spoke in a cracked voice. "His name's Robber, sir. Though I could never teach him to steal nothin' . . . He'll be a good friend to you, a good——"

The words were muffled by a hood thrown over the victim's head as the executioner made ready to proceed with his task. Without looking back, Richard and Theo walked on, leading the dog between them. There was a long tortured silence that neither could break. At last, several blocks away, Richard paused.

"I take back what I said a while ago, Theo."

"Yes? What about?"

"About not going into debt. I want one more loan from you."

Apel's response was immediate. "Good! How much do you need? Just name it."

Richard was thinking aloud. "I must have enough to take Minna and me out of Germany. The little Natalie can go back to Minna's parents." He stopped to pat the dog's head. "As for Robber here, I don't know who would take a hanged man's legacy. No, Robber had better come along too."

Apel looked baffled. "Out of Germany? Whatever is on your mind?"

"That—that fiendish performance back there is on my mind." Richard nodded toward the town square. "How can I make music in a land where people gather to watch a fellow human being done to death?"

Apel tried to soothe him. "It happens everywhere—in Italy, Russia, Sweden. Remember the French Revolution with its guillotine, and Restoration England where gentlewomen brought their needlework along with picnic baskets while waiting for the sharpening of the headsman's ax?"

"Yes, yes," Richard admitted. "All the same, I've read that there's a movement afoot, both in England and France, not

only to bar executions from public view but to do away with
the death penalty altogether. In any case, Theo, my mind's
made up. I need a change—a change of mental climate."

"Very well. Where do you intend to go?"

"I don't know. London, Paris——"

"How about America?"

"Ah!" A light came into Richard Wagner's eyes, but he shook
his head abruptly. "No, that would be too expensive. Paris
will do. All artists, I am told, find inspiration—yes, and recognition too—in Paris."

Apel reached into his pocket. "Paris it is. I have friends
there—Heinrich Heine, Alfred de Musset, Giacomo Meyerbeer.
I'll write you some introductions."

Richard laid a hand on his friend's shoulder. "Thanks. You
won't regret this." A wave of exultation swept over him. "Come,
let's tell Minna about it!"

Together they raced the rest of the way, arriving at the small
Wagner flat just as the clock in the church tower struck a quarter past twelve.

"I'm never home before one," Richard explained. "The table
won't be set. But you'll eat with us, of course."

He was wrong. On entering they discovered that dishes and
cutlery had indeed been laid out, while in the kitchen young
Natalie busied herself about the stove. Minna was nowhere to
be seen.

Richard's heart sank with sudden apprehension. "Hello," he
called to the girl, trying to conceal his alarm. "All alone?"

Natalie staggered under a tureen of steaming soup. "Minna's
gone," she said simply.

"Shopping?" Richard prompted, though his heart already
told him otherwise.

"No."

Offering no further comment, Natalie nodded toward the
bedroom. Richard followed and found his answer. Minna's
empty dressing table, the open cupboard, the bare upper shelf
where her travel bag had been kept bore out his worst fears.

"She's gone," Natalie repeated with finality.

He could not, would not, believe it. In a frenzy he ransacked the clothespress, the chest of drawers, the cartons and boxes that the possessive Minna had piled up, for she could give or throw nothing away. But she had learned her lesson: no tell-tale papers had been left behind. None, that is, save the small seesaw blotter on her desk. Held up to a mirror, it disclosed a blurred Berlin address.

Of course he must follow her at once. With a sheepish look at Theo he felt for the money that had just been given him for a far different purpose. Paris would have to wait. Nothing could be more important—the orchestra, his job, his future—than getting Minna back.

"Aren't you going to eat?" Natalie asked, seeing that the soup had gone untouched.

Well, he had better gulp a few spoonfuls and take along a piece of bread. Berlin, he remembered, was an expensive place and he did not want to waste Theo's funds on such ignoble matters as food. In a few minutes he had finished and was on his way, leaving Apel and the child behind.

The Berlin search proved fruitless. The fugitive wife and her old beau had gone a-trysting in some country hide-out; the manservant answering the door at the Dietrich mansion was unable to give any particulars. Within a week Richard had returned home, despondent. But here—oh, miracle!—a letter awaited him. It was from Minna. She was coming back! Her escapade had been a dreadful mistake, she explained, into which she had been lured by trickery and false promises; all she had wanted was a chance to help Richard by resuming her own career and thus contributing to the family cashbox. But Herr Dietrich's patronage (she did not mention that there was a Frau Dietrich, who had made short shrift of the clandestine idyl) had proved a fizzle. Contrite and crushed, Minna implored forgiveness.

Richard forgave. But that did not change the fact that he had lost his job. "How do you expect us to keep an orchestra together," asked the angry Königsberg management, "with a conductor who runs off whenever he pleases?" In addition, an advance unit of the Comédie Française had already arrived, causing all symphonic plans to be indefinitely suspended.

Now was the time to pull up stakes and leave for France. However, even with strictest economy, the journey to Berlin had cost a pretty penny, and Apel had meanwhile gone on his way. Also, Richard had vowed to himself that he would not again ask for help. There was no choice but to dispose of the household and to set out once more in search of work.

After repeated failures he made contact at last with the City Theater at Riga, in the Russian province of Latvia. Again it was only a temporary fill-in job while the regular orchestra director completed a concert tour. Furthermore, there would be language difficulties, as Richard spoke neither Latvian nor Russian. But it was a means to an end: the yearned-for flight to Paris.

In moving to Riga the little family had no packing problem. Most of the furniture had already been repossessed by the relentless Herr Gruber, and as for Minna's wardrobe, it was sacrificed now to help defray travel expenses. In her present mood of remorse there were no protests or wails; Minna herself carried the best of her theatrical finery to the costume dealer's and traded it for cash.

After they had all settled in Riga a new development presented itself. Minna was pregnant. Though her questionable past and more recent moral defection might have cast doubt on Richard's claim to fatherhood, he did not allow such speculations to take root. Instead his heart overflowed with solicitude for the prospective mother and child. It now became evident that the compassion he had always felt for animals was a sublimation of his love of all creatures and of life itself, the highest expression of which could be reached only through the wonder of conception and birth. With the promise of bearing him a son or daughter of his very own, Minna took unchallenged possession over his soul. Nothing and no one, he felt sure, could ever dislodge her.

The happy dream ended with a rude awakening. Forgotten creditors from Lauchstaedt and Königsberg, some of whom were still trying to track down the disreputable Bethmanns, got wind somehow of Richard Wagner's new location. As former *Kapellmeister* of the Magdeburg Company he was held responsible for that organization's bad debts, as well as some of his own. The latter he could take care of, but only a princely inheritance would have sufficed to cover the Bethmann arrears. As the impatient claimants threatened Richard with litigation there was no choice but, once again, to start packing. The Apel loan had been carefully husbanded. With a small nest egg of additional Riga earnings the long projected trip to France could be attempted.

The exodus, set for the summer of 1839, must be made without the knowledge of local authorities, since the creditors were ready with a warrant for Richard's arrest. Thus, to leave Russian soil he must obtain a Russian passport and a ticket for some vessel that would be cleared from a Baltic sailing point. A sympathetic cellist named Abraham Moeller, whom Wagner had befriended at the start of his duties in Riga, proved of invaluable help. Through influential relatives Moeller reserved passage for Richard and his family on a cargo ship named *Thetis*, after the classic Greek goddess of the sea. This vessel carried a crew of seven, the captain included. Space was at a premium, but—for a price—a corner would be made available to the travelers, deep below deck. As regarded passports, Moeller acknowledged defeat. The fugitives would have to be smuggled across the border into Prussia, where, in the port of Pillau, the *Thetis* would pick them up.

The overland journey took two days by stagecoach, after which the frontier crossing must be attempted within a few paces of the watchful Cossack patrol. Once these hazards had been negotiated the Wagners were to be picked up by a German accomplice, with a disguised peasant cart in tow. The last part of the way, finally, they must make on foot.

Actually the whole plan worked astonishingly well, including the skirting of the Cossack encampment. This was the more remarkable as the giant dog Robber, whom Richard could not bear to leave behind, remained a source of constant danger. Had the animal barked even once while in earshot of the Muscovites there would have been the devil to pay. But Robber was possessed of uncanny intelligence. Softly he padded along beside the fleeing family, as though fully aware of the terrible risk. Even on hearing a Cossack hound's ominous growl, only a short distance away, Robber ducked lower and held his peace.

Misfortune struck only after the worst appeared to be over and they were safely on German soil. The chartered peasant cart, a decrepit affair, sagged under its load and promptly turned over into a ditch. No bones were broken, but Minna suffered severe contusions and nervous shock. Before the journey could be continued she was overcome by a spasm of pain that ended in miscarriage.

From now on everything that happened took on the aspect of a nightmare. In pitch-black darkness the travelers reached Pillau, where the sailing vessel *Thetis* lay at anchor. They hastened aboard and found themselves shunted into the bowels of the ship, to a miniature cabin that could not have been meant to hold more than a single—and preferably undernourished—occupant. Well, they were by no means corpulent, what with stringent economies and not one square meal among them since departing from Riga. But with their ill-assorted bundles of luggage, and the enormous Robber taking up half the available space, the three humans found themselves wedged together like a catch of herring.

Minna's nerves were the first to give way. "I don't know why you had to bring that dog along," she chided Richard. "He'll eat up our last copper, besides leaving us no decent place to sleep!"

Richard gave her a long look. "Robber has already lost one master," he said quietly, "and he loves us."

"But he's a monster! Why not put him back on shore and let him fend for himself?"

On this Richard set her straight. "You can't do that, you know—just leave someone who loves you. No, not even a dog."

He did not disclose, at this critical moment, that the full story of Robber's origin had not been told. The dog had belonged originally to a Riga merchant named Armitstead, from whom he had been taken by the subsequently condemned housebreaker. Several times, on seeing his pet in Wagner's company, Armitstead had claimed Robber, but the animal was so attached by now to his newest benefactor that both men came to an amicable agreement. Had Minna known of Armitstead's existence she would of course have lost no time in leading Robber back to his first home. It was Richard's silence that caused the animal to be included in the strenuous voyaging that lay ahead.

CHAPTER 12

THE nightmare had only started. No sooner did the schooner *Thetis* put to sea than a violent storm arose which tossed the little craft before it like a broken toy. Within a half hour the inexperienced travelers went through the paradoxical phenomenon of seasickness, trembling for their lives yet fervently wishing they were dead.

After eight days of alternating panic and nausea Richard mastered himself sufficiently to appear on deck. Here a magnificent sight awaited him: the ship was approaching the green coast of Denmark. He hastened below again and dragged Minna and Natalie to the porthole of the tiny cabin.

"Look, there's the town of Elsinore, and Kronborg Castle, the scene of Shakespeare's *Hamlet!*"

But Minna and the child were too ill for literary enlightenment. Only Robber took a halfhearted interest.

The ship sailed on through the Straits of Kattegat and Skagerrak where, after a brief calm, the elements exploded anew, this time into a furious hurricane. Now even Robber refused to leave his hideaway under the cabin bunk, while half the crew members were reported sick. Richard, however, had got his sea legs. Hatless, he strode the deck, absorbing the full drama of the storm. He listened to a rugged old sailor defiantly singing a wild Norse chant, and his sensitive ear captured the tune. In the howling winds his mind conjured up visions of another Shakespeare drama, *The Tempest,* in which Caliban and Ariel battled—the one to destroy, the other to save—an equally storm-tossed cargo. Then a different picture took shape before his fancy: a scene developed by the poet Heinrich Heine concerning the Dutch mariner Vanderdecken, who had sworn a blasphemous oath that he would round the Cape of Good Hope against Nature and Heaven's opposition. For this he had been condemned like Ahasuerus, the Wandering Jew, to endless roaming. In Vanderdecken's case the aimless sailing over the earth's seas could end only if a virtuous woman gave him her lifelong love, the proof of which must necessarily be her death.

While the hurricane raged and the ship floundered past Norway's fiords, Richard reveled in a fever of creation. Already he had drawn a mental sketch for an opera to be entitled *The Flying Dutchman,* in which the sailor song just heard would be incorporated. Swiftly the plot crystallized as he saw, with eyes of his imagination, the phantom schooner, sails full-blown, of the accursed and lonely Vanderdecken.

Thrown off course by implacable elements, the battered *Thetis* was unable to reach France as scheduled. Instead she drifted into the Thames, where she hove to for repairs. The Wagners and their dog were dumped on British soil.

Not knowing which way to turn, Richard hailed a passing hansom cab. Into this the little family managed to squeeze itself, with Robber taking up most of the seat. They had no plans and scarcely any cash, but there was no room for them on the docks, so they had better go on a sight-seeing tour of London. On spotting the Houses of Parliament the idea struck Richard that the great Bulwer-Lytton might be found there and that "His Lordship" would be pleased to see the half-finished manuscript of *Rienzi.* But no, Bulwer-Lytton was not around, nor was he a peer or a political figure except by the grace of Richard's innocence. Furthermore, lest their remaining funds be dissipated altogether, the travelers hastened to dicker for passage on a Channel steamer to France.

As they were about to put to sea once more it was discovered that Robber had been left behind. Or rather, already aboard, the dog's recollection of the previous voyage might have induced him to skip back to shore. It took the combined persuasion of Richard's eloquence and the young Natalie's tears to delay the small vessel's departure until Robber was fetched from the dock.

The crossing was uneventful. The French coast soon came

into view, and the travelers prepared to land at Boulogne-sur-Mer, where the currently fashionable composer Giacomo Meyerbeer was vacationing. His operas *Robert le Diable* and *Les Huguenots* had won acclaim across Europe, and the artist was reported working on another sure triumph, *Le Prophète.*

Richard had Meyerbeer's address on a card signed by Theodor Apel. He now called on the prosperous master, paying tribute to the latter's achievements and requesting some introductions to the Paris music world. Meyerbeer, a large and exceedingly well-nourished gentleman, received the shabby-looking stranger with no enthusiasm and less courtesy. He accepted the phrases of adulation as his due, but for the rest he appeared little inclined to put himself out in behalf of an unknown greenhorn who might possess more confidence than talent. He handed the visitor a brief list of publishers who were known to employ orchestral arrangers or copyists, and wished him luck. No commendation, no bolstering references. The interview was ended.

By now the Wagners were bare of funds. In order to continue their journey they must trade one of their luggage pieces in exchange for the fare to Paris. Once in the famed City of Light, they did not repeat the London sight-seeing expedition but headed straight for the cheap market district of Les Halles. Here they found lodgings on the top floor of No. 33 Rue de la Tonnellerie, an ancient structure overlooking such avenues as Tripe Street, Fish Row and Cheese Alley. The sidewalk directly below the Wagners' lone window was littered with a mash of trampled cabbage leaves and fruit. But a stone bust above the street entrance informed passers-by that here within these venerable walls the poet-dramatist Molière had been born.

It was hardly the goal Richard had set for himself at the start of his long pilgrimage. But he had reached the end of his material resources and there was no other place to go. He, and Minna and Natalie with him, must stand his ground and make the best of what was to be had from it.

As they climbed the narrow stairs to their attic apartment Minna took in her surroundings with disgust. Richard had just paid the grubby landlord a full month's rent in advance, turning over each centime with utmost care. Now he tried to make light of the depressing setup.

"Well, here we are on the banks of the Seine, in the city of a thousand possibilities!"

Minna sniffed. "Do you realize we're right above a fish market?" She had opened the window, then quickly slammed it shut. "This is a cool day. But can you imagine what it will be like in midsummer?"

She was right, of course, in disapproving. He too would have preferred a better address. Still, they must adjust themselves to the inevitable.

"Let's not lose courage, dear," he told her. "Remember, we came here on borrowed funds and must put up with a few hardships."

"A few hardships!" She gave a mocking laugh. "In this chicken roost? We might as well be back in that ship's cabin among the bales of hay and the grain sacks. Where do we cook? Where do we eat and sleep?"

While she continued ranting, Richard and Natalie quietly went about unpacking their skimpy luggage and putting things to rights. When a semblance of order had been established they sat down to consider the next step.

"A little patience," Richard promised, "and we shall improve our lot. I've an idea for a new opera, a really good one this time. It came to me during that storm at sea."

Minna shuddered. "We were nearly shipwrecked! Who wants to hear an opera about a storm at sea?"

"You don't understand. The storm is only the background for a dramatic legend, the story of the Flying Dutchman."

Now Minna was thoroughly befuddled. "A Dutchman who flies?" She sneered in exasperation. "*That* ought to be good!"

He took her in his arms and kissed her. "Poor Minna, always so literal—but that's part of your charm! As for the Dutchman, no, he doesn't actually take to the air, like this." He flapped his arms, mimicking a pair of wings.

The little Natalie grasped his meaning. "He doesn't fly," she cried proudly. "He *flees!*"

"Exactly." Richard patted her cheek. "He is a man cursed to roam the oceans in atonement for a grave sin."

Minna was idly fingering an old newspaper that lay in a table drawer. Now she veered suddenly about. "Why can't you write something like this?" She held the paper before Richard's eyes, pointing at the theater notices. "Here, that's what people like. Something commercial, that will bring money."

He glanced over the page which contained announcements of Gioacchino Rossini's *Barber of Seville*, Gaetano Donizetti's *Elixir of Love*, and a Grand Guignol opening of *Papa s'Amuse*. Nodding good-naturedly, he laid the paper aside.

"Give me time, Minna," he pleaded. "Give me a little time."

It happened that this was all she could give him, for she was devoid of either faith or hope. And though she was not a woman of profound perception, her pessimism had a sound base. A winter of near starvation lay ahead.

Cramped into a pair of unheated rooms which must provide living and working space, the family shivered and endured. It soon became evident that Richard could not resume his career, either as composer or conductor, for Paris had more than its quota of both. Here in the City of Light were Offenbach, Gounod, the young Saint-Saëns, and a dozen others basking in public favor. The best that an unproved stranger could ask for was hack work as an adapter of opera hits-of-the-day for simplified piano or vocal use. It was an unusual stroke of luck that the printing firm of Maurice Schlesinger happened to need a young man for just this chore. Richard applied and was accepted.

Day after day for the next two months he carried home huge stacks of manuscripts. Far into the night he labored over elementary transpositions of the tritest passages in *La Fille du Régiment* and similar standard hits. And as he pocketed his miserable fee, which scarcely fed the family but allowed no balance for clothing or fuel, he regretted that Robber, that giant quadruped, had not gone astray on the London docks. It was almost impossible to care for the beast here in the penury and squalor of a Paris slum. Robber had shown little intelligence. England, citadel of animal lovers, would have been a good place to be lost in.

As for himself, Richard Wagner felt that he had truly gone

astray. He had always loathed mediocrity and compromise. Yet here he was stranded and might continue so for years, prostituting his gifts and wasting his energy on tasks that only furthered the exploitation of uninspired commercial trash.

Turning from his own frustration to view the progress of others, he questioned whether there was anything vital and new in the musical output of mid-century Europe. Where were the worthy heirs of Bach, Mozart, Weber, Beethoven? If only he, Richard, could rise above hunger and the wet cold of the Paris winter, he would show the world the true meaning of creative work! He would start where Beethoven left off, and lead tomorrow's harmonies into fresh and glorious channels. He would teach men a special approach to theater and concert stage, and to the marvelous offspring of both—grand opera. For the present, however, he must close his window and keep out the fumes of a carload of leeks, spilled the night before and turned by the morning traffic into a juicy carpet.

In her own way Minna was taking matters even more to heart. If she had hated the domestic treadmill in clean and bearable surroundings such as her honeymoon dwelling in Königsberg, the Paris interlude soon became for her the nadir of existence. Daily she wept for the good things she had left behind and which, in the light of present conditions, had been indeed wonderful. Her only release lay, unhappily, in nagging.

"Look here." She showed Richard another headline in a borrowed paper. "Meyerbeer is in Paris, celebrating his newest triumph. If you weren't so stubborn you would look him up again and get a lift to the top."

It was a highly dubious surmise, but in order to pacify her he agreed. He would ferret out Meyerbeer's address and pay the illustrious man another visit. Perhaps the flush of one more gaudy and pleasingly monetary success had rendered the proud Giacomo less stony of heart.

On a gray February morning, at five minutes past eleven, Richard stood in the foyer of an elegant residence in the district of Saint Germain. An aloof manservant asked for his name and bade the obscure and poorly dressed stranger to take a seat. Evidently Monsieur Meyerbeer was not at home to all and sundry, though a medley of voices could be heard through the door to an adjoining chamber. Perhaps an invitation or some special introduction was necessary? Well, there was Theo's note, which Richard had already used at Boulogne-sur-Mer to gain Meyerbeer's attention. It might serve the same purpose again.

Quickly he went through his pockets, searching for the much thumbed bit of paper. By the time he found it the impressive servant had returned.

"Monsieur Meyerbeer is very busy," he announced. "But he will receive you if you will make your visit brief."

How was brevity to be matched with an account of miseries so long endured? How could a plea for assistance, not financial but in the realm of professional comradeship, be framed on the run? Richard had no idea. But also he had no choice. Nodding politely, he followed the perfunctory summons into the next room.

CHAPTER 13

GIACOMO MEYERBEER'S Paris salon was actually an extension of his bedroom. That is, an intervening wall opened in partitions, permitting the sybaritic artist to loll comfortably in his pillows while receiving the daily parade of colleagues, sycophants, petitioners and friends who were ushered into his presence. A morning at Meyerbeer's, everyone knew, was not unlike the historic *levées* of Marie Antoinette or Madame Pompadour at Versailles—namely a spirited, conversational breakfast-in-bed, with social callers in attendance.

On this particular day in the waning winter of 1840 Monsieur Giacomo, rosy and fiftyish, sat propped up amid silken bolsters and frills, with a tray of gourmet delicacies across his lap. The semicircle of visitors standing (or reclining on Louis XV chairs) around him included political, literary and musical celebrities, both male and female, of the time. Outstanding among those present was the tall and extremely handsome figure of Franz Liszt, a striking sight with his shoulder-length blond hair and natural elegance. At the age of twenty-nine, two years older than Richard Wagner, Liszt was the undisputed concert idol of Europe.

Meyerbeer was in fine fettle. *Les Huguenots* had just been performed in a new and much improved version which had earned generous critical acclaim. Newspaper clippings were passed back and forth across the lacy counterpane with accompanying comment. "Bravo, Maestro Giacomo, you've done it again! What stupendous reviews! You will be the envy of the operatic world."

The object of these verbal bouquets sunned himself in his glory, though etiquette demanded that he pretend to make light of it.

"Fair enough, fair enough," he said with a casual air. Then, eyes narrowing, he swung sideways toward Liszt. "It seems to me that these notices are less extravagant than those earned by our prodigy here, the Fabulous Franz. The critics seem to like fireworks with their piano playing."

Liszt laughed, dismissing the barb. "Sheer trickery on my part," he said good-naturedly. "I happen to have exceedingly long fingers that permit me to indulge in, possibly, tradition-shattering acrobatics."

Nodding, Meyerbeer took several swallows of hot chocolate. Now his lips widened in a slow, taunting smile. "By the way, Franz, they say you've hit on another clever innovation—sitting sideways at the keyboard instead of with your back to the audience. What's the matter, snagged your breeches?"

A ripple of subdued chuckles from the hangers-on greeted this remark.

Again Liszt remained affable. "No. My tailor is quite dependable, but I'll remember your suggestion in case of an emergency." He paused. "As to my choice of seating, it's always been a puzzle to me why we . . . er . . . ivory thumpers customarily present our posteriors to the paying customers. I find it as easy, and perhaps more satisfying for the observer, to turn my side."

"Nonsense!" Meyerbeer addressed himself to the room. "He does it to show off his handsome profile!"

Once more a chorus of appreciative guffaws came from the clique of admirers. It was at this moment that the outer door opened and a fair young man of slight stature was ushered into the room. The servant preceding him made the announcement: "A gentleman to see you, sir. With a message, he says, from Monsieur Apel."

"Apel? Apel?" Meyerbeer frowned impatiently. It was obvious that this name had long slipped from his memory, as had his fairly recent confrontation with the visitor now facing him.

"My name is Richard Wagner," this insignificant creature in wrinkled clothes and badly worn shoes broke in. "I called on you at Boulogne, with a written introduction from our mutual friend . . ." He fumbled for the message and handed it to

Meyerbeer. "Here it is. You will remember reading it, I am
sure."

With fastidiously lifted wrist Meyerbeer took the grimy paper. He studied the almost completely faded script.

DEAR GIACOMO:
   The bearer of this greeting is my good friend Richard Wagner, who shows great musical promise. I beg you to help
him get a start in the unfamiliar world where you yourself
have reached such splendid heights. My warmest thanks.

                                           THEO

"Theo—ah, to be sure, Theodor Apel," drawled Meyerbeer
as, with bored gesture, he dropped the penciled note. "Bighearted Theo! No artist, but the next best thing—a man with
plenty of money." He seemed unaware of Wagner's presence.
"What's Theo sending me now, a piano tuner?"

Richard missed the remark, for something else had already
occasioned him a visible jolt. His eyes had taken in the opulent
scene before him—the gilt furniture, the satin hangings, the
plush carpets and the well-fed lord of all these riches. He
stared, openmouthed, for he had never before walked in on
anything like this. The assembled guests, on the other hand,
exchanged nudges and winks, some tittering or laughing out
loud at the uneasy, provincial bumpkin whose eyeballs appeared to be popping out of his head. Only Liszt stepped forward graciously and introduced himself.

"Good day, sir." He offered his hand. "I am Franz Liszt."

Richard gasped. "The phenomenal Liszt! Oh, yes. I would
recognize you anywhere from your pictures!"

Meyerbeer seemed a trifle piqued at this extravagant compliment directed at someone else. "Well," he broke in, eyebrows rising, "am I to learn the reason for this ... er ... uncere-
monious interruption?"

Escorted by the friendly Liszt, Richard approached the bed
where Meyerbeer waited with what appeared resigned patience, though his manicured fingers drummed irritably on the
food tray. The attending guests looked worried. Liszt executed a mock bow.

"And here is Buddha himself," he told the awed newcomer, "known to us lesser mortals as the Almighty Meyerbeer."

Wagner bowed too, but not in mockery. He held his hat crumpled between nervous hands while his gaze traveled from the proudly disdainful face of Meyerbeer to the choice tidbits on the breakfast tray. Obviously the shabby visitor had not been eating well of late; his palate reacted to the visual stimulus and he swallowed hard. Meyerbeer pointedly scanned the Apel note again for the stranger's name.

"Monsieur . . . er . . . Wagner, is it?"

"My respects, sir." Richard cleared his throat. "This is a supreme moment in my life."

Meyerbeer took this with characteristic hauteur. "Naturally."

Again Richard failed to notice the ironic tone. He was too full of what he had to say. "I am, like you, an opera composer—though without the magic Meyerbeer key to popular success."

The response was acid. "That makes you hardly unique." The great Giacomo sniffed, narrowing his eyes. "I presume you have come here hoping to receive the 'magic key' handed to you on a silver platter."

"Oh, no, nothing like that at all!" Richard was covered with confusion. "My friend Theo—I mean, our mutual friend, Herr Apel . . ." He broke off helplessly, then bethought himself and pulled parts of various manuscripts from his coat pockets. "Perhaps you might care to look at some of my work and to suggest a publisher."

Meyerbeer barely brought himself to glance at one of the proffered pages, then turned to his companions, vastly amused. "Here's something to captivate Parisians—an opera in German!" He gave Wagner a pitying look. "German is the language of plowmen and foot soldiers, haven't you heard? Hardly a medium for the lyric theater!"

Richard was baffled. "Beethoven's *Fidelio* is written in German, and so are the operas of Karl Maria von Weber, though not all of Mozart's."

"That could be why they are never heard on the important stages of the world—in Rome, London or Paris."

Meyerbeer let the manuscript page fall from his hand as he dismissed his dowdy young visitor by starting a private conversation with the coterie of admirers. Richard, hurt and offended, gathered up his papers and turned to go. It was now that his eyes met the friendly gaze of Franz Liszt.

"Don't take all this too seriously." The Hungarian made a waving gesture to include the assemblage. "Success does not like its memory jogged back to its own days of 'unsuccess.' That is why your presence here is unwelcome."

Richard did not understand. "But I thought I was coming to a fellow countryman." He indicated Meyerbeer. "At home we know him as the brilliant Jakob Liebmann Beer, born in Berlin."

The portly man in the bed had overheard this. He cut in with a sniping correction, uttered in an emphatic Gallic accent. "The name is *Giacomo Meyerbeer!*"

It was Wagner's turn to be ironic. "Of course," he murmured, "*Monsieur* Giacomo."

"And don't you forget it!"

"Whether *I* forget won't matter. The question is how long will the *world* remember?"

Meyerbeer groaned with vexation. "Spare me the snobbery of the frustrated! Since you yourself have never been heard of you pretend it's because you won't compromise your so-called 'ideals.' Well, I know your kind. And I say, let those fine 'ideals' fill your empty belly." He leaned over the edge of the bed, shaking a menacing finger. "But take this warning, you young upstart. I worked, and worked hard, to get where I am now."

"That is admirable," Richard agreed scornfully, "in view of your head start as a rich banker's son."

Meyerbeer was livid. "I'll have you know that nobody wrote letters of recommendation for me!" He searched for the Apel note and tore it to shreds. "Nor did I waste my time looking for sponsors with magic keys. It's because I was willing to struggle and even to starve, if necessary, that I became what people choose to call me—the great Meyerbeer."

"You seem to enjoy the adjective." Richard smiled in spite of himself. "But permit me to doubt that you really know what it is to be hungry. At least, your starvation period must have been short. Otherwise your . . . er . . . figure, no less than your musical integrity, would look better."

This was too much for Giacomo. "Get out of here, you Saxon peasant!" he exploded. "See that you don't keep the warden of the Debtor's Prison waiting."

Amid the cackle of the assemblage Richard headed for the door. Before he had reached the vestibule he felt a hand on his arm. It was Liszt's.

"You haven't exactly made a friend," the pianist observed regretfully.

"I don't need friends—not his kind anyway." Wagner looked back, his eyes taking in the opulence of the bed chamber. "If poor Minna—that's my wife—could have only a fraction of such riches!" He paused, then shook his head angrily. "No. I don't mean that. I'm not looking for charity but for a chance to show what I can do. I must believe in my talent."

"Yes, of course. Without faith no talent can survive."

Richard's face glowed with fierce determination. Again he surveyed the elegant Meyerbeer surroundings, then looked at Liszt. "Give me a year's time," he said, "and I'll have done as well as this."

Liszt's eyebrows arched. "Only one year? That's a narrow margin and a big claim."

"You will see." Richard's jaw was set in a stubborn line. "We shall meet again in a year's time."

They shook hands and parted, the one hastening downstairs into the cold gusty street, the other returning to the effete company that daily shared the Meyerbeer breakfast.

Fired with verve and determination, Richard sped home. He must tell Minna about the challenge he had issued to himself, and about the things he now knew he was going to do. He would describe to her the elegance and luxury he had just seen, so that she would have something to look forward to in the brief twelve months it might require for him to rise to equal heights. For, of one thing he was absolutely sure: what that windbag Giacomo had accomplished, he, Richard Wagner, could do, and better!

He arrived at the Molière house to find Minna, wan and disheveled, cooking a thin soup over a spirit stove. She received him with a drastic announcement: "You had better eat at once so we can start packing."

"Packing?" He looked at her nonplused.

"The landlord is tired of waiting for his money. He's got better tenants ready to move in." She pushed a limp strand of hair off her face. "We can take over a storeroom in the attic, or else start hunting new quarters—today."

The afternoon was spent not in bombastic speculation regarding an uncertain future, but with an acute realization of the stark present. Not much point now in regaling Minna with an account of Meyerbeer's cushy situation, or of the friendliness displayed toward Richard by the illustrious Franz Liszt. Minna and Natalie were hardly in the mood to listen. Their attention was taken up with bundling the few family belongings for Richard to haul up a dark stairway to a turret under the eaves.

Here, by the gray light that filtered through a dust-coated dormer window, Minna studied her face in a tiny cracked mirror. What she saw filled her with melancholy. Hardship and discontent had begun to etch premature lines on the soft cheeks. The brown tresses, formerly groomed to a silken sheen, hung dull and stringy, with a trace here and there of early gray. Also, despite the poor diet—or because of it—Minna's lithe and attractive figure was drooping with her spirits into an unmistakable matronly sag. Seeing her now, would anyone believe that male attention had centered on her as the hummingbird hovered about a nectar-bearing bloom? Alas, those days were gone beyond recall. Judging by the mirror's cruel revelations, not one of Minna's former "patrons" would deem her worthy of a second glance, while new admirers were an even less likely prospect.

Suddenly a wave of resentment welled up within her. Pulling the top of her soiled wrapper across her throat, she turned on Richard and screamed, "I used to pay hairdressers to fix my curls—before you came along with your artistic dreams!" Her shoulders shook as she burst into tears. "Now look at me! You've ruined my life. You've spoiled everything, everything."

It tore his heart to hear her, for of course she was right. Better than anyone else, he saw the change in his once loved and lovely bride. He bore the guilt of speeding her beauty's decline, and a great pity surged through him, the more so as the passion he had felt for her was spent. It had survived the double blow of Minna's premarital record and the subsequent Dietrich affair (all thoughts of the sausage maker had long been banished to oblivion), for Richard nursed no grievances. But the cultural and emotional chasm that from the beginning had separated their two natures was growing wider each day. To his regret Richard discovered that as a life companion Minna meant less than nothing—and this too was punishment for a special kind of sin, committed by him. He had chosen marriage as a means of becoming sole possessor of her body. Well, she had given him that. Was she to blame if she could give nothing more?

He did not know the answer to this or to his own flagrant failure as a husband and provider. Nor was there time just now for idle rumination. They had been moved, by special indulgence of the landlord, to the most ignominious corner of the Molière establishment. If Richard fell behind even with this reduced rental, the family would find itself out on the street.

CHAPTER 14

FRANZ LISZT rose from the piano to a thunderous storm of applause. The concert hall of the Paris Conservatoire was filled to bursting with a worshipful and frenzied public that could not get enough of the fabulous Hungarian's art. *"Bis, bis, da capo!"* cried jubilant voices, begging for encores which the tireless virtuoso was never loath to give. He bowed with the aristocratic grace that characterized him and turned back to the keyboard, when his attention was caught by a gesticulating stagehand in the wings. The latter held up an envelope that must have been marked "Urgent," considering the vehemence with which he waved it back and forth.

Liszt knew the value of compliance with audience demands. But he was also a ladies' man, lionized by Europe's fashionable women and himself a slave to the fair sex. The tributes and *billets-doux* that reached him through the mails could not be counted, yet each new missive held for him a tantalizing lure. Already, at thirty, he was the hero of many a love affair, each of which for a time appeared to be the passion supreme. But invariably there remained visions still unrealized, emotional heights yet to scale, dreams worth the dreaming. His poet's soul fed on romantic delusions, on implausible hopes and idealistic fancies that kept him in a state of perpetual suspense. Female perfection, though he had never seen it, must exist. He expected to run up against it at the turn of almost any corner.

It was thus tonight, at the end of his greatest concert of the season. The clamor of approval that re-echoed through the auditorium delighted the pianist's ear, and nothing would have suited him better than to prolong such huzzas by tossing off some pyrotechnical program addenda. Keyboard acrobatics were child's play to his long fingers and miraculous span, assur-

ing him of quicker rewards than could be earned by less spec-
tacular though sounder musicianship. But what cared he for
triumphs, either big or small, when a promise far more sweet
appeared to await him only a few paces away! With a definitive nod of farewell to his admirers the handsome Franz sped
offstage, there to receive the sealed missive that taunted his
curiosity.

He tore the simple envelope, noting—with a shade of disappointment—that the paper was of poorest quality and assuredly
did not exude the customary perfume. On unfolding the single scribbled sheet, executed in pencil, his throbbing spirits
drooped still further. Here was no adoring damsel's exquisite
penmanship. The message, in atrocious hentracks, read:

MONSIEUR!
One year ago today we agreed to meet again. As I am
personally prevented, by rather special circumstances, from
keeping our appointment, I beg you to call on me at the address below.
                                        RICHARD WAGNER
8th Arrondissement,
Debtors' Prison.

For a moment Liszt's face remained blank. The note and its
signature meant nothing to him. Richard Wagner? He was
quite sure he knew no one by such a name. "One year ago,"
the note said. Where had he, the widely traveled Franz, paused
between concert tours a full twelve months back? At this time
of year was he not always in France? Paris, the opera season,
Meyerbeer—ah, that was it—the Meyerbeer *levée*, and that desperate young caller with the heavy Saxon accent. Herr Wagner,
to be sure, who had boasted that in the negligible interval of
fifty-two weeks he would equal the prosperous Giacomo's success! Well, judging by the writer's current address a considerable delay, if not a definite change of plans, must have taken
place. With a wry smile Liszt crumpled the paper and tossed
it aside.

He picked it up again almost at once. Something, an intangible memory of that Meyerbeer gathering, rose before Liszt's inner eye and plagued his conscience. He was due for a champagne supper at one of Neuilly's more grandiose villas, attended by the cream of French society. No matter. At the risk of outraging his hosts he must heed the call of that unknown and impecunious wretch who, obviously, knew no one else to turn to.

A half hour later, still in full evening dress and with opera hat and cloak, the elegant Liszt was admitted to a grubby precinct jail and led down a dimly lighted corridor at the far end of which Richard Wagner languished behind bars. Hardly more than casual acquaintances, the two men met in awkward silence. It was Liszt who broke the ice, addressing Wagner for the first time by his Christian name.

"Well, Richard, this is scarcely the place where I would have expected to look for you!"

"Thank you." The prisoner rose to clasp the proffered hand. "You may be sure this is not what I had in mind when I made those high-flown boasts."

A turnkey unlocked the cell door and admitted the visitor, who sat down beside Wagner on the cot.

"My friend," Liszt murmured. "My poor friend! Tell me— what happened?"

The simple query tapped long-repressed emotions. The story of his sufferings burst now from Richard's lips. "What happened! How shall I begin to tell you?" He put his palms against his head, as if his whole brain ached. "When I left you at Meyerbeer's that day I walked the streets a long time. I passed a printer's shop with a display of books and sheet music in the window. The owner met me eagerly, but quickly lost interest when I pulled out my manuscripts. He couldn't publish any composition of mine, he informed me, unless I had a producer's contract."

Liszt nodded understandingly. "Go on."

"The next day, and for two weeks after that, I made the rounds of the theaters, including the Opéra. In every stage-manager's office I heard the same answer in reverse: 'Show us a publisher's contract and we'll see about producing your stuff.' Then there was the matter of language. I began to see that

Meyerbeer was right. There is no market for operas in German." He paused dejectedly. "I tried at least a dozen more places, with the same result, till at last there was no choice left but a return to my hack work at Schlesinger's."

"I know," said Liszt. "You sit on a high stool at a badly lighted desk in old Schlesinger's back room, ruining your eyes with the double job of copyist and arranger——"

"At a salary that's not enough to live on, yet too much to let me and my family starve, while all the while I was doubling the earnings of already prosperous composers by turning their intricate output into more simplified and popular form."

"The word is 'commercial,' I believe."

Wagner made a gesture of distaste. "It's destructive, corroding work, with nothing to show for it but a sense of inner shame and humiliation."

He went on describing the further depths of his descent. The scenes at home when the small family sat down to Minna's joyless cooking. The nights of waking, exhausted, yet forcing himself to make revisions on the *Rienzi* script while at the same time plotting the dramatic structure of *The Flying Dutchman*. Incredibly, amid the early-morning din of market cries and the late-afternoon miasma of garbage odors, the two operas had grown apace, as had four songs with French texts: "Dors, mon Enfant," "Mignonne," "Attente" and "Les Deux Grenadiers." The last of these gave musical form to the famous poem by Heinrich Heine, which likewise attracted the pen of Robert Schumann. Both composers employed the *"Marseillaise"* in their closing measures, Wagner perhaps even more effectively; yet Schumann, living at his ease on German soil, found quick acceptance of his version, while the work of his contemporary went begging in a Paris slum.

"What else have you done?" Franz Liszt asked, profoundly affected.

"You really want to know?" Richard drew a small notebook from his pocket. "Here is a listing of all my musical sins since I first entered the conservatory at Leipzig."

The tabulation was impressive. Liszt checked off several tightly scrawled pages:

1st Sonata in D Minor

Quartet in D Major
Arrangement (for 2 hands) of Beethoven's Ninth Symphony
Overture in C Major (⁶⁄₈ time)
Overture in B Flat
Pianoforte Sonata, B-Flat Major (Opus 1)
Polonaise in D Major (Opus 2) for 4 hands
Pianoforte Fantasia, F-Sharp Minor
Overture to Raupach's *King Enzio*
Concert Overture in D Minor
Concert Overture in C (with Fugue)
Symphony in C Major
Opera *The Wedding* (unfinished)
"*Glockentöne*": musical setting for a poem by Theodor Apel
Opus 5: seven compositions for Goethe's *Faust*
Allegro for Aubry's aria in *The Vampire* by Marschner
2nd Symphony in E Major (unfinished)
Overture *Christopher Columbus*
New Year Cantata "*Beim Antritt des Neuen Jahres*"
Opera *Das Liebesverbot (The Novice of Palermo)*
Overture *Rule, Britannia*
Overture *Polonia*
Romanza in G Major "*Sanfte Wehmut*" for Music Play by
     Blum
Folk song "*Der Tannenbaum*"

Franz Liszt exhaled loudly, his lower lip thrust forward. He stared at the notebook in utter amazement. "Good God, what an output!" he exclaimed at last. "You must be a glutton for work."

Richard shook his head. "No, not for work. It's food I was after." He ran a finger down the list. "Most of that stuff isn't worth the paper it's smeared on, but with it I hoped to entice some victuals into poor Minna's larder. You've got to do something *commercial*, I told myself—something that will sell. A musician with a family to feed has no right to waste his time on serious art. Well, the result is rubbish like *Britannia, Polonia, Columbus* and a superfluous cantata for any convenient New Year." He laughed, but his voice gave forth only a mirthless cackle. "It's all done with an eye to a purchaser, quite in the pattern of your proud friend Meyerbeer. Except for one distinction: my drivel doesn't sell."

With sadness in his heart Liszt gave ear to these self-accusations. He did not know what to reply, for much of what Wagner said happened to be true. Meyerbeer's success was indeed based largely on an astute compliance with popular taste rather than austere artistic integrity. But, unlike the average penniless composer who embarked on the same path of compromise, Monsieur Giacomo had had behind him the banking fortune of his father to ensure him a head start. In the music-publishing world, money not only talked, it sang!

Richard reached for his notebook. As he did so the pages flipped over to a second group of entries.

"Wait a minute. What's this?" Liszt cried. "You mean to say there's more that I haven't seen?"

The other gave a sheepish nod. "Since I got nowhere with music, I tried my hand at journalism, and with better results. Some of these literary efforts account for a fair supply of groceries, including—on one joyous occasion—a strip of sow belly. Here, take a look at Richard Wagner the author!"

Liszt took a look. The list was almost as lengthy as the previous musical tabulation, and it included short articles, essays, critiques and some narrative efforts, in both French and German. Some of this material appeared to have been published by the Paris *Gazette Musicale,* while other pieces were bought by various German publications, chiefly the *Dresdener Abendzeitung.* Payment was nominal, Liszt knew, since newspapers depended largely on contributors who asked for no reward other than the honor of appearing in print. But it was plain that Wagner had drawn some solace from the coppers earned by his pen. The titles of his prose pieces gave indication of considerable maturity in content:

The Nature of German Music
Pergolesi: Stabat Mater
The Virtuoso and the Artist
A Pilgrimage to Beethoven
The Overture
An End in Paris

The Artist and Publicity
Parisian Amusements
Parisian Pitfalls for Germans
Essay on "Der Freischütz"
Impressions of a Parisian Sunday
A Happy Evening
Critique of Halévy's "La Reine de Chypre"
On a New Paris Opera

Liszt closed the book. "An admirable record," he murmured. "Even at the risk of starving I should be unable to do as well."

"Don't be misled by the sow belly." Wagner shrugged as he answered. "The writer's career is almost as thorny as the unknown musician's. I managed to stay off beggar's row just so long—then the little girl fell sick."

"The little girl?"

"Natalie . . . er . . . our daughter. The doctor said it was anemia, brought on by months of undernourishment. He prescribed tonics and country air."

"How could you manage that?"

"I thought of selling my dog, Robber. An English traveler on the street one day had asked to buy him, and I had refused, perhaps with unnecessary rudeness. I tried my best to meet that Englishman again. But it was too late. Robber slipped out of the house that same night, no doubt at the insistence of his empty stomach. We never saw him again."

He could not go on. He could not bring himself to tell of the dreary trips to the pawnshop, bearing spoons, forks and the last of the wedding presents—the silver-plated sugar bowl from the diva with the black eye in Königsberg. The articles brought scarcely a dozen coppers, not enough to cover the doctor's prescription. Minna had done better with her coat; its sale paid for Natalie's treatments, with a small balance left for postage— to send one of Richard's operas to Germany, with a letter to the management of the Royal Opera House in Dresden. After all, Minna had argued, the King of Saxony, as a patron of the arts, ought to take an interest in a struggling artist abroad, an artist who, while starving, was still His Majesty's loyal subject.

Perhaps she was right. But no response came, either from

the King or the Dresden Opera's board of directors. Meanwhile the chronic need for money had grown critical once more. Swallowing his last vestige of pride, Richard had gone back to Meyerbeer's apartment.

"I rang the bell," he reported in a dull monotone, "and was shaken off by a glib manservant who swore that Maestro Giacomo was not at home, though through the slamming door I could hear the same chatter and merriment as on my first unhappy visit."

He paused, then went on in a near whisper. "So I borrowed from little people—the greengrocer, the butcher, the blind cobbler next door, none of whom could wait out the week for repayment. The end is obvious. When I fell behind they had me arrested. Who can blame them? They too must eat."

Liszt nodded, dismayed. He reached for his money pouch. "How much do you owe? When does your counsel meet the creditors?"

The other's head sank lower. "I have no counsel."

"But that's impossible! You can't remain here, locked up indefinitely without defense."

"Since I am unable to pay off, I have agreed to serve consecutive terms, till each creditor receives satisfaction."

Liszt was outraged. "It doesn't make sense. It's inhuman!"

"Not at all. They feed me here, and I have peace and quiet to finish my *Lohengrin*." For a moment Wagner's expression was almost happy, but it clouded over now with a frown. "What worries me is Minna and the child."

At these words Liszt jumped to his feet. "Look—I'll go to them immediately. What is the address?"

"Number fourteen, Rue Jacob, back entrance, where we've wound up after several moves, including a flat on Rue Helder and a farmer's cottage in Meudon. Rue Jacob has its fishmonger too, where you'll find Minna working." In reporting the latter onerous fact Wagner felt his face flush a deep crimson. Nothing underscored his degradation more grimly than the vision of his wife trapped in the same garbage stench that had surrounded their earliest Paris lodgings.

It was almost a relief to hear the heavy step of the prison

guard, who signaled Liszt that it was time to go. With a brief handshake the two friends parted.

Liszt halted for a second on the threshold. "This work you mentioned—*Lohengrin*—what is it about?"

Instantly Wagner's eyes lighted up with the fire of creation. "It's a story of chivalry and knighthood, ennobled symbolically by the quest for the Holy Grail." He broke off, realizing that his visitor had difficulty in following such metaphysical flights.

"Chivalry and knighthood," Liszt murmured as he scanned the miserable cell, then shook his head. "Er . . . I see." What he saw could not be put into words. It was the miracle of the human spirit, that rose on golden wings above the stone wall of confinement.

"Good-by, my friend," Wagner called from his bunk, where he was already engrossed in sorting manuscript pages prior to resuming work.

Rapidly Liszt walked away. In the jail corridor he collided with a thin, hollow-cheeked girl who had just been admitted by an outer guard. She looked awed and a little frightened by the prison atmosphere. With a mute gesture she handed an envelope to the turnkey. The latter glanced at the scribbled name, then stepped back to Richard Wagner's cell. Automatically Liszt halted in his tracks.

"A letter for you," said the turnkey, waving the missive through the bars.

Wagner tore the envelope flap and skimmed over the short message. "It's from Minna!" he cried. "She's got it! She's got it!"

Liszt was back beside him. "Got what?"

"My release! She was able to round up part of the money and to persuade the creditors to withhold further charges."

Pandemonium broke loose in the reopened cell as Wagner embraced Natalie, Liszt and the baffled turnkey in succession, dancing them about the cramped prison space.

It was Natalie who spoke a sobering word. "Herr Laube, our neighbor, thinks you could raise the rest of the money by sending another manuscript to Dresden, for a tryout."

Wagner's elation was punctured. "Dresden? A tryout? So

far they've ignored everything I've sent." He shook his head disconsolately. "It will be the graveyard for my works, this Dresden!"

Natalie displayed a seriousness far beyond her years. "Herr Laube says one must be persistent."

Wagner's innate optimism revived. "Well, there's the score of *Rienzi*, and I've finished *The Flying Dutchman*." He paused, annoyed by a petty, yet vital, consideration. "But the postage— it takes a fortune in postage."

Liszt drew Natalie aside and pressed a roll of bills into her hand. "Run along home," he urged *sotto voce*, "and see that those scripts go off immediately."

The child curtsied and kissed his hand. "Oh, thank you!"

As Natalie scurried off ahead of them Liszt and Wagner walked arm in arm through shadowy corridors to the jail portal and the Paris night.

A MONTH had gone by since copies of *Rienzi* and *The Flying Dutchman* were dispatched to Germany. Wagner had followed up with a bold letter addressed to His Majesty Friedrich August of Saxony, calling the monarch's personal attention to the submitted works and begging for royal intercession with Baron August von Lüttichau, director of the Dresden Opera.

The post moved slowly in those days and a quick answer could hardly be expected. During the time of waiting, Wagner took frequent walks through the cheap artist quarter of Montmartre where, in the company of other penniless Bohemians, he joined in philosophic and polemic discussions of the day. France had undergone some changes since her world-conquering splurge under Napoleon the Great. Two Bourbons had briefly restored the reactionary monarchy, only to be ousted in the July Revolution of 1830 which brought the liberal Duke Louis Philippe of Orléans to the throne.

Unfortunately Philippe's progressiveness did not extend to acceptance of much-needed electoral reforms, hence new dissension arose between government and working classes. French public opinion, from outspoken intellectuals down to the inarticulate man in the street, took issue with the ruling clique and kept the political kettle at boiling point.

This was something new to the German-born Wagner. Reared in a disciplinarian tradition that inculcated, above all else, respect for authority, he was vastly impressed by the general cynicism with which Frenchmen delighted in deflating their so-called betters. Never before had he encountered anything like the Gallic freedom of thought and speech. Some of these Parisians were irrepressibly voluble, ready to speak their

minds on any subject and at the drop of a hat. If th
in obscure back-street bistros where clerks and cab d
forth, it became even more manifest in the boulev
frequented by such personages as Alphonse de Lamar
fred de Musset, Victor Hugo, Théophile Gautier, Gustav
bert and Augustin Scribe. It was a stimulating time in
when Aurore Dupin under the pseudonym of George
wrote daring novels and advanced the emancipation of
sex. Honoré de Balzac, Charles Baudelaire and Ernest Rena
adorned French letters; Jean François Millet, Jean Baptiste
Corot, Théodore Rousseau, Rosalie (Rosa) Bonheur and Constant Troyon painted the contemporary scene; Chopin and
Liszt were concertizing; and an exiled German poet, Heinrich
Heine, was putting into verse the anguish of his homesickness.

Poverty alone did not keep the receptive Wagner on the
outer fringe of all this. He was discovering for the first time
a congenital handicap: his utter lack of polyglot leanings. Burdened from the start with the thickest of dialects, his native
Saxon, he had trouble even adopting "high" German speech.
The mastery of mellifluous French proved quite beyond him, a
fact which, in his need to cover his own failing, he blamed on
the country of which he was a suffering guest.

To add to his discomfiture, neighbors in the Rue Jacob, and
even the landlord himself, addressed him as Monsieur *Vagner*
(Vanyé), pronounced to rhyme with *gagner*, a twist he bitterly
resented. No, he was not equipped with the average immi-
grant's adaptability and gift for assimilation. Two notable contemporary Parisians to the core, the Polish Frédéric Chopin
and the Hungarian Franz Liszt, served by their example to
underscore this fact all the more.

Through stringent economizing Richard permitted himself
a gallery seat for one of Liszt's concerts. The thirty-year-old
keyboard magician continued to be the rage of Europe, garner-
ing a fortune by unashamedly building his programs with an
eye to mass appeal. In later years, as his artistry matured, he
was himself to admit this in his memoirs.

To Wagner, only two years younger than the Magyar wonder, such a profit-slanted compromise was a betrayal of the

...pose of art and a reflection on a performer's integrity. ...m being dazzled by Liszt's fame and financial eminence, ...ne away from the recital filled with disgust. Richard ...d have no part of a maxim fondly quoted by the uncritical: ...s making money, so he must be good." Money being some- ...g with which the struggling Wagner was not at all familiar, ...e scorned its use as a measuring stick.

Meanwhile his spiritual isolation grew. The nostalgia that beset him for the sight of German landscape and the sound of German tongue became gnawing. He realized for the first time the deep truth that to leave home was to rediscover one's roots. Not the provincial town in which he had been born but all of *Deutschland*, the earth that had bred Bach, Beethoven, Luther, Schopenhauer and Goethe—this it was for which he yearned with daily mounting need.

Idealized visions took shape in his fancy, painting his homeland to him in the colors of Arcadia. In long daydreams he recalled Teutonic folklore and legend wherein he identified himself as a lost wanderer seeking the mountain of bliss, or as a chivalric knight championing truth in a world of lies. Two separate hero themes emerged thus before his creative eye: Tannhäuser, the highborn minstrel turned pilgrim, and Lohengrin, the emissary of the Holy Grail. For the latter he found words of cryptic wistfulness:

> *Im fernen Land, unnahbar Euren Schritten,*
> *steht eine Burg, die Monsalvat genannt . . .*
>
> (In a far land that's alien to your footsteps,
> there stands a castle, Monsalvat by name . . .)

It was his answer to Paris, the French tongue, the people in whose midst he found himself unable to take root. Monsalvat, the mountain of salvation, lay elsewhere. His goal, the Grail of pure artistry, drew him home.

He fixed on this idea to the exclusion of all else. On leaving prison he had resumed working as copyist for various music firms. While performing these hack jobs in the cramped rear flat that served as parlor, bedroom, kitchen and laundry, he

kept one ear cocked for the postman's step. Surely there must
be news from Dresden this morning, this afternoon, or at the
latest by tomorrow's first mail. Daily Minna returned, drawn
and weary from her work at the fishmonger's, to find her husband at the window, staring down into the street.

"For weeks you've been standing there," she scolded, "waiting for mail. I should think you'd know by now that your
manuscripts got lost, or else nobody in Dresden has any use for
them."

He watched her go to the washbowl and start soaping her
hands. As she did so her expression changed to utter disgust.
"Ugh—this vile fish smell! Will we ever live to breathe anything else?"

Deeply humiliated, he turned away, agonized under the
weight of his failure. It was then that, through the grimy and
paper-patched windowpane, he saw old Brascassat's postman's
cap turn the street corner. Could it be true? Brascassat was
waving to him and grinning from ear to ear. Wagner flew from
the room and tore downstairs.

When he returned, breathless and on the verge of hysteria,
Minna was still washing herself. She took no notice of his cry
of joy.

"Minna, Minna, start packing! My *Rienzi* and *Dutchman* are
sold!" He held up the letter, pointing to a paragraph. "I must be
in Dresden next week to start rehearsals."

Her emotional apathy had become such that she seemed impervious to the best of news. She looked up glassily, then slowly
spoke: "Is that true?"

She did not really expect an answer, but he had seized her
shoulders. "Yes, yes, quite true!" He took her roughened hands
in his, kissing each finger. "Good-by, fish smell! Good-by,
Paris!"

The impulsiveness of his caress harked back—a long way—
to the days when they had been lovers. Minna's stolidity gave
way as her wan face began to light up. For yet another second
she swayed between scorn and doubt; then her defenses broke.
"Thank God!" she gasped in a voice that was more a sob. "The
nightmare is ended."

In the days that followed, joy alternated with despair as Richard scurried about town to assemble the necessary travel funds. A summons to the Royal Opera in Dresden was all very good, but no one in the Kingdom of Saxony had bothered to inquire into the Wagner family finances. The letter to the composer had been signed by an official, Baron von der Pfordten, who bore the impressive title of Minister of Education and Culture. Doubtless nobody of such exalted station was ever beset by economic qualms.

"I'll write this Pfordten," Richard declared at last, as every other avenue seemed fruitless. "If they want me in Dresden, let them pay for it!"

Minna warned against incautious action. There were other composers, other orchestra conductors, she pointed out, who strained to grasp just such an opportunity as this. A wrong move, a heedless gesture of defiance, might close the very door that had been opened. No, she had a better idea.

"What about your friend Apel?"

"Theo?" Richard shook his head. "Positively no! He's helped us out so often, without hope of repayment—I'd rather give up Dresden altogether than ask Theo for another copper."

Minna's lips tightened. "Then *I'll* ask him." She had suffered too much to shy at expediency, regardless of its cost in pride. Over Richard's protest she dispatched a desperate letter to the faithful Theodor, laying bare the whole pitiable crisis and imploring "one last greathearted proof of friendship."

Her instinct proved correct. Apel's reply, and a generous money draft, arrived by return post. With his good wishes for Richard's impending change of fortune Theo disclosed some news of his own. It was more tragic in import than anything the hapless Wagners had endured, for Theo was stricken blind. "You cannot imagine," his trembling hand spelled out, "what it is to live in darkness. More than ever, now, I seek comfort in music." In furthering Richard's career the pathetic Apel confessed that he was ultimately doing something for himself.

With mingled feelings the Wagner family set out from Paris on their journey home. The stagecoach carried them through the Rhenish Palatinate, Hesse and Thuringia, past Eisenach and the poetic meadows surrounding the historic Wartburg. Near by and above the castle rose a hill named Hörselberg, in the depths of which the Pagan goddess Venus was said to have found a hiding place after the advent of Christianity had banished the hosts of Jupiter from their Olympian thrones. Rain was falling along most of the way, but the Wartburg panorama appeared abruptly, blazing in clear sunshine.

"This is my setting for *Tannhäuser!*" Richard exclaimed ecstatically.

He had forgotten the realities immediately ahead: the *Rienzi première* set for October 20, 1842, at Dresden, and the Berlin debut of *The Flying Dutchman,* on January 3 of the following year. Those were already accomplished facts. His unbridled fancy leaped forward always to unborn works ahead.

It was a five-day trip from Paris, via the Rhine Basin to Frankfurt am Main, and finally Dresden. But before reaching his destination Richard insisted on a stop at Leipzig for a visit with his mother.

Johanna Geyer lived alone since the death, not long before, of her eldest daughter, Rosalie. In intermittent letters Richard had followed Rosalie's fate, from her rather late marriage to joyous anticipation of motherhood and its fatal outcome.

He stood now at this beloved sister's grave and realized anew how much of his own artistic fervor and idealism had taken nurture from her noble spirit. Quite subtly her presence seemed to pervade his work, if not in so secondary a creation as the pale Irene of *Rienzi,* then certainly through such tender and profoundly feminine characterizations as Senta in *The Flying Dutchman* and the Elsa of *Lohengrin.* To these his muse was already adding a third embodiment of Rosalie, the suddenly envisioned figure of *Tannhäuser's* gentle Elisabeth.

For the moment, however, more pressing considerations arose. Hotels were expensive and Richard's travel funds were shrinking fast. Did Mama have a guest room?

Well, there was a *Rumpelkammer,* or catch-all chamber, used on occasion by Richard's brother Julius, the bachelor in the family and its only nonartistic member, although it might be said that in his capacity as a traveling agent for a jewelry con-

cern Julius engaged in an aesthetic pursuit. In any case, provided Minna approved, the *Rumpelkammer* would be made
available.

The reference to Minna was deliberately pointed. Johanna
had not yet become reconciled to Richard's choice of a wife.
Minna's past history, no less than her Berlin escapade during
the early years of her life as a respectable Frau Wagner, had
reached the ears of Leipzig gossips. There was much sniffing
and dour headshaking, in which Johanna (quite unmindful of
the shady tittle-tattle surrounding her own youth) took active
part. After all, it was one of the prerogatives of old age to sit
in judgment over the sins of a new generation while drawing
a merciful veil across the indiscretions of one's own past.

In her starched bonnet and wool shawl Johanna sat rocking
by the fire. She rocked, and judged.

Richard, in typical masculine fashion, failed to catch the
poisoned overtones. Or, if he perceived, he chose to ignore
them.

"What about it, dear?" He turned to his wife. "Shall we
have a look?"

Minna gave her mother-in-law a sweetly disarming smile.
"That won't be necessary," she cooed. "I know it's a lovely
room."

Had it been a wet cellar or a windy garden shed, her answer
would have been the same. For every bone in Minna's body
ached from the one hundred and twenty hours just spent in a
clattering stagecoach. Any port in a storm, any roof over her
head, would do. She was fagged out.

CHAPTER 16

F ROM Leipzig it was an easy skip over the Meissen road to Dresden, where Richard presented himself forthwith, prepared to launch into rehearsals. He was burdened with misgivings for appearing a fortnight later than expected, but he soon found that he might have spared himself such alarms. The local playing schedule had undergone a last-minute change to make room for the much-touted Meyerbeer hit *Les Huguenots,* which likewise took precedence at the *Staatsoper* in Berlin. Not only did Wagner meet with no reproach for the tardiness caused by his money-raising efforts; the Dresden management seemed to have forgotten him altogether.

"Why don't you try Munich," Director Lüttichau proposed, "and come back when our playbill is less crowded?" He rummaged through a stack of papers on a sagging music shelf and handed the composer his manuscripts.

"To whom in Munich shall I address myself?" Richard asked, crestfallen.

"My secretary will give you some names." Lüttichau rang a bell. A moment later, with a scribbled memorandum in his pocket and two operas under his arm, Richard was back on the street.

He followed Lüttichau's advice and mailed his scores to the Bavarian capital, settling down in Leipzig meanwhile to await a reply. This was not long in coming, and the manuscripts with it. By Munich standards neither *Rienzi* nor *The Flying Dutchman* was acceptable, as both subjects appeared "too highflown and farfetched for German tastes." Dejectedly Richard received the news at his mother's house.

"We should have stayed in France," lamented Minna, who was easily discouraged nowadays. After years of suffering abroad she had looked for quick glory on Richard's return to German soil. When this was not immediately forthcoming her fretful nature rebelled. She looked back now and, with the short memory of the presently aggrieved, viewed the past in nostalgic rosiness. She wanted nothing now so much as to go back to "that dear and enchanting Paris."

Plagued by Minna's complaints, Richard wrote to his brother-in-law Avenarius:

The only sensible thing for me to do, I suppose, is to return abroad. Nothing will come of my operas. I have a formidable enemy to fight, one who schemes against me incessantly—my own wife! She has just told me, in a burst of tears, that she will do everything to make my operas fail here, so that I shall have no choice but to go back to her beloved Paris.

Yet despite domestic conflicts Richard continued doggedly in his search for a producer. He read in a Leipzig paper that *Les Huguenots* was opening in Berlin, with Meyerbeer present for the *première*. Again he cast pride to the winds and made his way to the Prussian capital, where he tracked down the great man in one of the elegant Kurfürstendamm hotels. Oozing success, Meyerbeer was in a gracious mood. Whether or not he recognized Richard was uncertain. But he generously introduced the younger man to Count von Redern, managing director of the State Opera House.

The Count was a polite man. He looked over the unknown composer's scores and declared them to be most interesting, but—alas!—this was his own last season with the *Staatsoper,* due to a tempting offer from abroad. He would therefore refer the matter to his successor, Herr von Küstner, as soon as that gentleman arrived in Berlin.

Richard's spirits sank. Küstner was none other than the manager of the Munich Opera, who had only a few days ago turned down the Wagner scripts. There was little point then in counting on favorable results in this direction. Crestfallen, he returned to Leipzig.

Here Minna received him with a new flood of reproaches.
She was bored with inactivity and nerve-wracked through in-
cessant worry. A doctor she had consulted during Richard's
absence diagnosed a cardiac weakness.

"He says I should take a trip," Minna declared, quickly returning to her specific tack. "You see, we must go back to
France."

Richard shook his head. "There are any number of spas here
in Germany specializing in heart cases. Or there's Bad Teplitz
in Bohemia, not far from here and certainly much cheaper."

His present restricted finances made even Teplitz too big an
expense, but Minna's health—or at least her soured state of
mind—called for some sort of treatment. Teplitz, then, was
chosen. Minna grumbled, for this was not the trip she wanted,
but she packed her bag and meekly followed Richard to the
station. He accompanied her on the scenic rail journey across
the Austrian border, fearing that she might suffer a heart attack if left alone en route. Lodgings were found in a modest
hostelry named "Zur Eiche," of which Richard reported in a
note to his sister Cäcilie:

Here we are in Teplitz, with a view of a castle on a mountaintop above our noses, and a cow barn beneath. . . . Ah,
this Teplitz, it has perhaps the most beautiful surroundings
I have ever seen. Right away this morning we planned to
climb the mountain, but Minna got a cramp in her leg. . . .

Two days later Richard was back in Dresden, importuning
Director Lüttichau of the Royal Opera for the promised tryout
of *Rienzi*, though without success. In ever-growing despondency he wrote to his Parisian friend Laube:

I really don't know what we shall live on by next summer.
. . . As you see, I am still *Hans ohne Geld* (Johnny-without-
money), rich in prospects but absurdly incapable of realizing
them. Minna prays for even worse luck so I will make a
contract with Schlesinger and return to Paris; poor Minna,
she thinks of nothing but Paris—as though it were Paradise!

A ray of light at last broke through this gloom. On one of his rounds of Dresden theaters Richard met the choral director of the Royal Opera, Wilhelm Fischer. This veteran music master, known to his colleagues as Papa Fischer, lent a sympathetic ear to anyone who chose the thorny path of musicianship for his own. With eager curiosity he read the *Rienzi* score and broke into warm praise of it. He promised to do battle for the luckless composer and not to let up until a *Rienzi* production was assured.

Instantly Richard's depression lifted. Through Papa Fischer he was drawn into a circle of congenial artists—small-caliber instrumentalists and composers to be sure, not one world celebrity among them, but all bound to one another in friendship and unity of purpose. It was good to know that others struggled too and found the going hard. Suddenly Richard felt no longer alone. He wrote Minna at Teplitz about his new companions:

At last, Minel my dear, I feel that I've really come home! We all meet at Papa Fischer's—wonderful evenings with boiled potatoes and salt herring—and the kind of hopeful conversation that children indulge in before Christmas. Affection, affection, affection—that is what we all need, all the more when fame seems so near yet is out of reach. . . . What is all the world's glory when there is no sharing of joy and affection? Joy, spark of Divinity! It turns salt herring and potatoes into veritable ambrosia! Oh, unique treasure in this life, the comfort of sweet friendship! The stars glitter in the night sky above us. Oh, German land! . . .

Minna read these effusions with scant enthusiasm. She saw no profit in Richard's association with "little people" who might know something about music but who had neither position nor authority to promote his cause. She said so in her reply.

It happened that she was wrong. Papa Fischer, the insignificant chorus master, kept his promise of pleading in Richard's behalf by going to the top arbiter of Dresden's Royal Opera, the head of the Ministry of Education and Culture, Baron von der Pfordten. A new reading of *Rienzi* was duly arranged for, with the result that the opera was officially incorporated in the current season's repertoire.

Heretofore Richard had commuted daily from Leipzig. Now it was imperative that he pack his belongings and move to Dresden, so as to be on hand for the coming rehearsals. While hunting for lodgings he spent a short time in the near-by village where Minna's parents had settled. He described this experience in a letter to Teplitz:

> The first night was terrible! Although I was very tired I could not close an eye. The towering feather bed was so suffocating I almost roasted. Then the mice, and the Town Crier who makes his rounds even far into the dark—it was a conspiracy! I feel wracked. . . .

But he had found an apartment and had obtained a six months' lease, so that Minna could return at once to Dresden and establish herself under her own roof. He wrote glowingly:

> All will go well, be assured! I hope you will return in good health, praising me for having managed things properly and to your satisfaction. Keep well and hurry back now to whom you call your
>   "Charming Richel." . . .

By return post he expected to learn the day and hour of Minna's arrival. But instead, by the end of the week, she wrote that she was prolonging her Teplitz stay. He protested in alarm:

> I am deeply saddened at your wishing to leave me alone so much longer! Dear Minna, we absolutely must not be separated for long periods, I feel this with a new and profound sincerity. No metropolis with its seventy thousand inhabitants can replace you for me. When I am idle I have the more time to grieve at being alone; yet after working all day and returning to my quarters at night without finding

you there I am sickened by all that means home, though normally my greatest comfort lies in domesticity—yet what I find outside the house truly does not give a minute's joy. . . .

At last Minna softened and gave ear to his pleas. She returned to Richard's side, though not without pointing out some faults in the apartment he had found. For one thing, it was too cold. Also, the neighborhood being strange, she knew she would be lonely. Members of the Wagner family circle had an answer to this. They gave out periodic hints, both verbal and in letters, that it was high time for Richard to produce some offspring. Most of his brothers and sisters were blessed with progeny and could vouch that parenthood left no room for feelings of abandonment. Richard wrote one of his sisters regarding this:

As to Cäcilie's queries about children, so far no luck. Since we don't seem to have any prospect of human issue, our solace lies in four-legged pets; we have another dog, only six weeks old, an amusing little beast. His name is Peps or sometimes Striezel (because he looks like one of those puppies from the Striezel Market). He is more manageable than Robber, our last one. However, it remains deplorable that we must resort to dumb creatures for companionship. I would far rather have a little Max, like yours—but he, of course, could not be duplicated anywhere in the world. . . .

Such melancholy thoughts did not depress Richard too long. Things were moving with regard to *Rienzi*, as Director von Lüttichau had at last set up a rehearsal schedule. A cast had already been chosen, including the renowned soprano Wilhelmine Schröder-Devrient, as well as Henriette Wüst and Joseph Aloys Tichatschek. Of the tenor Tichatschek, Papa Fischer said, "He is stupid as an ox and will take a lot of coaching, but his voice is magnificent." Minor roles, sung by Michael Wächter and Wilhelm Dettmer, were in competent hands.

From the start, optimism reigned at rehearsals. When a passage had been found particularly melodious, the singers themselves broke into applause. Tichatschek, carried away by the beauty of his own opening aria, pulled a silver coin from his pocket and slapped it on the piano. "This must be paid for," he cried. "Even in rehearsal nobody can have this free!" The others went along with the game, tossing a groschen into a collection plate every time an outstanding passage came up. Richard was more than flattered. He could use the money.

As a work of art, and in spite of the performers' enthusiasm, *Rienzi* left much to be desired. It was imitative, both musically and in story content, to a point just short of plagiarism. That is, with all his professed scorn for Meyerbeer, Richard had succumbed to a temptation common among beginners: he had modeled his opera after the tried and sure-fire successes of the older master. *Rienzi* was cast in the French grand-opera mold of *Les Huguenots,* and the resemblance became unmistakable, particularly in the patterned sequence of overture, martial pageant, ballet and massed choral finale.

Yet there was something more. Though buried in fusty traditionalism, the pulse of a new force made itself felt. "The young lion's paw is there," wrote Pitts Sanborn and Emil Hilb a century later, "strong and resilient, to smite the music into life!"

CHAPTER 17

THE plot of *Rienzi* closely followed Bulwer-Lytton's historic novel. In outline it runs as follows:

RIENZI

ACT I

The scene is Rome in the mid-fourteenth century. An aristocrat, Paolo Orsini, and his followers have succeeded in abducting a young girl, Irene di Rienzi (sister of the papal notary, Cola di Rienzi), from her brother's home in the dark of night. Before making off, however, Orsini is surprised by an enemy of long standing, Steffano Colonna, and the latter's armed clique. In the ensuing tussle Colonna's young son Adriano, in love with Irene, rescues the girl and restores her to her outraged brother. Rienzi, given authority by the Church, now arouses the populace of Rome to break the tyrannic rule of the nobles.

ACT II

Orsini and Colonna now join forces against a common enemy. Rienzi succeeds in subduing them, however, and his victory is celebrated with city-wide demonstrations and a dance festival honoring the Goddess of Peace. At the same time amnesty is granted the nobles so as to dispel future rancors.

ACT III

A false truce follows as, at the first opportunity, Orsini hurls a treacherous dagger at Rienzi, which is deflected by the latter's armor. Now mercy gives way to retribution: death sentences are pronounced against all ringleaders. Before these can be carried out, the elder Colonna is reported killed in a police action. Now the young Adriano feels duty bound to avenge his father, taking up arms against Rienzi the newly crowned Roman Tribune.

ACT IV

A conspiracy by Orsini and Colonna followers is undermining Rienzi's reputation among the citizenry, with allegations that he is in league with the Ghibelline Emperor Henry VII, whom all Italy regards as an alien intruder. An assassination attempt fails, but Rienzi knows that even the protection of Cardinal Raimondo cannot ward off further clashing of arms.

ACT V

Adriano is torn between two loyalties: family honor and devotion to Irene. In a final attempt to save the girl he joins sister and brother inside the walls of the beleaguered Capitolium. But mass frenzy amid the populace has been whipped to a peak. Incendiaries now set the building on fire and the three victims, Rienzi, Adriano and Irene, are trapped in the flames.

According to operatic tradition, younger male roles were written for women singers. Thus the curvaceous Madame Schröder-Devrient struggled with the problematic impersonation of Adriano, while Tichatschek and Fräulein Wüst assumed the far easier guises of Rienzi and Irene. It was an obsolescent device, this use of female voices in masculine parts, and soon Wagner would scorn the practice. Save in the characterization of a page boy or flute-playing shepherd, he was to emancipate himself of such archaisms altogether.

The Dresden *première* of *Rienzi* went off exceedingly well, though Wagner suffered agonies backstage. He worried about the opera's great length (there was an overture in addition to the highly cluttered five acts), which might tax the audience's patience. Thus during the third intermission he crept up a ladder, behind the drawn curtain, and set back the hands of the clock that hung above the proscenium, to hoodwink people regarding the passage of time. The ruse appeared to work, for the ticket holders stayed to the very end.

That same evening a gala reception was held for the
poser and his wife in tribute to the *Rienzi* triumph. A g
ing assembly of guests, including members of the royal
as well as worldly celebrities, moved through the theater
where the festivities took place. Favorable comments
be heard on all sides. Even King Friedrich August of Sᵥ
paused graciously to congratulate Richard and Minna, bᴏ
whom were overwhelmed almost to the point of forgᵉ
their manners. During their presentation to His Majesty,
ner managed at the last moment to give his petrified ᴠ
helpful nudge.

"Minna," he stage-whispered, "make a curtsy!" He hi
managed an awkward but reverent bow.

"Bravo, Herr Wagner!" the King said warmly. "All Saxony
is proud of you."

"Thank you, Your Majesty."

The monarch indicated one of his companions, a lean and
tight-lipped gentleman with penetrating eyes. "This is our
Minister of Education and Culture, Baron von der Pfordten,
who was instrumental in launching you here tonight. He
promises to take a special interest in your future."

Wagner and Pfordten shook hands, but they exchanged no
more than trivial formalities before the royal cortege made its
departure. Now the reception grew more relaxed. In the mingling of townspeople and artists the tall figure of Liszt suddenly
appeared. He rushed forward with arms outspread.

"You've done it at last! Congratulations!"

Richard was nonplused. "Franz! What are you doing in
Dresden?"

The dashing Hungarian smiled. "I read the newspapers. As
soon as the date of your opening was announced I planned to
be here."

A man of slighter build stepped up, on the arm of a companion. His sightless eyes stared vacantly, but the hands of
Theodor Apel sought Wagner. "Everything has been said, my
dear Richard," he murmured, "everything fitting and important. And you deserve it all."

The boyhood friends embraced, choked with emotion. It

was Liszt who lightened the moment by pointing to the buffet
tables set up in an adjoining salon. "How about some food?"

Richard and Minna, caught in a new round of handshaking,
turned only briefly to glimpse a Lucullan feast spread amid
gleaming candelabra and flower bowls of finest Meissen. While
responding mechanically to the ripple of well-meant platitudes,
they had difficulty keeping their minds off that tempting sight.
At last, in the foyer's congestion, Richard managed to break
out of the receiving line, dragging Minna with him. Together
they made for the dining hall, where their eyes bulged with
delight.

"Come, Minnie, let's stuff!" Richard cried exuberantly in his
unvarnished Saxon dialect. (*"Komm, Minel, nu woll'n mer
pampen!"*)

It had been years since they last gorged themselves—back in
Königsberg, at the impromptu celebration of their marriage.
To be sure, the victuals assembled on that boisterous occasion
might have looked skimpy beside the current lavish spread.
For the moment, then, Richard and Minna lunged for the edi-
bles, while Liszt and Apel kept themselves tactfully in the
background. Strangers continually moved up to address the
composer and to press him with questions regarding his rumored "modern" artistic theories. Richard, hands loaded with
canapés, mostly could not answer for swallowing. Having
known hunger for so long, he radiated childish happiness at
the mere discovery of so much food. Nor did Minna lag behind. After disposing of her first ample helping she led Richard on a second forage, this time away from the hors d'oeuvres
to the high spot of the menu.

"Look!" she cried blissfully. "Roast goose, liver dumplings,
suckling pig . . ."

Richard's nod was appreciative. "Now comes the main
course," he observed, smacking his lips.

Minna could not resist taking an advance look at the desserts.
"Oh," she gasped, "come and see the sweets! DoboschTorte,
cheese tarts and butter pastries with whipped cream!"

Joyously they heaped their plates and ate anew. At the end
of this splurge, finally, their gluttony was appeased and their

intemperance slackened. Only now did Liszt return and draw Wagner's attention away from prandial matters.

"Well, my friend," he repeated, "the ice is broken. You are well on your way to the top. Now what about your other operas, the *Dutchman* and that new work, *Lohengrin?*"

Wagner beamed. "I've signed with Lüttichau for the *première* of *Der Fliegende Holländer* right here in Dresden next January."

"Then why not let me have *Lohengrin?*"

"You?" Wagner looked puzzled. "My dear Franz, *Lohengrin* is no piano concerto."

Liszt grinned. "Oh, haven't you heard? I've given up the concert stage."

"No!"

Liszt's expression grew serious. "I have accepted a post as director-conductor of the Weimar Opera. With my family already installed there, I am looking forward to a quiet and rewarding life. No more touring. Time, perhaps, to try my hand at composing." He paused. "What do you think of it?"

Richard was too baffled for rational comment. "I hardly know, Franz. If anyone, *you* are a virtuoso, a born performer." He shook his head. "I'll have to get used to the idea."

Again Liszt smiled. "You will. But back to *Lohengrin*—the repertoire for the current Weimar season is not complete. You could do me no greater honor than to let me give *Lohengrin* a proper launching." He held out an entreating hand, which Wagner clasped after a moment's thought.

"All right, Franz, it's a promise. But not for this season."

"Why not?"

"There are rough spots in the script, and the score is incomplete."

"You can work on it right away, now that *Rienzi* is off your hands, can't you? I am prepared to wait——"

"Sorry, no." Wagner indicated a ribboned decoration pinned to his lapel. "After the final curtain tonight I was handed this . . . er . . . trinket and a written appointment as Royal Conductor in His Majesty's Court Opera. That means I am committed to yet another Dresden opening, my third."

"Not *Lohengrin,* surely!" Liszt protested. "You just promised——"

"No, not *Lohengrin.* I am at work on a new opera, to be called *Tannhäuser.*"

He would have liked to take Liszt aside and with him discuss the plot and technical aspects of this project, but a fresh wave of admirers had pushed into the dining hall to seek out the guest of honor and the comestibles. In the accompanying tumult any attempt at serious conversation was drowned out.

Disappointed, Liszt bade his friend farewell. For the rest of the evening Richard and Minna felt themselves whirling on a merry-go-round which did not slow down till the small hours. When they returned at last to their apartment, shortly before dawn, Minna took time to fetch a jar of bay leaves from her kitchen. She spread these under the bed sheets, so Richard could "rest on his laurels." It was her first gesture of acknowledgment and recognition. During this night that was ending she found herself for the first time believing in her husband's talent.

Minna's new-found faith was amply corroborated by the next day's reviews. "Better than Donizetti!" wrote the music critic for the *Dresdener Tageblatt,* whose words were intended as high praise indeed. A footnote, nonetheless, pointed out one flaw in the new composer's work: "An opera that lasts from six o'clock to midnight—has anyone ever heard the like? The audience could hardly keep its eyes open. We all felt beaten over the head. . . ."

As for Wagner, he arose from deep slumber toward noon of the following day, a man of good cheer and financial assets. The instant popularity of *Rienzi* caused the Dresden Opera management to seek immediate acquisition of all performing rights. The composer was offered a blanket sum of three hundred taler (approximately $240), which to him seemed the height of largess. He accepted eagerly, rushing home at once to lay his riches into Minna's waiting hands.

On his way thither he took time to stop at an apothecary shop for an ointment to treat a skin rash that overnight had broken out on his back. The bay leaves spread by Minna under his sheet had concentrated, through the sleeper's movements, in the area of greatest weight. Being dry, they had pricked through the linen and left a pattern of sharp speckles that soon gave rise to an intolerable itch.

Richard confided in a colleague, Ferdinand Heine, who described the mishap in a letter to their mutual friend, Kietz:

> ... His wife put our great man's laurels (in all innocence, of course) where they were most profanely crushed. Richard slept splendidly [*prächtig*], but he is now careful how he sits down. . . .

CHAPTER 18

SCARCELY two and a half months after his first modest touch of fame Wagner saw his second work presented on a Dresden stage, this time under the personal sponsorship of the King. The opera was *The Flying Dutchman*, and in conjunction with its opening on January 2, 1843, the composer was promised a lifetime pension—paid out in the form of an annual salary of fifteen hundred taler, or slightly over $1000—in his new station as *Königlicher Hofkapellmeister* (Royal Court Conductor).

Great anticipation filled the first-night audience, which still thrilled at memories of the romantic bravado and vivid clash of arms in *Rienzi*. No one knew what to expect from a Dutchman who was said to "fly," but theater customers waited in unison for a big action drama that must surely surpass its predecessor as a stage spectacle. They were bitterly disappointed. The new opera was a complete departure from Meyerbeer's established blood-and-thunder formula, with its crowded stage, picturesque ensembles, oratorical climaxes and general hullaballoo. For the first time Wagner was bringing mysticism and the supernatural into play.

The story of *Der Fliegende Holländer* belonged to legend. It was a part of Dutch literature and had been borrowed by the poet Heinrich Heine in his *Reisebilder (Travel Tales)*. Wagner himself, during his stormy sea voyage from Riga, had outlined a libretto on this subject and later tried to interest Léon Pillet, director of the Paris Opéra, in contracting for the music. Monsieur Pillet did not wish to take chances on an unknown composer, but he liked the libretto well enough to offer buying it for one of his regular hired composers. When Richard recoiled in outrage he was coolly informed that Paul Foucher, brother-

149

in-law of Victor Hugo, happened to be working on just such
a theme, with a dozen top musicians itching for the privilege of
collaboration. His spirit wilted. Pillet further pointed out that
his own production schedule was set for the next seven years,
with not a chance in that time for a work of Wagner's to break
into the Paris Opéra. Already harrowed by dire poverty, Richard was in no position to resist. He surrendered his script to
Pillet for five hundred francs (less than $100), committing him-
self to supply an additional ballet intermezzo, since Parisian
theatergoers could not give acceptance to an opera that dispensed with dancing.

It happened that Pillet promptly passed the libretto to one
of his pet composers, Pierre Louis Philippe Dietsch, who blew
it up into a grandiose offering titled *Le Vaisseau Fantôme*.
This was presented to the French public on November 9, 1842,
and proved a signal failure, because of both the eerie strange-
ness of the narrative and the totally inept musical treatment.

Copyright laws in those days did not prevent an author from
giving new form to story material already sold. There was no
agency to stop Richard from going to work on another *Dutchman* libretto, tailored this time to German rather than Gallic
tastes. While still fighting starvation in the Rue de la Tonnellerie, he had jotted down the essence of the wild seaman's
legend once again, giving it a new and original twist. The
definitive Wagner outline ran as follows:

DER FLIEGENDE HOLLÄNDER

ACT I

Daland, a Norwegian skipper, is faced with rough seas and
the necessity of taking shelter in a harbor some distance from
his home port. Another vessel arrives—the ghostly ship of the
Dutchman, Philip Vanderdecken—with high black masts and
blood-red sails. This is the time, in the seven-year cycle specified by an ancient curse, for Vanderdecken to step ashore and
seek a woman whose love will end his interminable voyaging.

The two captains meet on land and talk of their affairs. Vanderdecken mentions a great treasure stored in his ship and
promises good pay to anyone who will give him a night's lodg-

ing. Daland could use some money. When the stranger asks suddenly, "Have you a daughter?" and gives indication that he is marriage-bent, a happy gleam comes into Daland's eyes. Straightway he asks Vanderdecken to be his guest. As the weather has cleared, the two ships weigh anchor and move out to sea.

ACT II

At Daland's house in the next port young Senta, the skipper's daughter, sits among her girl companions who are busy at their spinning wheels. It becomes evident that the legend of the Flying Dutchman is very alive in the region, and much talked of among romantic maidens. On the wall above Daland's door there is even a fanciful painting, showing an imaginary Vanderdecken with black beard and a Spaniard's cape and hat, which plainly holds a fascination for Senta. She is given to daydreaming in front of the portrait. Teased by her friends, she sings a ballad about the Dutchman and confesses that she yearns to be the woman who might lift the curse from him.

Her words are heard by the lovesick woodsman, Erik, who vainly has hoped to make Senta his wife. As he now pleads his case anew, the giggling girls depart, soon followed by the dejected Erik. Senta is left staring at the image on the wall, when, almost unnoticed by her, the door opens and Vanderdecken stands there in the flesh, with Daland at his side. A long and searching look passes between the towering dark adventurer and the fair-skinned girl. For his part, Daland would like to push matters along by mentioning the foreigner's great wealth and also commenting on his daughter's more than ordinary beauty. But this is hardly necessary, for Fate already binds those two. When Daland tactfully leaves the room the enraptured Senta opens her heart to Vanderdecken and accepts his impassioned troth.

ACT III

That same evening, while the Dutchman attends to his ship, Erik seeks out Senta once more and accuses her of fickleness and treachery. This unhappy scene, taking place near the docks, is witnessed by the returning Vanderdecken, who concludes that if Senta jilted one man she would be faithless to

another. He rushes back aboard and takes off with his vessel
for seven more years of desperate sailing. Senta, beside herself, runs along the rocks, crying after him that her love is true
until death—a pledge she proves by throwing herself into the
sea. At that instant the curse is lifted, the phantom ship is swallowed by the waves, and Vanderdecken—whose soul has sought
release for so long and hopeless a time—is seen joined to Senta
in a heavenly mirage.

In treating this subject Wagner began giving emphasis to a
concept that would grow and expand throughout his later work
—namely, the glorification of womanhood. He had seized on
Goethe's phrase *"Das ewig Weibliche zieht uns hinan!"* ("The
eternal feminine draws us upward.") This he was hoisting for
his banner.

Also, for the first time, he was experimenting with a device
in musical composition, evolved by himself and called the "leitmotiv"—the association of a definite tune or even a mere fragmentary passage with an individual personage in the plot. Not
yet perfected as it would be in his later operas, Wagner gave
to his *Flying Dutchman* cast a rudimentary means of recognition; that is, each singer came on stage preceded, as it were, by
his or her own musical theme.

As to style, the composer still floundered in borrowed techniques. His Senta and Vanderdecken delineations leaned
heavily on Weber, while Erik's sad songs sounded like the
plaint of poor Nemorino in Donizetti's *L'Elisir d'Amore*, with
overtones from Marschner. Daland, the scheming father with
a marriageable daughter on his hands, he derived straight from
the classic French *opéra comique*.

Nevertheless, over these appropriated idioms there already
hovered a hint of that special magic which one day would be
described as Wagnerian. It appeared only for moments, as yet,
forming a shimmering tissue here, a stronger fabric there, before losing itself ultimately in the tyrannical dominance of accepted formulas. Enough of the nameless new element stood
out, however, for critics to speak of the composer "painting an

ocean canvas with his music brush" and creating "tone rhythms that convey the motion of the sea."

Needless to say, for his German version of the tragic *Holländer* story Richard furnished no ballet, deeming such an appendage not only anticlimactic but indeed grotesque. He did, however, write a stirring overture to key the opera's high pathos and set its mood.

At the Dresden opening the role of Senta was sung by the soprano of the hour, Schröder-Devrient, who made much of the somewhat ethereal part. Vanderdecken was unfortunately entrusted to a corpulent and mediocre baritone named Johann Wilhelm Wächter, for whom no likely maid would have jumped off a cliff. The *basso buffo* did well enough by Daland, while an obscure tenor listed only as Reinhold made a touching Erik.

Whether due to Wagner's grimly mystic theme or the avoirdupois of the play's hero, Dresden listeners were unanimous in condemnation of the work. Legends and tales from the supernatural were not the genre of the hour, as critics quickly pointed out. People preferred elementary action dramas, with swordsmanship and swashbuckle, and a minimum of cerebral motivation. In short, they wanted Meyerbeer.

Wagner was summoned for a conference with Saxony's Minister of Education and Culture, von der Pfordten. "Why not give us another *Rienzi?*" proposed this sagacious gentleman. "You might use a Greek setting this time, and an earlier century."

Richard demurred. He was scarcely done with *Holländer* rehearsals and the strain of his conductor's task at the *première* when another subject, heavy with metaphysical overtones, took hold of his imagination. This was the cherished *Tannhäuser* saga. It had lain dormant in his mind since that overland journey from Paris, when he and Minna had first looked on the fabled Wartburg. Here at last was an intrinsically Germanic story that would permit the re-creation of a figure long cherished in Middle-European folklore—the wandering *Minnesänger*, or minstrel knight. Singers and bards abounded in pre-Reformation Germany, engaged in lute playing and ballad composing when not drawn into chivalric duels or jousts. These gallant heroes chose love (*Minne* in ancient Teutonic speech) for their muse, and sang the praises of all womanhood even while each extolled the virtue and beauty of some specified damsel known to himself alone. Music contests were held not only to evaluate the merits of a song but to establish whether the fair lady who might be its subject was truthfully honored and did not herself do injustice to its claims.

While occupied with this romantic topic Richard Wagner was no longer deeply in love with his own wife. But it pleased him to point out that her name, though actually derived from Wilhelmina, bore a phonetic relation to the classic *Minne*. In evoking the era of minstrelsy for his newest operatic effort he was, subjectively, casting himself in the role of supreme balladeer behind the scenes.

Alas, his flesh-and-blood Minna failed to see things in the same light. The short run of *The Flying Dutchman*, ended after four performances by Madame Schröder-Devrient's tactfully requesting a vacation, cut off any hope of revenue outside Richard's fixed salary. This meant, in Minna's eyes, that the time and effort expended on the dreary sea drama (to which she had been opposed all along) must be reckoned a total loss. She agreed fervently with Baron Pfordten.

"What's the use of bothering with riddles that nobody understands?" she goaded. "Why don't you write something that will sell?"

She still had Meyerbeer in mind. She still saw no degradation in her husband's embarking on a slavishly imitative course so long as the formula he employed was sure of a ready market. Already that formula had known its best days. Its threadbare fabric showed the heavy wear of several decades in Italian and French repertory. The wonder was that it still held together.

"You are asking me to start backward," Richard replied, separately, to Minna and Pfordten. "You want to hear the jingle of the box office before you lend ear to either my words or my music."

He spoke the truth. But it did not win him the friendship of the Minister of Education and Culture, any more than it could sway the stubbornly entrenched opinion of a wife.

CHAPTER 19

ORIGINALLY Wagner had planned to name his Tann-häuser opera *Der Venusberg (The Mountain of Venus)*. Under this title he submitted his first completed manu-script to the Dresden Court Theater management, only to meet with an acidly mocking rejection. In his almost naïve unworld-liness, which even a three-year sojourn in Paris had not dis-pelled, Richard failed to see the danger of *double-entendre* to which his simple caption might give rise.

"My good fellow," Baron von Lüttichau explained, "it's really most embarrassing. After all, we have a famous medical school here in Dresden." He coughed. "I dread to think what the anatomy students would make of it!"

At last the unsophisticated Richard understood. He made quick amends by giving the opera the name of its principal character, and, to forestall all possible salacious interpretation, he added an innocuous subtitle, *The Singers' Contest in the Wartburg*. Under this dual identification the *première* was held on Sunday, October 19, 1845. The cast included Tichat-schek as Tannhäuser, Madame Schröder-Devrient as Venus, Anton Mitterwurzer as Wolfram von Eschenbach, Wilhelm Dettmer as Landgrave Hermann, and among lesser roles such repertory singers as Schloss, Wächter, Curty and Risse. The opera's heroine, Elisabeth, had been assigned to the composer's young niece Johanna, daughter of his eldest brother, Albert Wagner.

The performance could hardly be called a smashing success. All through the rehearsal period there had been difficulties be-tween podium and singing personnel. For one thing, the tenor Tichatschek lacked imagination and seemed hopelessly incapa-ble of breathing life into the story's hero. He sang Tannhäuser's lines with such lethargy, particularly the climaxing adagio measures of the last act, that even members of the orchestra were lured to sleep. Secondly, Schröder-Devrient raised a delicate point: how was she to be costumed as Venus? Classic portraits of the goddess dictated undress rather than dress, a fact which gave the demure diva palpitations.

"I can't wear a sash around my middle and let it go at that," she stormed. "The whole idea of this Venus creature is absurd and . . . and indecent!"

Only after repeated pleadings and the promise that her voluptuous charms would be shielded by tricot tights and veritable clouds of gauze did the skittish soprano accept the role.

To German ears the plot of the opera was of course familiar, since it derived from medieval Teutonic legend. Tannhäuser, a young minstrel knight of thirteenth-century Thuringia, was wont to take part in amicable contests of balladeers and minnesingers who met in the great hall of Wartburg Castle near Eisenach. But on an adventurous outing in the surrounding forest the romantic lad found himself trapped in a cave which led to the subterranean hideaway of the Pagan Aphrodite, or Venus, and her riotous court. With understandable zest he threw himself into the joys and revelries here offered, forgetting the world and human company he had left behind. Here the synopsis:

TANNHÄUSER

ACT I

SCENE 1: Preceded by an overture, the action opens with the Hörselberg cavern, where Tannhäuser has lived for a whole year. Love, lust and lechery have been his pleasure in such measure that monotony has set in. Not only the nymphs and handmaidens of Venus but the goddess herself can stir no further appetite within him. His senses are jaded and he longs for nothing so much as a return to earth and its simple delights. Even a singing contest would look good to him. Venus lets him go.

SCENE 2: Through a miracle of lighting and prop shifting, Tannhäuser next finds himself in a green Thuringian valley, where a shepherd's flute mingles with the chorus of a group of pilgrims on their way to Rome. Immediately thereafter Landgrave Hermann and his hunting party, among them many of Tannhäuser's former fellow minstrels, come upon their "lost" companion and welcome him back into their midst. A song tournament is immediately arranged for, in which all promise to take part. The theme for the occasion is to be Nature's Beauty, and the Praise of Pure Love, with the victor's prize no less than the hand of the Landgrave's niece Elisabeth. It is not known that Elisabeth has long yearned for Tannhäuser; only the Knight Wolfram, in love with her himself, has guessed her secret.

Act II

In the hall of the Wartburg the contest opens in the presence of the assembled court. Each minstrel performs for the judges, in turn. Tannhäuser, however, finds such lyrical treatment of "virtuous passion" both insipid and untrue. Memory evokes for him far different sensations, hardly to be compared with these pallid and feeble phrasings. He has known erotic delights at their carnal best, without euphemism or concealment. When his turn comes to strike up the lute it is not Sacred Love but Profane Passion of which he sings, thereby revealing to his friends what they had long suspected: his sojourn in the forbidden Hörselberg with the temptress Venus.

Outraged, the respectable ladies of the Landgrave's court stalk from the hall, while the men draw their swords and close in on the boastful sinner. Only Elisabeth's intercession saves Tannhäuser, who thereupon is ordered by the Landgrave to do penance by joining another band of pilgrims that is just starting for Rome. Contrite and won over by Elisabeth's devotion, the young rake vows to seek absolution.

Act III

During his absence the gentle Elisabeth has herself donned nun's garb. Daily she prays at a forest shrine to speed Tannhäuser's salvation. Watching over her, Wolfram sings his sad song to the Evening Star, revealing his own hapless love, but to no avail. Elisabeth retires.

In Rome, meanwhile, things have not gone well. The Holy

Father is adamant where sins of the flesh are concerned. Holding his papal wand aloft, he cries: "As on this staff no green will sprout, so shalt thou not escape the fires of Hell!"

A weary and tattered Tannhäuser returns to the forest clearing outside the Wartburg and reports this desolate outcome to Wolfram, unable at the same time to conceal his bitterness at such intransigence on the part of the Church. In his resentful mood a vision rises before him in a roseate light: the Hörselberg, with Venus beckoning him to return into her arms. As he stands, transfixed and sorely tempted, a chapel bell rings from the Wartburg tower, for Elisabeth has died of sorrow and is being carried to her grave.

The funeral procession passes Tannhäuser presently, and he drops to his knees beside the bier, while the Hörselberg vision and its lures fade forever.

True remorse has cleansed Tannhäuser's soul, and final proof of heavenly pardon now arrives as messengers from Rome report that the Holy Father's staff is burgeoning fresh leaves.

Thus the Wagner libretto. In the ancient folkloric version of the Tannhäuser saga there is no such pious denouement; instead of repenting, the hero answers ecclesiastic implacability by flinging himself willfully back into Aphrodite's realm, never again to emerge.

Neither ending, whether Wagner's or that of hallowed legend, pleased the Dresden opening-night audience. German operagoers were accustomed to the libretto formula of Karl Maria von Weber, with a dependable finale in which everything turned out for the best. In Wagner's *Flying Dutchman* and the new Tannhäuser there was solution but hardly the proverbial happy end. Disappointed listeners went away shaking their heads.

Further trouble arose from religious quarters. For some time a neo-Reformation had been afoot throughout Germany against fresh encroachment of the Catholic Church. The movement was called the Czersky and Ronge Dispute, and its Protestant participants accused Wagner of being in the pay of Rome for making his *Tannhäuser* a vehicle for Vatican propaganda, while Catholics in turn looked on Meyerbeer's *Les Huguenots* as the subversive tool of heresy. Both views, of course, were wrong. The extrovert Meyerbeer was unburdened by questions of dogma, and in any case he did not write his own dialogue; his interest lay in composing tunes that would sell. As for Wagner, he was by no means a rebel against any given theology, though he visibly leaned toward mysticism. Actually, in propounding the theme of *Tannhäuser* as the struggle between humanity's higher and lower natures, he respected a convention of his time —namely, that good and evil must not be embodied in one female person. The current ideal of womanhood demanded that there be no compromise or indecorous blending of weakness and strength. Hence the figure of Venus stood for sinful pleasure and temptation, while Elisabeth was given the qualifications of a saint. Masculine standards of the day were less demanding; no canons were violated by combining in the single role of Tannhäuser both spiritually sublime and carnally impure promptings.

Musically the new opera represented another step forward toward the Wagnerian concept of the future. As yet Richard had not freed himself of the old structural conventions providing for independent arias, duets, trios or sextets, which had no thematic bearing on—and could be freely isolated from—the main text. But again, as in *The Flying Dutchman,* there was evident in *Tannhäuser* a strong effort to make the whole opera count, rather than to let dramatic values, choral effects and orchestral contribution serve merely as backdrops for the vocal display of individual stars.

Richard still did not know how to sublimate song units into the "symphonic flow," but already his melodic line had psychological overtones. That is, his performers did not sing merely pretty tunes, or grandiose or heroic ones, but what they sang was beginning to paint character and *emotion-relevant-to-plot* while lending a lasting identification to a role. Heretofore classic opera, from Mozart and Gluck through the Berlioz, Giordano and Donizetti school, had furnished typical solo or group numbers that, as far as text was concerned, rambled off from the libretto and became concert-stage offerings for which all operatic action was temporarily halted. This practice left no doubt in the listener's mind that most of the ensemble business was secondary in importance and calculated to serve as a mere filler till the next aria came due. From such a realization evolved a practice, widespread among less musical opera supporters, of remaining in their stalls only long enough to hear what obviously was tailored to be a high spot, and skulking off during the duller sections to find solace in the smokers' foyer or the theater bar.

Richard fiercely resented such audience behavior and he was bent on seeking a cure. In *Rienzi* he had not yet tackled the problem musically, but in obedience to Goethe's dramatic dictum for all stage works—"Let things *happen!*"—the libretto was studded with visual factors, from elaborate scenic paraphernalia and costuming to movement-producing skulduggery, swordplay, leaps from high balconies and the like. With so much going on behind the footlights, thirsty boxholders and gallery occupants alike were willing to forgo their champagne or beer rather than miss what might turn into a fascinating fracas.

With *The Flying Dutchman* physical action was still dominant: a huge four-master sailed onstage and later was demolished by a raging sea, all within sight of a thunderstruck audience. But Wagner was now on the track of something for which he had no name. It was the art of tonal painting, the wielding of a musical brush. Not drama alone, nor occasional melodic fireworks, must draw people into the theater for the duration of some favorite scene; he meant to hold them there, from start to finish, by an indissoluble unity in which he would clothe his work. He still did not recognize the aria as the true culprit which he would one day escape. But he was blending its too-pat singsong structure into the fabric of conjunctive music that thereby was given greater importance. In so doing he bridged pauses and mastered awkward gaps between "numbers" by simply permitting no singer to step into a spotlight for his or her "number." He still wrote arias, but he led up to them and away from them by repetitive phrases, thereby stumbling upon that most effective Wagnerian device, the leitmotiv.

In *Tannhäuser* the classic structure continued to defy him.

Again he did not know how to keep solo passages from standing out, sore-thumb fashion, as solo passages. Yes, he had arias, clean-cut and detached from the opera's web, like *Lieder* offered in a voice recital. There was an overture, however, that richly worked these separate entities into a tapestry of sound, with overlapping threads that managed to reappear from act to act, creating an outward effect of union. The leitmotiv rose a notch nearer perfection, as in the Venus music of the first Hörselberg scene and its reprise when, near the opera's end, Tannhäuser sees the goddess in a vision. But the greatest forward step was none of these. It lay in Wagner's initial handling of an all-German theme. He had found his roots and his idiom.

He had come home.

I F *Tannhäuser* was not destined for a long Dresden run, its few performances were attended by a select public. In the opening-night audience sat Franz Liszt, with a box party that included the fashionable Madame Kalergis, a niece of the Russian Chancellor, Count von Nesselrode. Madame Kalergis was renowned as a patroness of the arts, ever on the lookout for new talent to sponsor. On Liszt's word, she came to the *Tannhäuser première* with high anticipation, only to find herself quite bored. Hers was the conventional spectator attitude: she went to the theater "to be amused." That is, she liked a fair balance of everything—a bit of farce, a touch of tragedy, and the merest flip of naughtiness for spice. In opera, besides love songs and bloodshed she thoroughly enjoyed the ballet. *Tannhäuser* had no ballet.

On the other hand, if she was disappointed in his work, Madame Kalergis took rather a fancy to the young composer. She found Richard Wagner both personable and exciting. Certainly he bore watching. She paid him a carefully worded compliment: "You have a great sense of color. The costumes and sets are magnificent!"

Richard bowed. "I shall transmit Madame's praise to our designer, Ferdinand Heine, and the set painter, Herr Dieterle."

Another listener in the first *Tannhäuser* audience was the thirty-five-year-old Robert Schumann, whose pianoforte compositions—*Fantasie, Kinderszenen, Kreisleriana, Carnaval,* etc. —had gained steady fame during the past decade. At present Schumann was himself trying to invade the operatic field with a work—his only effort of this nature—entitled *Genoveva*. Already the artist's wife, Clara Schumann (nee Wieck), surpassed her husband on the concert stage, so that Robert deferred to her virtuoso talent and dedicated himself almost exclusively to composition. Here, though not in opera itself, he would reveal his particular genius, becoming one of the heralds of modernism in instrumental music.

To Schumann the *Tannhäuser* performance was an unqualified delight. Despite the severe migraine headaches that attacked him with increasing frequency, he returned for a second and third hearing, each time rushing backstage to congratulate singers and orchestra alike. For Wagner he had words of glowing encouragement: "The world will one day recognize you among its greatest! I do so now."

Richard needed this friendly boost to his shaky confidence, particularly as the miscast Tichatschek grew worse with each appearance. To stir some spark of life in him the tenor was plied, before curtaintime, with wines and liqueurs, but he rejected these in favor of beer, which he could down in prodigious quantities. Far from vivifying him, however, the hops-and-malt beverage only aggravated Tichatschek's apathy toward a role which at best he but vaguely grasped.

With Schumann it was possible to talk shop. Richard confided some of his projected and later discarded plans, such as an outline for a three-act opera to be called *The Mines of Falun*, which never developed beyond the original sketch. Another and more ambitious attempt in five acts, *The Saracen*, begun in Paris, had reached libretto form before it too revealed itself as mere literary carpentry. The music for it was never written.

"Have you tried anything outside opera?" Schumann wanted to know.

Wagner winced. His hack days were not over. As a salaried court employee he was expected to produce not only special arrangements but original compositions for use at ceremonials and during feast-day services in the Royal Chapel. What made these obligatory efforts less onerous was the fact that an exceptionally fine vocal ensemble had been put at his disposal. Thus the King's favorite male chorus dealt nobly with several Wagner cantatas, among them the "Love Feast of The Apos-

tles," an arrangement of the Triumphal March from Spontini's
La Vestale, a chorale in honor of the New Year, and various
eulogies to the Saxon dynasty. Though well orchestrated and
enhanced by skillful use of trombone flourishes and horn or
trumpet fanfares, these varied productions leaned toward the
melodic commonplace, and Wagner knew it. He was still guilty,
even in *Tannhäuser,* of lapsing now and then into the easy tune
clichés of his era. Even the commissioned funeral music he
furnished for the reinterment at Dresden of Weber's remains,
in December of 1844, was on the whole too pedestrian, considering the surpassing esteem in which, since his own boyhood, Richard had held the older composer.

He led the conversation into less embarrassing channels. "I
have done some prose writings. Autobiographical sketches for
a periodical published by my friend Laube."

"Ah, yes! *Zeitung Für Die Elegante Welt*—a journal for the
upper classes."

Wagner smiled wryly. "To whom the account of my shabby
miseries must have made quaint reading, if only by way of
novelty."

A gleam of understanding lighted Schumann's face. He too
knew the thorny road walked by the insolvent musician. Worse
off than ever Richard had been, Robert had a large brood of
children for whom he could not provide save with the help of
their mother's grueling concert tours. This humiliating fact
contributed unmistakably to his early breakdown and death,
eleven years hence, as an inmate of an institution for psychotics.

No such grim portent hung over the lives of two English
ladies, Mrs. Taylor and her eighteen-year-old daughter Jessie,
who attended the *Tannhäuser* opening. They were traveling
on the Continent, taking in sights and artistic events. Both
loved music and found themselves entranced at their first contact with Wagner's symphonic form of opera. Breathlessly
mother and daughter made their way backstage to shower the
composer with encomiums. More than that, Mrs. Taylor was
a wealthy widow of philanthropic bent who delighted in lending aid to struggling artists. She begged Wagner to accept a

monthly stipend that might assure him of needed leisure to write further masterpieces.

The offer was an unexpected windfall. Richard's salary tied him to numerous tasks that well might be delegated to copyists and arrangers; if he but could afford to pay for such services and thereby release his own energies for weightier work, an ideal situation would result. The mere thought of such a possibility set his brain awhirl. There was the revising to be done on *Lohengrin*, which he had promised Franz Liszt yet saw no chance of completing. Always there were rehearsals, imperfect orchestrations, new choral requirements for the Royal Chapel and a thousand other routine matters making demands on him. Liszt might as well be told to forget about *Lohengrin* altogether. Unless, of course, Mrs. Taylor's largess were accepted.

And why should it not? No feelings of unseemliness or diffidence arose in Richard's mind to cloud his answer. Money in itself meant nothing to him. Food, clothing, shelter, love, and indeed life—all were for him wrapped up with one purposeful obsession: music. Here was the delicious, supreme thrill, the joy one could almost taste, the magic mission for which he believed himself put on this earth. Whatever served the consummation of that mission was good and must not be repulsed. Blessings upon the head of that most charitable Briton, Mrs. Taylor! Posterity might one day owe her a debt far greater than could ever be realized, for she was setting Wagner on his feet at a time when not even he himself could have guessed that he would become WAGNER. Hers was the reckless gamble, the bold and lofty faith. Since she did not happen to be a young or pretty woman, her gesture precluded coquetry. It was uncalculated, with no strings attached. Only a fool would have turned it down.

In many ways Richard was just that—a fool. He lacked all sense of practicality and earth-bound realism. Childishly willful and naïve, he actually believed that creative artists were a breed apart for whom Providence accepted full responsibility, or at least *ought* to. In published articles and personal letters he often stated this belief, adding that civic authorities, as logi-

cal executors of a Divine Will, should subsidize those gifted
starvelings who might provide the world with immortal beauty
though they had not enough common sense to fill their own
bellies.

Beyond doubt Mrs. Taylor was precisely such a deputy from
on high, a discreet confederate of God. Richard accepted her
as such. He also accepted her money. Coin in itself meant
nothing to him. But security for the pursuit of his work, and
the comforting knowledge that Minna need suffer no want—
these were his constant gnawing concerns. The royal wage, supplemented by the Taylor bounty, promised an end to such
pangs.

One other person derived intense happiness from the amicable contact. This was Mrs. Taylor's daughter, Jessie, an impressionable young woman who had never before met an opera
composer face to face. At sight of the blond Wagner, whose fire
and vivacity made him appear far younger than his thirty-two
years, Jessie experienced a breath-taking thrill. She remained
mute throughout the eminently proper discourse between her
mother and the artist (Mrs. Taylor was a lean, starched lady of
high principles whose benevolent impulses were above romantic suspicion), but secretly Jessie's heart engaged in a delicious
and accelerated pit-a-pat. Had Wagner himself been less infatuated with his muse he would surely have noticed this flattering turmoil that kindled the girl's gaze and cheek. But he
was agog with plans for a final refurbishing of *Lohengrin*, a
task made feasible by Mrs. Taylor's help. Alongside such
vivid agenda the person of Fräulein Jessie looked pale indeed;
all Richard would remember of her was an uneasy stutter and
the cold feel of her nervously damp palm.

The work on *Lohengrin* moved now into high gear. With
means at hand to escape Dresden distractions, Wagner left the
remaining few performances of *Tannhäuser* under an assistant
conductor's baton while he repaired with Minna to the small
health resort of Marienbad (Mariánské Láynè) in Bohemia,
thirty-six miles from Pilsen. Here mountain air and the silence
of great pine forests combined to give him restful concentration, while Minna benefited from the tonic waters of the region.

By the end of 1845 the libretto had received a thorough going over and Wagner was ready to map out the music. But the brief respite was cut short by a call from Dresden, where a series of court concerts required his attention. Wagner was, after all, a jobholder in the King's pay, a fact his regal sponsor did not intend to let him forget.

Through most of the following year the Hofkapelle Choir took up the composer's time. There were motets to be rehearsed (the court was Catholic and very pious), voices tested and applicants groomed for solo parts—all tasks that left no leisure for private musical pursuits. Mendelssohn's *Elijah* came out during the summer and was given an inspired *première* at Birmingham, with its Hamburg-born author, an ardent Anglophile, in attendance. Reports of the performance reached Saxony, where Wagner was promptly ordered to include this choral work in his repertoire, following an earlier and very ambitious rendering—with full orchestra and singers—of Beethoven's Ninth Symphony. It was not until late September that *Lohengrin* was picked up again.

By now the score had almost completely taken shape in Richard's mind, with melody line and harmonic structure all but crystallized. So well did he see his opera before him and hear its polyphonic sounds that he was able to work backward, writing the third-act music first. Acts I and II followed in quick succession, and by August of 1847 the Prelude took shape. Even now he was interrupted by extra-routine chores, including a commissioned arrangement of Gluck's *Iphigénie en Aulide*, and a requiem program on the sudden death, at thirty-eight, of Mendelssohn. Only with all this behind him could he tackle his orchestrations.

Before he finished these there were other intercurrences to block completion of the work. The year 1848, politically fateful for Europe, brought personal sorrow into Richard's life. On January 9 his mother died without having seen him again since the *Rienzi* days. The burial took place in Leipzig during a heavy winter freeze which caused the traditional handful of earth, dropped in farewell gesture on the coffin, to rumble like a load of rocks. Laube accompanied Wagner and found his friend looking not only sorrowful but haggard and drawn from overwork. The heavy Dresden schedule showed no sign of letting up: an arrangement of Palestrina's difficult *Stabat Mater* was next on the calendar, besides which Richard again took up his journalistic pen. He had resumed the study of Germanic mythology, including the Norse Eddas and the Wälsung Saga. These furnished him with material for two weighty essays, *"Die Wibelungen"* (A Legend of World History) and, with new spelling, *"Die Nibelungen"* (A Drama Sketch). In addition, the 300th anniversary of the founding of the royal Hofkapelle loomed ahead that year, calling for dignified observance. Richard was only a hired orchestra conductor, but it was the King's whim to exact from him a suitable ceremonial address.

He knew next to nothing about speechmaking. Nor could he think of an adequate subject other than the purely chronological recital of the music chapel's record to date, which turned out to be just what his royal master wanted. It proved a tedious task for speaker and listener alike, besides taking an unconscionable amount of pointless research.

To break the monotony of this effort, Richard sought refuge in poetry, dashing off his first narrative strophes about a Nibelungen figure that had captured his fancy—the hero Siegfried. As in the case of the *Lohengrin* music, he began at the end. His poem was entitled "The Death of Siegfried." At the same time another semimythological theme dwelled on his mind as a possible new operatic subject—the obscure story of the Hohenstaufen Emperor Friedrich I, surnamed Barbarossa (Redbeard), who ruled over the Holy Roman Empire during the middle of the twelfth century. It was a tale steeped in pugnacious action and heroic mysticism, partially anchored in factual history yet colored by centuries-old popular superstition. Ultimately, however, Richard would cast Barbarossa aside as too unyielding in imaginative range. He turned instead to yet another consideration, a Biblical topic. Why not an opera dealing with Jesus of Nazareth?

A surge of inspiration swept through him. He worked on this noble idea through most of the summer and autumn, completing a tensely dramatic script before the start of the Advent season. But the time was not right for sacred subjects. Europe boiled in the throes of social upheaval that reached across borders and threw the accepted political order out of joint. Revolution broke out with special vehemence in France and Germany, attended by a characteristic rejection of churchly restraints. Against the mild face of the Christ loomed the image of a new messiah, the thirty-year-old Karl Marx, engrossed in launching a gospel for the future within the covers of his book *Das Kapital.*

No. An opera on Jesus of Nazareth was hardly opportune.

CHAPTER 21

DURING Richard Wagner's sojourn in Paris the throne of France had been occupied by a well-meaning but ineffectual ruler, King Louis Philippe. No despot, this Orléans dynast strove to retain the thread-worn mantle of monarchic tradition while at the same time ornamenting his royal head with Liberty's peaked cap. He called himself Philippe Égalité and spoke in democratic accents. Yet, when called on by the National Assembly to institute much-needed electoral reforms the sovereign lost his taste for tolerance. He balked and withdrew coyly behind the ramparts of tried and familiar absolutism, a choice that cost him his crown. For, under leadership of an upstart Bonaparte, Louis Napoleon, nephew of France's great Emperor, an uprising was staged in Paris and carried to a triumphant conclusion—the establishment of the Second Republic.

Louis Napoleon carried off a plum by winning the presidency of the new French State. But he was as much an actor as Égalité had been. For two years he impersonated a benign representative of the people before, in 1850, throwing off the mask of republicanism and proclaiming himself Emperor Napoleon III.

Though France's Second Republic proved short-lived, the factors that had brought it about were kindling fires of revolt in other parts of Europe. They swept across Holland and Belgium into the loose aggregation of states that formed the German homeland. Here a string of princelets, hereditary dukes and kings clung to their jeweled scepters and ruled as individual, now benevolent, now tyrannical, autocrats.

In particular, the political breeze blowing from the west gave rise to demands in Frankfurt am Main for a constitution uniting all provinces of German speech under a centralized government at Berlin. No infringement of individual states' liberties was implied in such a union; but the small autocrats, in a body, were against the plan. In Saxony the pouting Friedrich August locked himself up in his castle, refusing to parley with any representative of the reform party.

Richard Wagner had been too long exposed to French liberal thought and free expression not to be affected by the German struggle. He lined up wholeheartedly with the Constitutionalists, putting even *Lohengrin* aside for the writing of patriotic pamphlets and speeches against the royalist die-hards. Early in the campaign there appeared over his name such challenging dissertations as "Republican Ideals vs. the Monarchy," "Art and Revolution," "Man and Existing Society," and a departure into the field that remained his particular concern, with "The Need for Theatrical Reform."

He had a knack for demagogic phrasing. "Dynastic rule is on its last legs," he proclaimed, "and the privileges of birth must yield to the free rights of honest labor. . . . Fifty years from now royalty will be reduced to mere symbolism, or else be relegated to waxworks and museums. The dawn of social conscience is approaching!"

For a time these inflammatory postulates were spouted by others. But soon Richard's own oratory supplanted his pen. In company with his friend Theodor Apel he sat in on political discussions at taverns and coffeehouses where on occasion eloquence conquered discretion as Richard's tongue ran away with itself.

Minna disapproved of such gatherings, particularly when they began to take place in her own living room. She had been bickering again over the fact that a new Meyerbeer opera, *Le Prophète*, was making headlines, while Richard's *Tannhäuser* had quietly faded out and *Lohengrin* remained on the shelf. Her refrain was always the same: "I don't know why you insist on picking such unusual subjects. Can't you write something commercial? People come to the theater to be amused, not instructed in some ancient mythology."

His defense, too, was the same. "Folklore is something a nation should be proud of. Ours in particular can help explain to the outside world a few mysteries about the German character."

"German character! Who cares about German character? If you don't watch out, your music is going to sound like a tiresome political tract. And we can thank dear Theo and his socialist friends for that!"

He was startled. "What do you mean?"

"It's Theo who always talks about reforms for the fatherland, as if that were *his* concern. We have a king, haven't we? It's the King's job to worry about the fatherland."

"The individual counts for something too, Minna. That's what Theo wants—to improve the lot of the individual."

She bristled. "Well, I don't like the company he keeps and, moreover, I don't want you to bring them here. Those fellows— Blum, Huebner and Bakunin—are notorious rabble rousers, while their chief instigator, Röckel, just got himself in trouble with the police."

Richard shook his head, smiling. "Poor old Röckel. All he did was make a speech advocating that the workers band together and stand up for their right to a living wage."

"Whatever he advocates, it's against established authority and you ought to be careful about getting mixed up with him."

Richard nodded placatingly. "Yes, dear. We have a king. And according to you that takes care of everything." He kissed her good-naturedly, then reached for his hat and music roll. One avenue of escape never failed him; he could always plead being late for rehearsal.

Debates with Minna were not, however, the only thorns in his path. The Minister of Education and Culture, Baron von der Pfordten, presently summoned Richard to his office. "Word has come to me," the stern official said in a cool, clipped voice, "that you, Herr Kapellmeister, are abusing your position."

"In what way, sir?"

"You were appointed to run the Royal Opera along cherished traditional patterns, not to revolutionize His Majesty's orchestra. And speaking of revolution, what's this I hear about your outspoken sympathy for a disgruntled element among the backstage personnel?"

Richard was undaunted. "All theater people, musicians in particular, are flagrantly underpaid. I would strongly urge, sir, that a general increase in salaries be considered."

"That's very interesting." Pfordten's tone was sharp with irony. "But the next time you have advice for us on financial matters, pray wait until we ask for it. Good day."

The interview should have been a warning. Richard had drawn unfavorable attention on himself, from the highest quarters, and it certainly behooved him to watch his step. But he did nothing of the kind. Directly from Pfordten's office he strolled to the beer cellar of the Green Lantern, where Apel and his cronies were wont to gather over a noonday drink.

"Bravo!" he was greeted in chorus. "You're just the person we've been waiting for."

He shook hands with Michael Bakunin and Robert Blum, who urged him to sit down. "Sorry, but I can't stay long. I'm conducting *Orpheus* tonight and there are some cuts to be worked out."

Apel rose. "We've something important to discuss, Richard. It will take only a moment."

"All right. What is it?"

"You heard about August? He's been arrested."

"You mean Röckel? Yes, Minna told me."

Bakunin cut in with harsh Slavic consonants. "The workers are holding a torch parade tonight. It's to be a city-wide demonstration." His eyes narrowed. "We need you."

Richard caught his breath. "Among the marchers? That's impossible. I've already told you I'm conducting Gluck tonight. And in any case, I don't believe in mob scenes except on stage." His tone changed to banter. "Also, after seven hours on the podium day after day, my feet hurt. Sorry, parades are out."

"We're not asking you to march, Richard," Apel spoke up, his fingers tapping on a paper held before him by Bakunin's hand. "What we want is your help with a broadside that is to be distributed."

"A broadside?"

Bakunin took over. "Yes. You have lived in France, where

men are already experienced in the ways of freedom. And you can write better than the rest of us." He pressed the paper into Richard's hand. "Here is an outline, covering the main points. It will take no more than half an hour for you to whip them into shape."

Richard studied the notes and found them reasonable. The workers' arguments would make a fair and convincing manifesto. He saw no reason for refusing to write it for them. More than that, when Bakunin proposed postponing the torch parade until Richard was free to walk in it, the latter recklessly promised to take part.

On May 3, 1849, the signal for a labor uprising was given and the demonstrators massed for a march on the royal palace. In their midst, head carried high, strode Richard Wagner. When the King's Cavalry came charging through the palace gates the marchers grew enraged and hurled themselves against a hastily raised line of barricades. The melee lasted several days, with Richard appearing at one time in the bell tower of Dresden's Church of the Holy Cross, from where he addressed the crowd in sonorous phrases. This last piece of Quixotism earned him the fullest royal wrath. When the mutinous clamor ended in failure the top leaders, Wagner among them, came under sentence of death.

He had yet to be caught, of course. Under cover of night he raced home and urged Minna to make ready for immediate flight. They must be on the move again, not on account of debts this time, but as political refugees. A shock awaited him. Minna was not on his side.

"Well," she received him, "is your silly parade over? And did you succeed in making a thorough fool of yourself?"

He motioned her to silence. "Ssh-sh! We're in trouble. The King's troopers have been called out and there's shooting in the streets."

Minna exploded in sudden fury. "What do you mean, *we're* in trouble?" She pointed a thumb at herself. "Not *me!* I warned you, didn't I? I told you to stay away from that bunch of world fixers and lunatics. A man in your position, with a fine government salary, taking that kind of risk—it's stupidity, sheer stupidity, that's what it is!"

He tried to pacify her. "Yes, yes, you're probably right, but there's no time to quibble now. The police are going from house to house. You must come away with me, right now!"

"Come away with you!" she cried, beside herself. "Are you crazy?"

"Get your things together. Hurry, hurry!"

He pulled her into the bedroom, then hauled clothes from a cupboard and started rolling them together. Minna stood by in stubborn passivity.

"Hurry!" she drawled. "*I'm* not going *anywhere*. I had no part in all this foolishness, and there's no reason why I should suffer the consequences."

He seized her shoulders, pleading. "You can't mean that. We belong together, you and I, through thick and thin!"

"Through *this* we don't. I'm staying here."

If he doubted his ears, the set expression of her face convinced him. Perhaps what he was asking was too much for any wife. With an agonized look at Minna's turned back he pulled up his coat collar and, drawing his hat down over his eyes, rushed from the flat.

In town the fracas between demonstrators and the King's police had not yet ended, though the paraders had been dispersed and their leaders sent into hiding. Here and there small groups of malcontents continued to reassemble for further harassment of the authorities. They would be disposed of piecemeal, to be sure, but for the moment their activities threw the city into a state of siege. To escape capture or even a stray bullet Richard had to steer a wary course, keeping to dark byways that led to the edge of the Elbe and the forest beyond. Where he would turn next he did not know. Only one thing was clear: he must keep on going.

From one of the river bridges—he was too distraught to recognize which—he looked back toward the agitated center of town. There, on the left bank, lay the elegant promenade known as Brühl Terrace, its ancient baroque lampposts flaming quietly amid bursts of sudden gunfire. Alongside could be seen the high tower of the Hofkirche, where tomorrow there would be no choir practice. Beyond this lay the magnificent Zwinger, or landscaped vestibule of August the Strong's great palace, the northeast wing of which formed the famous Picture Gallery, or Royal Museum. A paradoxical thought came to him in this moment of extremity and haste: in all the years of dwelling in or around Dresden, from early childhood through the recent attachment to the Court, he had been too pressed by circumstance to permit himself a leisurely visit to the gallery. Its celebrated treasures—Raphael's "Sistine Madonna" and Correggio's "Holy Night," the Titians, Veroneses, Tintorettos, the Spanish, Flemish, Dutch, French and German masterpieces—when would he see them now?

It was too late for such contemplations, too late for anything except keeping on the run. And even of that he could not be certain.

CHAPTER 22

KING FRIEDRICH AUGUST stood on the balcony above the main portals of the royal palace. For the past two hours he had been watching the ruckus in the streets below without becoming unduly excited. A man of patriarchal sentiments, he felt a fatherly indulgence toward his subjects and permitted them considerable leeway in matters of self-expression. Absolutism could afford this inasmuch as no amount of noisemaking or stone-throwing could dent the bedrock of authority. The engine did not blow up and run out of control simply because it was allowed to let off steam.

Unworried, His Majesty looked down on the spectacle. He found it quite interesting, really. Rather a break in the monotony of regally dull living.

Around the monarch stood a corona of ministers, plainly more nervous than he. The torches lighting up the night also disclosed flashes of fear and misgiving among lesser palace personnel, from major-domo to lowliest footman. But most of all there shone anxiety in the eyes of Baron Pfordten.

The Minister of Education and Culture addressed his master *sotto voce.* "Your Majesty is taking this too lightly, and with excessive patience. That shouting rabble means danger."

A chorus of officials joined in. "A tumult of this sort is close to insurrection, and an affront to Your Majesty's government."

The King adjusted an ornate and rather inadequate spyglass, then peered through it with a squint. "Oh, I don't know. A simple parade seems harmless enough. As a matter of fact, I like parades."

A servant stepped from the shadows, bearing a printed handbill which Pfordten took and quickly examined before passing

177

it on to the King. "Perhaps this broadside will change Your Majesty's mind. It lends some support to our warnings."

Stepping back into his study, the monarch dutifully scrutinized the paper, which contained a workers' manifesto and ran in part: "Röckel unjustly imprisoned! We want freedom of expression and a constitution guaranteeing the rights of the working class. If these rights continue to be denied us the days of monarchy are counted."

Friedrich August's brows narrowed into a pensive frown. "Hmm. Rather rough, isn't it?"

"It's much more than that, Sire." Pfordten slapped the back of his hand on the printed text. "This document contains an unvarnished threat to sovereignty. Your Majesty ought not to stand for it."

The King looked at the semicircle of faces. "You think so, gentlemen? What . . . er . . . am I to do?"

Before they could answer, Pfordten pointed through the open French windows. "Send out troops with orders to scatter the crowd."

"You mean—shooting?"

"Why not? If the demonstrators refuse to break up quietly, they must be shown force."

The King raised a reluctant hand, and an attendant stepped forward to receive an order. Pfordten smiled approvingly. "Well done, Sire."

A short time later the dust clouds and the smoke of torches rising toward the royal balcony mingled with the tattoo of infantry action. Sandbags were being piled up around the palace, while workers and soldiers tangled in hand-to-hand fighting. Cries of "To the barricades!" and "Long live the Revolution!" alternated with the ringing of church bells and the clatter of saber-swinging cavalry.

At his desk the King took a more somber view. A second handbill had been put before him. Its daring text caused the royal choler to rise. "Demands for a constitution, indeed!" Now Friedrich August took the whole affair as a personal insult. "Since when, gentlemen, do we let the rabble instruct us in the business of government?"

Pfordten nodded. "Precisely, Sire." The semicircle cried, "Hear, hear!"

"I want the name of every pamphleteer, ringleader and agitator." The King's anger gained momentum. "They shall die as traitors!"

A secretary stepped up with a penciled list. At a nod from Pfordten he read: "August Röckel, Gustav Kietz, Robert Blum, Michael Bakunin—"

Pfordten made an interpolation. "So-called intellectuals, all! Stuffed heads are more dangerous than empty stomachs."

"—Rietschel, Huebner, Tschirner, Todt, Roempler, Koechly, Bieberstein . . ."

The royal wrath reached a peak. As the list ended with two more names—the respected architect Gottfried Semper and the court conductor Richard Wagner—His Majesty grew apoplectic. Jumping to his feet, the King bellowed, "Richard Wagner! Isn't that the composer fellow we fetched home from a prison in France? Pfordten, it was your Ministry that sponsored this Wagner. What have you to say for yourself?"

The Baron's face twitched. "I was . . . er . . . hoodwinked, Your Majesty. It has lately become clear that France is a hotbed of republicanism, despite that newly crowned Bonaparte. As for Herr Wagner, he appears to be a typical example of political contamination."

"Is there proof of his taking up arms against us?"

The secretary stepped forward, breaking in with sudden ardor. "Oh, no, Sire. This man Wagner, he is a friend of the lowly and poor." Momentarily he cringed at a sharp glance from Pfordten, then recovered his nerve. "Herr Wagner helps in writing the workers' speeches."

Pfordten pounced on this. "A dangerous weapon, the pen!" He pointed to a document on the table. "The hungry musician whom Your Majesty so graciously honored has had a hand in drawing up this shameful manifesto."

"I never would have believed it." The King was genuinely shocked. "This Wagner is a Constitutionalist, a traitor to the state!"

"Exactly. A price must be put on his head, to set an example." Pfordten grew more confidential. "Once the working classes have a say in government, Sire, the power of monarchy is broken."

"True, true. We are indebted to you, Pfordten, for having brought the miscreant back from abroad, where he might have plotted even worse mischief against us. As long as he is here he can be kept in check."

The Baron clicked his heels. "Shall I order his arrest?"

"Yes. And have his confederates pulled in too. Also, Pfordten, you may personally give notice to every theater management in Saxony that the works of Richard Wagner are banned."

"Very good, Your Majesty."

The royal audience was at an end. As the King retired to his private chambers the ministers disbanded, each beset with trepidation at the scrimmage going on outside the palace gates. Only Pfordten marched off with head high and eyes agleam with satisfaction. His was the exhilarating role of avenger on a personal enemy.

That same night the police set their bloodhounds on Wagner's track. As Minna had feared, a uniformed squad searched the apartment, turning trunks and cupboards upside down. They went through his papers for incriminating evidence, but found only a series of essays, among them "The Art-Work of the Future," "Art and Climate," and the first sketch for a dramatic project, *Wieland Der Schmied.* There were also some notes on "Judaism and Music," which were confiscated on suspicion of anti-Semitism.

"I told him not to write that," Minna protested. "He was angry at Meyerbeer's success at a time when we were down on our luck. Professional jealousy—nothing else."

"The judge will decide that" was the police sergeant's reply as he folded the papers and stuffed them into his pocket. "Now if you'll tell us where your husband went . . ."

In all honesty Minna did not know the answer. No amount of prodding or threats could draw from her even a suggestion of Richard's whereabouts. She was at the moment so enraged at him herself that she did not really care whether she ever saw him again. Dashed and disgusted, the constabularies clumped downstairs.

While the futile chase expanded now to cover the entire city, the fleeing quarry had long left the Elbe banks behind. By way of Chemnitz, Zwickau and Gera, Wagner was making his way to Jena and Liszt's home at Weimar, just beyond. This was still Saxony, where Friedrich August's might held sway, but the fringe of Thuringia's forests enveloped the traveler and lessened the chances of pursuit. By the time Dresden troopers were on his track Richard hoped to have crossed Hesse and the Rhenish Palatinate on his way to foreign parts.

At Weimar a gratifying surprise awaited him. Rehearsals of *Lohengrin* were in full progress, the edict of the King not having yet reached this provincial outpost. On attaining the town at dusk, after two days of wandering, Richard found his way to the Hoftheater, which he entered without making himself known. Behind the footlights the last act was at its height, with the hero singing the great aria *"Im Fernen Land"* and Liszt conducting. With bated breath the fugitive listened as the closing lines rang through the auditorium:

> *"Mein Vater, Parsifal,*
> *trägt seine Krone . . .*
> *sein Ritter, ich,*
> *bin Lohengrin genannt."*

> ("My father, Parsifal,
> its crown doth bear . . .
> His knight am I,
> With Lohengrin for name.")

At the opposite end of the theater a slim young girl with braided dark hair and startlingly grave face crept unseen along a backstage corridor. She reached a spot in the wings from which, wide-eyed, she could survey actors and orchestra in the mild glow of rehearsal lights, when a finger tapped her shoulder.

"Your father will be very angry, Fräulein Cosima, if he sees you up here."

Cosima Liszt recognized Heinzelmann, the theater factotum. Her smile was reassuring. "Don't worry, Heinzelmännchen. Papa always forgives me. He knows Mama won't bring me on opening night—I'm too young, she says. Heinzelmännchen, who ever heard of thirteen being too young?" She exaggerated. She was a precocious twelve.

The old stagehand shrugged noncommittally. "Your mother no doubt has her reasons, Fräulein. Last February's performance of *Tannhäuser,* for example, wasn't exactly suitable for a young ladies' seminary."

"Oh, I heard about the Love Goddess in her pink tights. As if girls my age didn't know what an undressed woman looks like! Besides, with all that gauze around her, Papa says Frau Venus was practically invisible—nothing but a head mounted on a huge blob of meringue." Cosima could not suppress a giggle.

"Sh-sh, your father is looking this way now."

On stage the tenor had launched on a reprise. Majestically the Castle of the Grail was described, to the accompaniment of a shimmering obbligato wrung from the highest reaches of the violins.

Cosima shivered blissfully. "It's wonderful, wonderful!"

"That fellow Wagner, who wrote this music, ought to see you," commented Heinzelmann. "Bet he'd be glad to know that young folks enjoy it."

"Papa has been trying to get him here for one of the performances." She sighed. "But there was a letter from Frau Wagner, saying her husband has been appointed conductor of the Royal Orchestra. That means he won't have much time for traveling."

The music rose anew to a climax and Cosima was silenced by its enveloping rapture. Here was the miracle of which she had heard, from her father's lips, for years. As a child, in Paris, she already idolized the mere name of Richard Wagner, after listening to his transcriptions (those dreadful commission jobs, he himself would have called them!) which first brought him into print. She also knew of his rebuff at the hands of Meyerbeer, and the vicissitudes that had led him into debtors' prison. Yet—and this was what made him a hero in her eyes—through all his hardships and defeats he held to one dream, the mission of beauty, sublimity, creation on the highest plane. Young though she was, Cosima had a grasp of these things, primarily through exposure to a brilliant paternal example, but also by virtue of her own precocity. She had a good musical ear and lately was taking piano lessons from a Leipzig Conservatory graduate, Hans von Bülow. Yes, she knew what Richard Wagner was about.

Today, while watching rehearsals, Cosima for the first time clothed her idol in the guise of Lohengrin, Knight of the Grail. She had no clear grasp of the Grail's meaning beyond the fact that its brotherhood was removed from commonalty and earthliness. But was this not true of Wagner himself? Stranger and apostle of a new art, he dwelled in a world apart. She had her father's word for this.

As for the *Lohengrin* story, Cosima felt enraptured by it. The setting itself was new to her: the Duchy of Brabant in the Netherlands, under the early-tenth-century rule of King Heinrich der Vogler (Henry I, surnamed "The Fowler") of Germany. This royal huntsman and equestrian champion spread his love of horseflesh throughout Europe, furthering the shift from foot-soldiery to mounted troops and the panoply of the chivalric age. The opera synopsis runs as follows:

LOHENGRIN

Act I

Following a musical prelude, the action opens with King Henry arriving at Antwerp. He has just subdued the Slavs in Poland and Bohemia and is faced now with a Magyar invasion, against which he hopes to levy Brabant troops. But the Duchy is in a state of upheaval. Gottfried, the young son of the late Duke of Brabant, has disappeared, and his sister Elsa is under suspicion of having murdered him. Count Friedrich von Telramund, a former suitor of Elsa but now married to Ortrud von Friesland (a collateral claimant to the ducal throne), makes public accusation, whereupon Elsa must face trial before the King. It is agreed by custom that Heaven shall decide guilt or innocence, through a duel fought by the accuser and a voluntary defender of the accused. The royal court and populace have gathered in a clearing along the river Scheldt. Telramund is ready, but gossip and superstition have worked against Elsa, and neither noble nor yeoman raises a sword in her behalf. The distressed lady prays to God for succor, mentioning a heaven-sent knight who has appeared to her in dreams. Almost immediately the prayer is answered: on the river a launch is seen approaching, drawn by a majestic swan. Now a helmeted figure steps ashore, gleaming in magnificent silver armor. The stranger greets the assemblage and announces that he will champion the young woman's cause. He puts forth one condition, however. As a protector of the oppressed and unjustly persecuted, no matter where they are found, he professes allegiance to no nation or race, hence must not be asked his origin or name. This warning is aimed at Elsa in particular, for she has offered her hand in marriage to the man who will save her.

The Silver Knight's demands are agreed to and the duel begins, with Telramund soon worsted by his opponent's steel. The innocent duchess is vindicated and carried off with her knight on the soldiers' shields. A wedding feast is ordered to be prepared for the morrow.

ACT II

The enraged Telramund, now in peasant garb, for he has been deprived of title and estates, plots vengeance with his wife Ortrud. It is night and the castle courtyard lies in darkness while the gentlemen carouse in their special wing called Pallas, and Elsa with her retinue has retired to the Kemenate, or abode of the ladies. A window opens now and the white-robed duchess appears on her balcony, singing of her happiness. Ortrud quickly sends her husband away while she creeps toward the balcony and calls woefully to her noble cousin. Her plea for pardon and for reinstatement of Telramund is heeded by the compassionate Elsa, who rushes down herself to comfort the outcasts. In the shadows Ortrud has time for a frenetic invocation to the heathen gods of her father Radbod against the Christian factions in Brabant, to whom the ruling family belongs. She then faces Elsa with well-feigned contrition and manages even to plant a seed of doubt in her ducal cousin's mind regarding the Silver Knight's identity, since the latter has been appointed by King Henry to the post of Protector of Brabant and commander of the province's newly levied troops.

Furthermore, she argues, should not a would-be husband render full account of his past? Brooding on these matters, Elsa leads the ragged Ortrud into the warm shelter of the castle.

On the following day the two ladies emerge in festive array for the wedding. But as the procession moves across the courtyard to the chapel, Ortrud reveals her true colors by demanding precedence in rank. At the same time she taunts Elsa with not even knowing her bridegroom's name, while Telramund reappears to alarm the gathering spectators with the accusation that the "foreigner" is a sorcerer. King Henry and the Silver Knight order the conspirators banished, and the wedding proceeds as planned, though the bride is visibly troubled by the poisonous promptings.

ACT III

SCENE 1: To the strains of the Wedding March the young pair is ushered into the bridal chamber. After King Henry and the guests depart, Elsa thrills to her husband's embrace, but cannot throw off the urge to pry into his past. Point-blank she asks the forbidden question. At the same moment, sword in hand, Telramund and four of his followers burst into the room. Horrified, Elsa picks up her husband's weapon and hands it to him in time to ward off a fatal blow. The Silver Knight in turn strikes dead his enemy, who is carried off by his cowed companions.

Another kind of retribution, however, is also at hand. The frightened bride has fainted, but is revived gently by her groom, who then summons her ladies and orders them to leave her in the King's charge, while he himself makes ready to depart.

SCENE 2: The opera closes with a view of the clearing on the banks of the Scheldt, where the Silver Knight bids farewell to all and discloses himself as Lohengrin, son of Parsifal, who is King of the Grail. On the river a boat is again seen approaching, drawn by a swan. The evil Ortrud, in a last vengeful gesture, cries out triumphantly that the missing child Gottfried is imprisoned by witchcraft in the swan's body, never to be released. At this, Lohengrin sinks to his knees in the silent ritual of the Knights of the Grail. A moment later his prayer is answered, as the Divine Dove of Monsalvat, symbol of the Holy

Ghost, descends from the skies to touch the swan, which is transformed instantly into the young heir of Brabant.

While all present bow in homage to the child, Lohengrin steps into the boat and moves silently downstream, the Dove of Monsalvat flying before him. Elsa cries after him, "My husband! My husband!" and the crowd too breaks into laments as the grief-stricken woman sinks lifeless at her brother's feet. It is too late. The heaven-sent visitor had not been taken on trust, his fight for truth and goodness had not been disassociated—by those for whom the fight was waged—from paltry ulterior motives.

Suspicion was no climate in which virtue could dwell.

CHAPTER 23

A MOONLESS night blanketed Weimar.

Hungry and weary (how often would such a state obtain in his life?), Richard Wagner walked through the streets toward a tree-circled area of the town. Here he peered carefully at name plates and numbers on gates that opened into spacious gardens. Eventually he entered the grounds of a white villa crowning a gentle knoll. He found the iron knocker, shaped like a woman's hand emerging from a cuff and holding a small ball. The tapping sound was louder than he intended it to be.

A thin young girl, in appearance no more than a gawky adolescent, opened the door. He hesitated, then summoned his failing nerve to ask, "May I . . . er . . . is this the home of Herr Franz Liszt?"

The girl nodded. "Yes. Do you wish to see him?"

"If you please."

Her gaze was penetrating, intense. "I am Cosima Liszt," she said with unconscious pride, "his daughter. Do come in."

The visitor's face had been half hidden under a wide hat brim. As he stepped across the threshold into the lighted hall, Cosima studied his features. She sensed something special about him and cast sidelong glances at his person as she led the way. The door of a pine-paneled study opened and Liszt stepped out with a cry of instant recognition.

"Richard! My God, how did you get here?"

"By shanks' mare. Take a look at my boots." Only now did the wanderer himself become aware of the mud he had tracked into the polished mansion. "I am sorry to be tramping across these rugs."

A manservant who had appeared in Cosima's wake, obviously

187

nettled at his young mistress for answering visitors' knocks,
underscored Richard's apology with mute disapproval. But
Liszt's mind was not on floor coverings. He took his friend's
arm.

"You must be tired. Come and sit down." There was a pause,
just long enough to be significant. "I've been hearing about
you, Richard, and the things I hear disturb me. In fact, only
this evening, after the *Lohengrin* rehearsal . . ."

"Yes?"

Liszt's brows met in a frown. He forgot his daughter's presence, so anxious was he to unburden his thoughts. "A dispatch
was handed me, from Dresden, with orders—orders, mind you—
that no work composed by you is to be given performance on
Saxon stages. The document was signed by Minister von
Pfordten. I ask you, Richard, what does it mean?"

"It means just what it says. I am *persona non grata.*"

"Obviously." Liszt was picking his way carefully, not wishing to hurt his friend. "Other shreds of news have reached me—
rumors that you have tangled with the authorities, made socialistic speeches and such. Forgive me, old man, but is there
something to this foolishness?"

"Foolishness?" Wagner's tone was offended.

"Well, really, an opera composer mixing into politics and
getting himself proscribed! What do *you* call it? And anyway,
just what seems to be the matter with you?"

"The misery of my fellow workers, that's what. Not the court
orchestra, of course, but all those struggling musicians in minor
jobs. I've known them to go without salaries for months. I've
lived through it myself. And no law courts to help, or any
voice to speak in their behalf."

"But lately, at least, that hasn't been true in your case. Your
luck turned, and there are big things ahead——"

Wagner broke in impatiently. "You sound just like Minna.
So long as one's own stomach is full, why worry about the next
man's?"

"Sorry. I deserved that." Liszt smiled apologetically, then
raised questioning eyebrows. "By the way, where *is* your
wife?"

"At our flat in Dresden, though I presume she'll pack up and go back to her parents." He passed a weary hand over his brow. "I'm a hunted man, you see. I can't ask Minna to share any further risks."

Liszt's expression became guarded. "Risks?"

"I must get out of the country without delay, to France or Switzerland. That's why I've come to you, Franz, to ask for help in obtaining a false passport or some sort of travel permit."

"A false passport? How could I manage that?"

"You are a big man here in Weimar, with an official position. You hire and dispatch musicians, guest artists, foreign celebrities."

At this point Cosima, who had been listening in the background with ever-growing concern, stepped quickly forward. "Papa, that poor Professor Werder who broke his ankle last week won't be traveling for some time." Her eyes took on a cloak-and-dagger gleam. "Herr Wagner could use the professor's papers and send them back by mail long before they will be needed again."

"What?" Liszt gasped with surprise, then shook his head in astonishment at his daughter's cleverness. "That's a capital idea!" He turned back to Richard. "We have a fellow conspirator in the house, a strategist, no less."

Wagner's luminous gaze rested on the girl. "A guardian angel!" he whispered while kissing Cosima's hand and leaving her entranced.

The rest was easy. With Liszt's co-operation the Werder passport was obtained that same night and Richard was shunted off to Paris. Here his hopes of finding asylum were promptly dashed due to a raging cholera epidemic which had already taken a toll of 1,300 dead. He therefore moved on by the next train to Bordeaux, where his British benefactress, Mrs. Taylor, lived with her daughter Jessie. Just what he expected from these two ladies he hardly knew himself, except that Mrs. Taylor had long urged him to seek her out when in need of professional mediation or advice.

On reaching Bordeaux, Richard learned of a change in the Taylor family status. Jessie had married a local wine dealer,

Eugène Laussot, while her mother had gone home to England. When Wagner called at the young couple's flat the bride's greeting was cordial, to be sure, but a honeymoon establishment included no provision for house guests. Furthermore, a startled Monsieur Laussot chanced to be at home and demanded explanations.

Quickly Wagner withdrew, not wishing to disturb the hymeneal bliss. But it was already too late. Unwittingly he had become a provocation for the pretty little wife's first quarrel with her husband. After a stormy scene Jessie flounced out and sought Richard at a near-by pension to which she had thoughtfully directed him. In the interview that followed she heaped invective on the ill-tempered Eugène's head.

"I hate him!" she cried disconsolately. "Take me away, take me away!"

Richard was appalled. He couldn't take anybody anywhere, what with a faked passport and very little cash.

Jessie had been reading Lord Byron. "Take me to Cephalonia or Missolonghi," she sobbed, then paused at his puzzled look. "That's in Greece," she added helpfully.

He talked to her like a German uncle, with the result that she calmed down after a bit and was persuaded to return home before Eugène caught up with her and perchance put a bullet through the composer's head.

The matter was not to end there, however. Before Richard could leave town Jessie called again, this time to promote an understanding between the two men. Having cooled down, Eugène grew reasonable and looked on the visitor as a platonic and altogether harmless adjunct out of his bride's innocent past.

That's where he was wrong, as things turned out. If formerly no hint of romantic attraction had arisen between Jessie and her mother's protégé, circumstances were different now. She was no longer a vestal fledgling but a woman initiated into adult passion, with the sharpened susceptibilities springing therefrom. She knew what to look for in a man. In Richard Wagner she believed she had found it.

From admiration to adoration was a short step and one which

the emotional Jessie negotiated swiftly. As for Richard, he found himself faced with a flattering dilemma to which he reacted in logical masculine fashion. Gallantry alone forbade the rebuff of a delectable young creature who seemed to think so well of him. Indeed, Jessie's own attractiveness increased in exact ratio to her appreciation of his own virile allure. Richard began to see in her an uncommon measure of charm, to which he responded with growing sympathy and warmth.

At this juncture Mrs. Taylor arrived from England, providing an agreeable excuse for tea parties and dinner gatherings at the Laussot home, to which Wagner was bidden. Propinquity thus nurtured the spark of a mild flirtation into an unquestionably crackling blaze. Before long the observing Eugène reverted to his original opinion: the German visitor was an obnoxious customer.

Mrs. Taylor was loath to agree with her son-in-law, but in the end she too could not deny the testimony of her eyes. The infatuated Jessie was behaving in dangerously indiscreet fashion, while the composer, his vanity highly gratified, did nothing to dispel her madness.

Richard found time in the midst of these complications to write to Minna, reporting his whereabouts and sending on small sums of money earned by various Bordeaux jobs, chiefly music lessons. He also made mention of his friends, without, however, describing the thickening atmosphere that was beginning to cloud the Taylor-Laussot household. As Minna got it, "Eugène is a most amiable and trusting young fellow who accepts me with quite indescribable joy." In later diary notes which were to form the basis for Wagner's autobiography, *Mein Leben,* other facets of the situation emerged.

Jessie's intelligence and unusual grasp caused me to realize that she is the only human being who at that time truly understood me. I soon recognized the gulf separating me, as well as her, from both her mother and her husband. While that handsome young man spent his days in pursuit of business interests, and the mother's deafness discouraged three-way conversation, Jessie and I exchanged ideas upon many

absorbing matters until an ever greater confidence grew between us. It was inevitable that we soon found the people
around us a vexing element in our association.

In the words of Ernest Newman, *"The people around us* is
Wagnerian for *the lady's husband and her mother."* As for the
"intelligence and unusual grasp" attributed by Richard to Jessie, this claim too must be taken with a pinch of salt. It would
hardly have favored his ego to admit that he was encouraging
the coquetry of a physically matured but mentally vapid young
baggage of no more than adolescent judgment.

One thing was certain: the Bordeaux entanglement became
eventually untenable. Though hard of hearing, Mrs. Taylor
was not blind. Foreseeing the end toward which the flirtation
was heading, she resolved to do something about it. A stern
colloquy between mother and daughter brought Jessie back to
her senses, while Wagner's ardor was dampened in an even
more effective manner: Mrs. Taylor simply cut off the annuity
which she had promised him for life. Abruptly the tea parties
ceased and there were no more intimate and "artistic" tête-à-
têtes. Richard was given back his manuscripts (he had read
aloud to Jessie from his projected *Wieland Der Schmied* and
the long narrative poem entitled "Siegfried's Death") with an
injunction not to darken the Laussot door again. If the unwelcome visitor needed any further persuasion, Eugène furnished
it by threatening to go to the police.

In such vexing circumstances there was nothing left for Richard to do but to start packing. He wrote Minna several garbled
and highly inaccurate versions of the Bordeaux events, and
then he left town.

Via Paris, Montmorency and Geneva he made his way to the
Swiss music center of Zürich, where Minna presently joined
him. She had been able to raise a little money through sale of
the Dresden household goods. The sum, small as it was, helped
tide them over the first difficult weeks in a new land.

Hotels being expensive, the couple took a room at an inn
called "Zum Abendstern," near the outskirts of town. Their
quarters were dismal and noisy, with a violin student engaged

COSIMA WAGNER: Franz Liszt's Daughter and Wagner's
Second Wife

in constant practice next door, a soprano running through her strident scales across the way and a blacksmith hammering on his anvil just below the room's only window. But the hostelry's name, "Evening Star," evoked memories of *Tannhäuser* and might indeed be deemed a good omen. In any case, the price suited their pinched pocketbook. With a safe roof over their heads, the Wagners believed they could take minor annoyances in their stride.

CHAPTER 24

MINNA had come through Weimar on her way to Zürich, and she had seen Franz Liszt, from whom she brought bad tidings. Under official pressure it had been necessary to drop all *Lohengrin* plans. Special sets representing Antwerp and the ducal palace of Brabant were painted over for Lammermoor Castle in Donizetti's *Lucia di Lammermoor* while Minna stuffed Richard's manuscript and music score into her bags.

She wept as she unpacked them now. Would luck ever again smile on them? Would things ever be set to rights?

Richard covered up his own dejection. "Splendid!" he cried. "I happen to have some changes in mind and rather regretted Franz pushing ahead so soon."

To back up these words he sat down and made a few superficial revisions based on research in the Germanic History Section of the Zürich Public Library. Here he was attracted again to a favorite subject, Norse mythology, and its kindred theme, the Nibelungen Saga. Soon he was working on two things at once—the *Lohengrin* elaborations and an operatic outline of the life of Siegfried.

In shaping the latter he saw a parallel to the Laussot episode he had just been through, and, poet-fashion, he cheerfully made use of it for a sequence later to be called *Die Walküre*. Jessie Laussot emerged in this as the gentle Sieglinde, her unaccommodating husband would become bad Hunding, while the author saw himself mirrored as romantic Siegmund (future father of Siegfried).

Through all this the small cash reserves brought by Minna from Dresden were soon exhausted and the money problem again grew acute. Richard appealed to friends back home—

Liszt, Apel, a family named Witte, and his brother-in-law Hermann Brockhaus. With slight variation of phrase the message was the same. He wrote:

> If only I had the wages of a middling good mechanic, I could spend the rest of my life composing operas. For anything else I am unfit. I want to sell my *Lohengrin*, skin and bones, or pawn it! Then maybe someone would commission my *Siegfried*—the price is cheap. . . . Surely in this villainous tradesman's age we must help one another, or what honor art? I need firewood and a warm overcoat, but shall do without these as I have not the knack of earning money. Cannot music lovers provide for creative artists so that these may be in a position to give them pleasure in return?

In short, he believed the world owed a living to its men of genius, and he counted himself among the latter, without false modesty or pose.

But no funds arrived, for even sincere well-wishers in Germany could not risk corresponding with or giving aid to a politically marked man. Richard must therefore lay aside his manuscripts and return to job hunting. He filled in as substitute conductor for various provincial orchestras, in addition to acquiring a number of piano pupils, all of them singularly untalented. The task of teaching these hapless barbarians drove him nearly out of his mind. As the cacophony of inept keyboard thumping blended with the violin scraping overhead, the soprano bleats next door and the anvil pounding from the smithy belowstairs, Richard tore his hair.

"I've in mind to write an opera," he shouted over the din, "about some horrible noisemaking little monsters who bring on the destruction of heaven and earth!"

Spontaneously, without intent, his tortured mind envisioned a nether world of Nibelungen (creatures of the fog), with twisted dwarfs pumping bellows and hammering metals in an underground forge. All the same, piano lessons brought enough money to pay the rent and food bill for himself and Minna, as well as for the parrot Papo, who likewise had made the trip from Dresden.

Papo, an African gray, was an entertaining and friendly pet. At mealtime, if Wagner was too engrossed in his labors, the bird "Papchen" issued a loud summons: "Richard! Siegmund! Ha, Liberty!" This brought the great man running.

For the rest, life in Switzerland was not without satisfactions. Friends from Germany passed through on holiday and stopped to call, bringing news from home. The novelist Gottfried Keller, the composer Theodor Uhlig, the chorus master Wilhelm Fischer—all gave Richard assurance that in his fatherland he was not forgotten. This mattered most. For, like the oak tree in Heine's song of homesickness, *"Ich Hatte Einst,"* Wagner had roots that burrowed deep and could not be torn up. His was one kind of music only, and one kind of tongue. Though his art one day would gain world-wide appeal, its source remained the special earth that he called home.

Exile was hard on Minna too. She had left Dresden with great reluctance, impelled only by a sense of wifely duty. But there were moments in the tight quarters at the Abendstern when old resentments reawakened.

"Things were going so well for us in Dresden," she lamented, especially in the presence of visitors from Saxony. "If only Richard had stayed out of politics!"

Also, she took up the old refrain regarding the "uncommercial" nature of her husband's musical output. Her present rantings were directed against the incomprehensible Nibelungen material. Who ever thought of calling a river Father Rhine, with "daughters" living underwater and dwarfs ruling the bowels of the earth! Again the taunting jibe was resumed, "Why can't you be clever, like Meyerbeer?"

By now these were fighting words. Never had Wagner forgotten the older composer's lack of generosity when approached for helpful introductions to Parisian music circles. Beginning with his own beloved stepfather Ludwig Geyer, Richard had cherished many Jewish associations; but his hatred of Meyerbeer became, in time, markedly tinged with racial antipathy. To this was added now a growing bitterness against Minna herself for persistently gushing over the successful rival and rubbing salt into the wound she inflicted thus on her husband. Finally, Minna knew something of the Laussot affair. That is,

Richard had had to explain in as innocuous a manner as possible just why the benevolent Lady Bountiful, Mrs. Taylor, had cut off his allowance. The account he gave was innocent indeed, conveying the idea that Jessie's enthusiasm for his art had been misinterpreted by evil-minded busybodies. Minna, however, employed wifely reasoning in putting two and two together. Here was something she had not reckoned with: the mate whose devotion she had taken so long for granted might be susceptible to outside allurements. She grew suspicious, watchful, letting him know that he must not bank on her gullibility. A sharpness entered her voice and a faint jeer curled her lips when the Bordeaux interlude came up in conversation.

He did his best to keep this from happening. His conscience, after all, was far from clear. For the rest, he sought relief from growing marital tensions by putting Minna into one of his scripts—namely, the Nibelungen project of which she especially disapproved. He immortalized her as Fricka, shrewish wife of the god Wotan. Her bickerings he chastised with withering blank verse:

> *Nichts lerntest Du,*
> *wollt' ich Dich lehren,*
> *was nie Du erkennen kannst*
> *eh' nicht ertagte die Tat.*
> *Stets Gewohntes*
> *nur magst Du versteh'n:*
> *doch was noch nie sich traf,*
> *darnach trachtet mein Sinn!*

> (Nothing have you learned
> of things I would teach you,
> nothing do you grasp
> save light-of-day facts.
> Only habitual custom
> do you comprehend—
> whereas the uncommon, never-before-seen,
> captures my thought!)

Minna had far too little interest in his work ever to read the above lines. Outside of her complaints regarding the unprofitable nature of his efforts she did not bother her head about either Richard's music or his operatic dreams. Passion spent— and their union had been based on nothing else—husband and wife were left with scarcely a point of contact.

Lately Minna was beset by the first shadowy qualms of mid- dle-age. In her early forties, climacteric symptoms were mak- ing an advanced appearance and coloring her trend of thought. The difference in age between herself and Richard loomed larger now, causing her to look with distrust at all younger women. She began checking her husband's movements, as though in his present penurious state he could afford, or indeed attract, feminine attention. What about the twittering soprano upstairs? Or that young librarian at the *Züricher Bibliothek*, a snippy little thing who was all smiles when Richard came to borrow those tiresome tomes on ancient Germanic lore, yet who scarcely looked up from her desk if it was Minna who chanced to return the self-same books.

Then there was that Laussot episode, not yet thoroughly digested; Minna began working backward over it as over a meal, the bones of which were incompletely gnawed. Meticu- lously she picked each shred of memory and held it to the light, not sure whether she hoped or dreaded to find something to get her teeth into. No, she was not fully at ease regarding the Laussot matter. Had it been as harmless as Richard presented it to her? Why, even back in Dresden at the *Tannhäuser pre- mière*, Minna recalled, the Taylor woman and her daughter had gushed about the composer and showered him with flattery. And the court ladies, too, had they not turned coquettish wiles in his direction?

At the time Minna had been too pleased with Richard's chances of financial success to fret over romantic dangers. Yet now, when he was truly friendless, the fading wife looked for temptation in the flick of every eyelash, the rustle of any silken skirt, the timbre of a feminine voice. Paradoxically, though she resented poverty, she wondered now whether it was wise to goad him on to success if that meant throwing him into the path of some chit of a rival like that frivolous Jessie Laussot. On the other hand, the prospect of continued misery was even

less alluring. Those days of hunger in Paris had not been forgotten. They could be remembered only with dread. It was
a conflict that split Minna's soul.

Truly by 1850 the tables had been turned. Once the lovesick
Wagner had suffered torments over Minna's early promiscuity,
as disclosed by her confessions after she had lured him into
marriage. In those days, even following the Dietrich escapade,
she rather enjoyed thinking of herself as a siren chained to a
mooning Galahad for whom no other woman could exist. This
had been true. But what Minna failed to reckon with was that
the husband she took for granted might one day be coveted by
ladies more ardent than herself. Today, between menopausal
hot flashes, she foresaw this possibility as distressing in the
extreme.

Thus it happened that, before there was any proof of Richard's actually having strayed from narrow domestic paths, in
Minna's breast the demons of self-torture were putting in their
advance stabs. As her looks faded and her dull spirit turned
in on itself the poor woman seemed bent on inviting disaster.
She anticipated it by visualizing, many times over, just how
and by what evil sorcery Richard would be stolen from her.

When the fated moment came it could no longer bring surprise. She had already suffered the blow, in theory and lux-
uriating under its pain, a thousand times.

PART II

Mathilde

CHAPTER I

HERR OTTO WESENDONK, a German silk importer of Dutch ancestry, always enjoyed visiting his branch offices in New York. Business had boomed during the second quarter of the century, causing him to wonder whether he ought not to open a new plant in some internationally favorable spot like Switzerland.

As he stood at the ship rail, watching the Manhattan sky line disappear, he put the matter up to his twenty-three-year-old wife, Mathilde.

"Maybe we could close the outmoded little Rhineland office and move to Zürich. What do you think?"

"Yes, dear."

Mathilde's soft voice carried a tone of deference. She was in awe of her husband's power and importance, and it would never have occurred to her to contradict him. Also, she felt no particular enthusiasm for her birthplace of Elberfeld, with its noisy textile mills, its malodorous chemical works, its vile, damp climate. The baby Myrrha, almost two, would certainly thrive better away from the fog and smoke-laden air. "Zürich," she approved, "will be fine."

Wesendonk was pleased. He stroked his ample square beard, which already showed flecks of middle-aged gray. It gratified him anew that, almost committed to bachelorhood, he had switched about in time to choose not only a beautiful young wife but a wise one as well. Mathilde appreciated her masterful husband. She respected his judgment, as befitted her inexperience and sex. In 1850 women (the well-bred sort, at any rate) were, like children, to be seen and only condescendingly heard. In the best social circles a girl found marriage essentially a shift of authority from a more or less despotic male parent to a mate of similar stripe. Except for its functional bedroom phase, wedlock brought no change of pattern to the sheltered female with no mind of her own.

It was Herr Wesendonk, then, whose decision pointed to Zürich as the family's future residence. While lodged in temporary quarters at the fashionable Hotel Baur au Lac, he surveyed the city for a proper home site. This was soon found on a wooded elevation called *Grüner Hügel* (Green Hill), in the suburb of Ende. Price being no object, the purchase was made and an architect hired to crown the summit with a handsome Italian villa.

Builder and decorator were finished in due time and the family, enlarged meanwhile by the birth of a second child, moved in. It was only after settling in their new surroundings that the Wesendonks discovered, adjoining their elegant property, a shabby little cottage that might easily attract slipshod and undesirable neighbors.

Otto disposed of the problem. "We'll buy it. I'll have it converted into a gardener's lodge."

He was like that. He marshaled his business interests, and affairs at the villa as well, so that there remained little for Mathilde to do. Servants took care of the household and a trained nanny looked after the children. The young mother was left with time on her hands, either to be wasted in idleness or spent in some artistic or cultural pursuit.

She chose the latter. Zürich offered much to attract and stimulate an inquiring mind. There was the National Museum, containing, among other treasures, the finest collection of stained glass in the world. Pretty dull just the same. Then there were first-rate theaters, a botanical garden, an astronomical observatory, lecture halls and a concert auditorium. Pressed by her husband, Mathilde visited them all and, in her peregrinations, formed contacts with the city's intellectual element.

It was thus that she came face to face one day with Richard Wagner. The occasion was a Beethoven concert held by a local music group, and the desperate Richard had managed to obtain an evening's engagement as symphonic conductor.

"A very talented fellow," commented Otto, who called for his wife before the end of the program. "Who is he?"

Mathilde didn't know. But an informal reception followed the concert, during which the Wesendonks and Wagner were introduced. They met again soon after, when the same music society sponsored a private showing of the refugee composer's newly completed *Lohengrin*. It was to be a condensed version, in concert form, calculated to attract financial backers.

This time the impressionable Mathilde fell headlong under the Wagnerian spell. Never had she heard music of such sensuous and intoxicating quality. Not the uplifting Grail motif alone but the shimmering delicacy of Elsa's Dream and the wedding magic evoked from her an immediate response. In the course of this evening she found words for her rapture. During a brief conversation with Wagner her eyes shone. "You are a god!" she whispered.

The phrase, to Richard, was music more exquisite than his own. No one had ever before called him a god—least of all, Minna. How he wished his wife had come along on these last two engagements and convinced herself that there was some merit after all to the man she had married! "A god," that fine lady had said. He sprinted away on air to his dreary Abendstern lodgings where Minna snored peacefully in the dark. He rushed in to waken her, then thought better of it. She might laugh and only start harping at him again to write "understandable" operas like *Lucia di Lammermoor* or *Guillaume Tell*. Tonight he wanted no nagging. He was enveloped in a golden cloud.

The Wesendonk contact might have stopped there. The gracious and properly reared Mathilde had not the remotest idea of seeing Wagner again except across an orchestra pit or perhaps one day over the plush-edged balustrade of an opera box. But she failed to reckon with Otto. That benevolent gentleman had overheard a favorable remark or two regarding the promising German composer. Perhaps this Wagner fellow was worth cultivating.

"Let's invite him over," he told Mathilde, "for your next musical soiree."

"Oh!" She caught her breath in an access of nervous doubt. A girlish shyness caused her to shrink from the role of a great hostess, such as Otto wished her to be.

"What do you suppose I built this house for?" persisted her hearty and sociable husband. "People in our position have responsibilities. This isn't Elberfeld, you know. You'll have to get over your small-town ways."

"Yes, dear."

She could see that Zürich wasn't Elberfeld. Also, she was beginning to adjust to life in the oversized house and to the round of entertaining that gave Otto so much pleasure. With earnest effort she planned the musical evening and asked him to approve the guest list as well as the seating at table.

"By the way—" Wesendonk emphasized a minor point—"be sure to wear one of your New York gowns. I would prefer the blue satin with the train."

He was indulging a vain man's folly in showing the world his treasures, unaware that he might thereby risk loss of not only some valued material bauble but also of his beautiful young wife.

As to the guest list, invitations were penned promptly in Mathilde's fine hand and sent out through the post. But she did not have Wagner's address, hence Otto delegated one of his office clerks to track down the musician and put a note in his hands. The message in this case was signed by Wesendonk himself and its tone leaned to businesslike brevity.

Minna, first to read the invitation, tossed it scornfully aside. "Somebody's offering you a meal in return for an evening of free music," she commented dryly. "You surely won't be fool enough to accept."

He scanned the short note and a warm glow came over him. "We ought to go," he told her eagerly. "They're really nice people."

"They?" She gave him a faintly puzzled look.

He was suddenly on his guard. Only an instant ago he had been ready to discourse at length on the lovely Mathilde, but instinct warned him that this was not the moment.

"Oh, they—the Wesendonk circle, of course." He tried to

keep his tone cool and detached. "My friend Otto, you understand, is a man of prominence."

This was truth mixed with a generous slab of prevarication. Richard's relations with the man of prominence had as yet failed to reach a point of intimacy warranting the reference "My friend Otto." Minna's quick suspicion should have fastened on this rather transparent exaggeration. Characteristically, however, she missed the pettifogging and chose instead to doubt what happened to be cold fact.

"I'll bet he's important, this Wesendonk type you've picked up!" She crumpled the note. "You're a stranger in town, without a steady job, so right away the eminent citizens beg you to their houses. Bah! Don't make me laugh."

He found himself not minding her attitude as much as he ought to have. The prospect of going to the Wesendonks by himself was gaining in appeal. Still, he made a hypocritical stab at persuading her to join him.

"I wish you would come with me, Minna."

He held his breath, fearing that he had made too strong a plea. But long experience should have reassured him. Frustrated and disgruntled wives reveled in opposition.

"Not me," she snapped back. "I'll pick my own friends." She had had enough trouble and humiliation accruing from the Dresden cronies who had got Richard's name on the political black lists. If she must share his Swiss exile, she at least intended watching her own step, even if he seemed incapable of learning his lesson.

The upshot of the mild wrangle was that Richard went alone to the Wesendonk reception. He arrived on foot, considerably later than the other guests who owned private carriages or at least could afford hiring a hack. On entering the mansion he paused first to warm his hands and feet before an open grate in the vast foyer, for he had a persistent and neglected cold. Here the hearty host soon came upon him.

"My good fellow, there you are at last! We were beginning to think you had forgotten or, worse, you were going to snub us altogether." He laughed uproariously, underscoring the humor of so preposterous a suggestion.

Wagner murmured a vague apology, but before he managed to stammer some excuse he felt himself propelled into a brightly lighted ballroom and presented to what seemed an interminable receiving line. Somewhere in that sea of bobbing faces the lovely Mathilde stood out, for a moment only, and his lips brushed her slender outstretched hand. Then, with Wesendonk's grip still firm on his arm, Richard found himself suddenly before the magnificent concert Bechstein.

"You will favor us with a number, I trust."

Wesendonk's tone made an answer superfluous. Already the hubbub in the room subsided as, with a field marshal's gesture, the host caught everyone's attention. On cue the chattering assemblage transformed itself into a listening audience. Musical evenings at the Wesendonks obviously were already a tradition.

Just as he had long ago at Meyerbeer's, Richard felt awed by the surrounding elegance and splendor. True, he had walked in palaces and tasted royal patronage in Dresden, but that interlude had been brief and impersonal, as were all forms of official opulence. No sense of luxury emanated from any but private wealth. It was the alchemy of personal ownership that furnished the missing element of exultation. Richard became its victim now, anguished and thrilled at one and the same time as his mind drew a quick comparison between two ways of life—the pinched dispossessed and the prodigally endowed. How inescapably he seemed doomed to the former! A cold sweat broke out over his body and his clammy fingers clenched as though in impotent protest. What was he doing here amid all these fine uppity people? There must be some back door through which he could slip out and make a hasty escape.

"Ladies and gentlemen—" Herr Wesendonk was addressing the room—"I have the honor of presenting to you a new artist."

A ripple of voices, followed by warm applause, drowned out further identification. To be on the "Green Hill" villa guest list was, plainly, enough reward, regardless of *who* might furnish the evening's entertainment. A lavishly generous host and hostess were being applauded, not the obscure and certainly unimpressive musico they chose to take under their wing.

Benumbed, like an automaton, Richard sat down at the piano. And then a wondrous thing happened. All awkwardness and constraint fell from him. The blood welled warmly through his veins and there was heart in him again. Why must he look for things to resent or fear? Had he not chosen the greatest of the muses for his life's devotion? No earthly treasure could compare with this, and they who sat here under the glittering chandeliers would recognize it—he would show them —the moment he began to play.

There was no fixed program. He chose the first movement of Beethoven's *Sonate Für Das Hammerklavier* and a number of Schumann themes, then inevitably glided into the iridescent pool of his own melodies.

"*Lohengrin*," Mathilde Wesendonk whispered to her husband, who had joined her on a Directoire sofa near the piano. "The new opera he mentioned to us the other day, remember?"

Wesendonk was not so musical as his highly sensitive wife, but he pressed her hand and nodded agreement.

Elsewhere in the audience there were spurts of subdued conversation. Two ladies in the front row raised long-handled lorgnettes and studied the blond man at the keyboard, then turned to each other.

"Who on earth is *that*? I thought the Wesendonks collected only top-rank celebrities?"

"Fellow named Wagner. Not Otto's discovery, I'll bet, but Mathilde's." There was a pause during which the lorgnettes wandered in the direction of the sofa. "Hmm. She seems quite taken with her protégé, doesn't she?"

Frau Wesendonk's eyes were indeed fixed on the pianist in a rapturous trance. Once her white fingers closed over her husband's wrist as though in a gesture of gratitude. The two gossiping females near by exchanged meaningful glances, depreciating the matrimonial caress.

"My, my, it's lucky they *both* like music, otherwise . . ."

"Otherwise?"

"Well, I was only thinking, a young mother with two babies. . . . It's not every husband who would encourage . . . er . . . artistic pursuits."

"No, not every husband. My Hugo for one, God rest his soul, he would have read me the whole of Leviticus, and sharply too."

The lorgnettes clicked busily. From the Bechstein, meanwhile, wave upon wave of glorious harmonies poured forth. It was Mathilde now who could not hold back speech.

"Just listen, Otto," she whispered. "Isn't he phenomenal? That's from *Tannhäuser*—Wolfram's solo, 'To the Evening Star.'"

Wesendonk nodded approval. "Admirable, admirable."

At this moment the music broke off as Wagner was beset by a fit of coughing. Mathilde jumped to her feet. "Oh, he's sick, the poor man! I've heard that he lives in the most awful quarters. No heat, and probably no one to look after him."

Wagner resumed playing, though only long enough to wind up the Abendstern coda.

Wesendonk, meanwhile, leaned over to soothe his wife. His smile was expansive. "All right, Lady Bountiful, I know what is going through your pretty head." He pinched her chin affectionately.

Mathilde blushed. "We do have that spare gardener's cottage, on high ground and full of sunshine." She waited for his nod, which was almost a certainty. It came, lifting her spirit to joyous heights. "Oh, thank you, Otto! You've a heart of gold!"

"A pocketbook, you mean." He smiled, not without vanity.

Now the pianist had finished. He bowed only briefly to the audience, then turned to his hosts and apologized under cover of the generous applause.

"I am sorry. I shouldn't really have come. I don't feel very well."

Mathilde was all solicitude. "My husband and I would like— I mean, would you allow us to help you?"

"Help me?" He shook his head, not sure of her meaning.

"You don't know Zürich very well, we suppose." She was trying to be tactful. "Newcomers often choose the wrong place to live."

He coughed again. "I am afraid, Madame, with me it is not a matter of choice."

"There's a dangerous fog here because of the lake. The lower parts of the city are always damp."

Wesendonk stepped forward. "What my wife is trying to say, Maestro, is that we have an unoccupied lodge at the far end of our grounds. Nothing would please us better than to have you make use of it."

Richard hesitated, visibly tempted, then shook his head. "That is very kind, sir, but this—this luxurious neighborhood is quite beyond my means."

"Who said anything about cost? You are to be our guest, of course."

"Oh." Richard gulped. "I would have to talk that over with Minna. That's my wife."

Mathilde suppressed a gasp. "Your wife?"

"Yes. She's under the weather, the same as I. Otherwise she would have come along."

Otto Wesendonk put a hand on Richard's shoulder. "Isn't that all the more reason for accepting our offer? Surely you don't want Frau Wagner to become seriously ill."

"No, certainly not."

"Well, then, that's settled," Wesendonk boomed. His tone was that of a man unaccustomed to refusals. "Shall we see how the champagne is keeping?"

Wagner shrugged helplessly, while the young woman's face beside him lighted up with happiness. A hired gypsy band began playing on an upper balcony as the guests wandered into the adjoining salon.

CHAPTER 2

MINNA took the news in an analytical mood. She wanted to know a little more about Richard's extraordinary new friends before giving serious thought to their hospitable offer.

"This Wesendonk, you say, is a rich man?"

"Very rich. It would be no burden to him at all if we moved into the empty lodge."

"And his wife? Tell me about her." Quite casually Minna directed the conversation while Richard stumbled ingenuously into her trap.

"Oh, Frau Wesendonk," he cried enthusiastically. "She is much younger than her husband, and quite beautiful."

Nothing could have settled the matter more neatly. "We are staying here at the Abendstern," said Minna, "where we pay our own way and don't have to kowtow to anybody."

Richard's face fell, but he did not waste any time in lamentation. The Wesendonk offer might have been an ideal solution of his problems, but if Minna didn't want the lodge, that was that. He certainly would not force the issue. On the following morning he wrote a polite letter of refusal.

Contact with the Wesendonks did not end because of this, though the promising intimacy suffered a quick blight. Otto and Mathilde continued patronizing musical events in town. On occasion, when Richard was lucky enough to get an evening's job, they rushed up to greet him. Sometimes Mathilde came alone, in the company of friends, that is, when her husband was detained by business or had gone abroad. Minna knew of this and kept a watchful eye on Richard's every move. She accompanied him to concerts nowadays, waiting for him offstage and personally meeting all who came to pay him tribute. Thus she and Mathilde were introduced, and Minna was able to take stock of this young creature in whom she instinctively sensed a formidable rival.

She might have spared herself much worry. Richard was at this point entering an intensely creative period that lifted him far out of his physical surroundings. News had reached him from Franz Liszt that, despite the ban issued by Saxony, a *Lohengrin première* had been held at the Weimar Court Theater on August 28, 1850. The Grand Duchess of Weimar herself, a friend and patroness of Liszt, had vouchsafed her protection in defiance of all royal edicts.

The performance, before a chosen and necessarily limited audience, was warmly received. It added up to a *succès d'estime*, rather than a financial plum. Even so, here was heartening encouragement that fired Richard to new effort. He again took up the study of ancient Germanic mythology and folklore, particularly the absorbing drama of the Nibelungen. On November 20, 1851, he wrote Franz Liszt:

You will remember that in the autumn of 1848 I mentioned for the first time having outlined a version of the entire Nibelungen Saga, to which I now lay an author's claim. My immediate effort after that was the formulation of a principal catastrophic element in this story, namely *Siegfried's Death*, as straight drama for our German stage. . . . Then, after long hesitation, I decided in the fall of 1850 to develop the whole production along musical lines after all. Acceptance of so stark a theme seemed unlikely, however, unless some sort of preliminary episode prepared the way. I therefore fixed upon *The Young Siegfried* for this purpose. Thus all the dramatic events which in "Siegfried's Death" are told in narrative dialogue and must be presumed to have happened long before could actually be seen happening on stage in all their freshness and reality.

The text took form and was completed quickly. To be sure, this *Young Siegfried* too is only a fragment, incapable of full evaluation except as part of the whole plan, in which the "Death" already occupies its climactic place.

With two music-plays in mind, I still found myself with

an abundance of plot complications to be handled through long stretches of dialogue or else left to audience deduction. Some of these involvements were really too vital to be given summary treatment or else left to spectator conjecture. In short, I convinced myself that any work of art—and the drama in particular—can be effective only when the poetic purpose, in all its essential moments, is manifested fully to the senses. No creative artist, having recognized this truth, can afford to violate it. In order therefore to make the whole Nibelungen Myth properly understood, nothing must be left in the realm of assumption. Unsophisticated audiences are entitled to as graphic a presentation as possible.

Two factors remained yet to be clarified, both occurring in my *Young Siegfried* script, and there only by inference. The first is Brünnhilde's recital [concerning the Nibelungen curse] after her awakening in Act III. The second is the story told [of the gold stolen from the Rhine] in a dialogue passage between the Wanderer and the dwarf Mime, in Act I, and the Wanderer and Mime's father Alberich, in Act II. You realize of course that technical demands alone do not govern my obsession with this matter, but the glorious and dramatically so effective quality of those unused story elements, which you would recognize yourself on closer inspection. Just try to visualize the wondrous ill-starred love of Siegmund for Sieglinde, and Wotan's mysterious involvement in that passion; then the god's rupture with his wife Fricka, his angry self-abasement in permitting Siegmund's slaughter (to satisfy moral dictates); and finally the marvelous Walküre, Brünnhilde, dearest and most trusted of Wotan's daughters, defying and provoking his divine punishment. . . . Imagine this wealth of inspiration, which is barely suggested in my Wanderer scene and later in *Brünnhilde's* monologue, worked out as a separate play preceding the two "Siegfrieds." . . . Surely you can see that not cold craftsmanship is carrying me along, but sheer, wild enthusiasm. Now then, I am set in my task of building three dramas:

1. *Die Walküre*
2. *The Young Siegfried*
3. *Siegfried's Death*

But still the picture is not rounded out unless I have a prologue to raise my curtain. Its subject—the loss of the

Rhinegold. On stage the Nibelungen Hoard is to be shown, glowing at the bottom of the river; then the theft of it, and the casting of the curse on which the full three-part drama is based.

The clarity achieved by such expansion of my original outline will permit deletion of superfluous narrative dialogue, or at least considerable condensation thereof. I have now a spacious framework in which to develop and build emotional factors that formerly had to be pruned and enfeebled to fit the limitations I first had in mind.

No longer can I now think of separating the four units into which this work has grown, unless I allow its very purpose to be destroyed. The entire project calls for performance in unbroken sequence, which I can see realized only in the following manner: the Nibelungen Trilogy and its Prologue ought to be offered within the plan of some great festival, one which can perhaps be formulated expressly for this purpose. The main dramas should be set for three successive daytime performances, with the introductory *Rheingold* given on the eve of the festival. Once such a composite production has been achieved in its entirety it can be repeated in the same manner. But I have no objection to future separate performances of the four dramatic segments, since each remains complete in itself. I am only insisting on the original impression of unity. That is, the whole should be seen prior to consideration of the parts.

Where and under what circumstances such a Nibelungen Festival will be possible is not at the moment my concern. After all, I have as yet to buckle down to the enormous task. This will, if I manage to keep my health while engaged in it, keep me busy for at least three years. . . .

Considering postal facilities in those days, Liszt's answer came promptly. It was dated December 1, 1851, and ran:

Your letter, my glorious friend, gave me great joy. You have set out on an extraordinary path toward an extraordinary and noble goal. This purpose of shaping the Nibelungen Epos into a stage work, and composing the music for it, is truly worthy of you. I have not the faintest doubt regarding your monumental success with such a work. My sincerest interest and warmest sympathy toward you are so manifestly assured that there is no need for further protestations. . . .

Despite such glowing praise and encouragement, Wagner's confidence suffered all kinds of setbacks. He fell into repeated periods of pessimism and despair. On January 30, 1852, he poured out his heart—in a different vein—to the good Franz:

> As regards the prospects of my Nibelungen cycle, you, my kindest of friends, are probably too optimistic. I am not counting on an actual performance, or, rather, I don't think I shall live to see it. For an audience I can imagine only an assembly of personal friends who might gather at some remote and quiet spot, away from the smoke and industrial pestilence of our urban civilization. . . . If I continue with the huge task, despite my doubts, it is only to escape and forget the misery of my daily living. I have no other purpose, and I shall deem it happiness merely to lose myself in work until existence itself fades from my consciousness. . . .

With creative fires burning high, what was bringing on this access of negativism, this *Weltschmerz,* or world-weariness?

In part such abrupt changes of mood, from ecstasy to black despond (Goethe's "*Himmelhoch jauchzend, zu Tode betrübt*"), must be ascribed to overwork. By spring Wagner was to complete the outline of the full Nibelungen project, which he no longer thought of as a trilogy with an introduction but "a tetralogy, each of whose parts equals the others in merit." On May 29, 1852, the following line occurs in a letter to Liszt:

> My whole Nibelungen Tetralogy is finished in rough draft; only a few months longer, and the blank verse too will be ready.

He corresponded also with some of his Dresden friends, among them Uhlig, to whom he confided two days later:

> I am more than ever possessed by the overwhelming majesty of my subject, in which my whole philosophic outlook

[*Weltanschauung*] finds its fullest expression. After this work I shall probably never write another line, for this is the highest to which my pen could aspire. Once the book is done I shall again turn composer, with the hope that at some future time I may become a stage director, pure and simple.

As to the critics, if they choose to separate harmonic values from instrumentation, they will wrong me as much as if they regard my music apart from the libretto, or the melody itself without the text. Unfortunately I committed the error of voicing my credo [of single authorship, without collaborators] too early. I still owe the world the work of art—actually long ripe within me—which is to prove all this.

By early summer Richard showed symptoms of nervous exhaustion. He suffered splitting headaches and sleeplessness, aggravated unquestionably by mounting domestic discord. Minna was giving him little peace. Her surveillance of his daily movements, punctuated by inquisitorial cross-examinations regarding the Wesendonks, disrupted his powers of concentration and halted the progress of his work.

In justice to Richard, his friendship with Otto and Mathilde contained at this time no element of guilt. The undeniable attraction between Frau Wesendonk and himself was inspired, on Wagner's part, by an intense and inextinguishable response to beauty, tact, gentility, and on hers by sheer overpowering admiration of his genius. The young woman's diary of this period contained the notation:

> Knowing that I loved Beethoven, he [Wagner] played the Sonatas for me. If a concert loomed in prospect, for which he was hired to conduct a Beethoven symphony, he never tired, before and after rehearsals, showing me its main passages on the piano until I felt completely at home in them. It made him happy when I was able to follow, and to fire my enthusiasm from the spark of his own.

Had Minna read this she would not have approved of Mathilde's "enthusiasm." Also, she would have taken exception to the informal music lessons that appeared to mark Richard's random visits to the Wesendonk home. In any case, Minna did what she could to douse any incipient blaze. Under her recurring innuendoes and reproofs Richard's composure at last gave way. Early in July he received from Liszt a modest royalty payment on *Lohengrin,* which led him to an abrupt decision. He must drop his work and seek a rest from discontent and strife. He would go away, alone, on a vacation.

CHAPTER 3

ON JULY 15, 1852, from the small resort of Meiringen, Wagner reported to Theodor Uhlig:

> For six days now I've been traveling through the Bernese Oberland. I do plenty of tramping over the countryside, and my legs seem fit. Only my head continues unsatisfactory, my brain bursting with neuralgic pain. Emotional upsets, exhaustion, lack of rest—these are the causes. Nor is there any chance of improvement. No cure in the world can help, save one: to be someone other than I am. . . .

The letter closed with a flash of insight. "I keep withdrawing from people, yet I really yearn to be with them!"

He took up mountain climbing. Soon he was negotiating such peaks as the snowy Faulhorn and the Sidelhorn, then crossing the dangerous Gries Glacier and descending into the Formazza Valley as far as Domodossola and Baveno on the Lago Maggiore. Here he became intoxicated with his first breath of Italian air and the indescribable enchantment of south-European skies. Soothed by the mellow climate and cheery surroundings, he thought of poor joyless, cantankerous Minna. What a world of good this trip would have done her! He was a cad not to have brought her along. His troubled conscience revealed itself between the lines of an exultant note to Otto Wesendonk, written at Pallanza on July 20:

> I should have to be the world's biggest ingrate not to think of you in this lovely spot. Here I am sitting beside the Lago Maggiore and smoking the first of your cigars, which are fit for the gods! . . . I don't know whether I can get off a letter to my wife today. Tomorrow, however, I shall press her to

join me here. If everyone I love could only be at my side
right now! If only *you* could come! Today I go on to Loc-
arno, and to Lugano tomorrow. I shall want to come back
here sometime, though not alone. I feel very lonely and am
a burden to myself.

How is *Donna* Mathilde coming on with her harmony
studies and the bass clef? I hope she will have finished her
first fugue by the time I return. Then I shall teach her how
to write an opera *à la* Wagner. . . . You can see what absurdi-
ties have been inspired by your delicious cigar. If I smoke
a second one I shall go quite fey, confirming what some already think of me!

Minna did join the latter part of Richard's tour, but his funds
were already running low and, in any case, she was not much
good at cross-country hiking. They were back in Zürich by the
end of July. Unfortunately the benefits accrued during the
short vacation were quickly dissipated under the cramped,
noisy living conditions at the Abendstern. On August 9 Richard confided to Uhlig:

One wish possesses me with such overpowering force that
I am determined to carry it out at any cost. I long for a small
house and garden somewhere in the country, far off, with a
view of the Zürich Lake. There I could cultivate the earth
and surround myself with flowers and all sorts of animal pets,
as well as furnish a hospitable retreat for friends to visit.

He worked hard all that summer on his Nibelungen tetralogy, completing the colossal poem by Christmas. In February
of 1853, pinching his already tenuous budget to defray the cost,
he had the text printed so as to gain confidence from the mere
fact of its existence in permanent form. Now he was ready to
tackle the music. On February 11, 1853, Richard reported to
Liszt:

As to its over-all pattern, the musical text is already completely finished in my mind. Never have I been so at peace
with myself regarding any composing effort as I am on this

occasion. The only thing I need is the right stimulus to keep me in a buoyant and uplifted mood which will allow the melody line to burst from me in joyous motifs.

Some time ago I complained to you bitterly, asking for some means of escape from the deadly situation in which I find myself here in Zürich. I hoped for some possibility of returning to Germany, to that section where I am not banned and where I could witness a performance of my earlier works, otherwise I shall wither here from lack of incentive. You could answer my plea only in the negative, urging me to be patient. Please remember that patience can at best sustain a mere naked existence; the vigor and fullness that alone can enrich life and render it creative in the highest spiritual sense, these no man has yet drawn from patience and utter stultifying abnegation. I too shall fail in the attempt.

To lift himself out of the dullness of a daily existence that seemed bogged down in bickering and pettiest domesticity, he visited public libraries, where the limitless world of books offered escape. This led to his discovery of the Persian poet Háfiz (pseudonym of Shems ed-Dín Muhammad, one of the Orient's greatest lyric talents) concerning whom Wagner told his friend August Röckel, "I am actually shocked: here we are, with all our pompous European culture, put to shame by the serene and gracious achievement of an Eastern mind!" He pursued his studies avidly, learning that Háfiz was born at Shíráz, where he spent all his life, dying there in 1389. Due to the sensuous sweetness of his poetry, Háfiz was epitomized locally as "Sha-karlab" ("Sugar Lip"), a term of droll association to modern Western ears. But the mystic and often esoteric element in his writings also caused him to be referred to as "Lishan el-Ghayd" ("Voice of Mystery"). In any case, the poet's tomb had been magnificently adorned by princes and wealthy viziers and was visited through the ages by pilgrims from many Oriental lands. Wagner's acquaintance with the odes of Muhammad was made through the collection by Kasim Anvárí, entitled *Diván-i-Háfiz*, available in German translation. The wealth of imagery and lavish word painting he thereby absorbed would be reflected in many an ecstatic passage of his own future work.

The sense of ennui and stagnation continued. Twice, in short succession, he complained to Liszt: "I can live only by extremes: the greatest activity and excitement, or complete peace." And again: "More and more I become convinced that people like you and myself are really doomed to misery except in moments, hours, and days of productive impetus; then, however, we revel and rejoice far beyond the capacities of our fellow men. That is the way it is."

Seemingly Richard's feeling for Mathilde was deepening into a more than platonic emotion. A letter to Röckel, June 8, 1853, contains a hint between the lines:

> This much I can tell you, that my art is becoming more and more the song of the mesmerized and yearning nightingale, and that this art would totter into nothingness if I were but allowed to embrace the reality.

He composed a waltz and a sonata, both in E-flat major, for Frau Wesendonk, sending them to her husband together with an explanatory note so as not to put the lady—or himself—in an equivocal position. The weightier of these works, to be published later under the title of *Albumsonate*, bore a poetic line for its motif: "Know Ye How This Will End?" *(Wisst Ihr, Wie Das Wird?)*

By late August of that year the migraine headaches had returned with renewed fury. Though Richard abstained from smoking and the use of alcoholic drinks, he sought relief by taking snuff. On medical advice, however, this small indulgence had to be discarded. Insomnia now plagued him and he was told to undertake another hiking tour that might rest his nerves and vitalize blood circulation.

He returned on a brief excursion to northern Italy, where, at Genoa, he set up headquarters. From here he undertook long marches through pine forests and olive groves, as far as the Gulf of Spezia, where, thirty-one years earlier, the poet Shelley had met his death. At the Spezia docks a strange experience befell Richard. Overcome with fatigue, he took a room at a port inn, dropping instantly into not placid sleep but a disturbing somnabulistic state. Half awake, he felt himself submerged in a vast body of water, the rushing of which filled his ears with ever new variants of the E-flat-major chord. Frequent structural changes, from open arpeggios to closed thirds and fifths swept over him like watery waves, now slowly, now stormy and wild, yet never surrendering the purity of the tonic E-flat-major starting point. He noted in his diary:

It seemed as if the persistence of this chord wished to give everlasting significance to the very element in which I was drowning. With a feeling of complete submersion I suddenly awoke from this half-slumber. Instantly I now recognized that the orchestral prelude to *Rheingold*, long laboring within me yet unable to take form, had achieved birth. At the same time I grasped a special truth, that inspiration must be sought inwardly rather than derived from some external source.

He rushed back to Zürich and plunged into work on the *Rheingold* harmonies. At Spezia he had made his customary jottings, for piano only, from which to build the operatic structure. A bold urge seized him now, namely to write in full-orchestration, or partitura, format, simultaneously composing for every required instrument. In a first draft this called for such condensing of notations and signs that, if interrupted by the slightest outside disturbance, Richard found his own manuscripts a maze of undecipherable stenography. Only through agonizing effort was he at times able to re-create the substance underlying his hasty hieroglyphics.

Most of Richard's suffering in this respect derived from his inveterately noisy neighbors whom he had no means, nor right, to silence. In addition there was Minna with her household worries, her budget, and the bill collectors at the door, not to mention intermittent husband-and-wife debates regarding the Wesendonk friendship.

One interruption, however, during early October, proved most welcome. Franz Liszt was in Paris on one of his ever-rarer concert engagements, for the great man's ardent public would not permit his absolute retirement. Thoughtful as always, he kept an ear to the ground for some opportunity to help his friend, and presently he summoned Wagner to the French capital as guest conductor for a week's appearance with a student orchestra. The pay was modest, but Franz secretly supplemented it out of his own pocket, thus making the trip profitable indeed.

The young Cosima Liszt, now almost sixteen years old, had accompanied her father. She appeared so grown and mature that Richard failed to recognize the Weimar adolescent; in his diary he made an absent-minded entry "October 15, 1853. First meeting with Liszt's daughter Cosima." In the presence of his friends he read aloud the text of *Siegfried's Death,* which would remain for the girl an unforgettable experience and for Liszt an undeniable testimony to Wagner's future greatness.

Characteristically, after two days in the City of Light, Richard regretted having left Minna behind. What a treat it would have been for her to roam through the busy metropolis where once she had known nothing but stark penury! Confound it, he could not enjoy himself alone while she sat in their stuffy Zürich room, moping and bored. Without further ado he sent Minna a railroad ticket and urged her to join him forthwith. This amiable though reckless impulse prolonged the Parisian sojourn beyond its original intent and diminished its profit quite palpably. Beguiled by the city's *boutiques* and elegant shops, Richard and Minna lost their foolish heads and set out on a buying spree that underscored again their incapacity to handle money. In a letter to her bosom friend, Frau Schiffner, Minna reported on November 14, 1853:

> Richard heaped rich presents on me. For example, a boudoir wrapper of blue silk that would not shame a queen; then two hats, much smaller than the one you wore last summer, more like a bonnet (of which he also gave me two); also a little coat of a strange woolen material. But the greatest surprise came after our return from Paris, for he had ordered some red plush furnishings to replace the old things in our flat, adding even new window hangings of the same color with panels of embroidered tulle. . . .

THE LIBRARY IN VILLA WAHNFRIED, WAGNER'S HOME
IN BAYREUTH

It was no wonder that Wagner confided to his sister Cäcilie that same winter, regarding the French holiday: "It seems that I gained somewhat in fame. As to money, that's no burden—I never have any."

For the rest, he plunged headlong again into the musical score of *Rheingold*, which in itself was to contain the thematic base on which the full tetralogy was to rest. On January 14, 1854, the first of the Nibelungen operas reached completion. Its half-symbolic, half-legendary story was summarized in Wagner's early outline of the entire epos:

DAS RHEINGOLD

SCENE 1: The curtain rises, disclosing a scrim-veiled stage representing the depths of the Rhine. With an open-pedal E flat in the bass the orchestra conveys the river's endless flowing, while on a rock offstage center the gold hoard is seen gleaming. Three of the Rhine maidens, Woglinde, Wellgunde and Flosshilde, custodians of the treasure, play about in the water when from a dark ledge the dwarf Alberich of the Netherworldlings (Nibelungen) appears. He tries to embrace one of the water nymphs, but they all mock and escape him. Soon he is distracted, however, at sight of the gold and straightway covets nothing else. Woglinde, to the melody of the gold motif which will recur throughout the subsequent operatic segments, explains that only he who forswears love can forge from the gold a ring that gives superhuman power. At this Alberich hurls a curse on love and leaps forward to snatch the treasure, rushing off with it while the happy song of the Rhine maidens turns to shrill lament.

SCENE 2: The Rhine has vanished and in its stead the towers of a fabulous castle, Valhalla, peer through the mists of dawn beyond a valley where the river is presumed to flow. The god Wotan and his wife Fricka have just acquired the castle, built by two giants—Fasolt and Fafner—who, impatient at not receiving payment for their labors, decide to seize Freia, the goddess of Youth. Loge, the god of Fire, protests such highhandedness and warns Wotan to ransom Freia at no matter what cost, since without her all other gods lose their immortality and begin at once to grow old. Together Loge and Wotan set out for the cave leading into the underground world of the Nibelungen, where, it is already known, the stolen Rhinegold is kept.

SCENE 3 shows the dwarf Alberich deep in his cavern, gloating over his riches and the power he has gained over his fellow creatures. He taunts his brother Mime by demonstrating the magic power of the Tarnhelm (a sorcerer's helmet), which makes the wearer invisible. During his disappearance Wotan and Loge arrive and listen to Mime's awed report. Now Alberich returns, driving a herd of slaves before him with his whip. Craftily Loge asks for a new demonstration of the witching headgear, and the vain Alberich quickly accedes by transforming himself into a toad. Wotan loses no time in putting his foot on the small creature, at the same time snatching the Tarnhelm from its head. This restores Alberich to his own shape, but shackled as a prisoner of the gods.

SCENE 4 brings Wotan and Loge to the earth's surface, dragging the enraged Alberich after them. As they demand the Rhine's treasure, and especially the gold ring which the dwarf fashioned as his talisman of power, Alberich lays his curse upon all who dare touch the Ring of the Nibelungen. The earth goddess Erda rises now out of the ground to warn Wotan not to keep any part of the treasure but to pass it on at once to the giants, Fafner and Fasolt. This done, the ransomed Freia is led back in freedom. A quarrel, however, breaks out between the giants over division of their riches. Fafner kills his brother and rushes away with the huge sack of treasure. A storm breaks in his wake, then clears away to reveal a shimmering rainbow bridge leading to Valhalla. Proudly Wotan bids the gods to the lordly castle, while from the valley below can be heard the lament of the Rhine maidens for the twice-stolen gold.

DIE WALKÜRE

ACT I

Wotan's earthly son, Siegmund the Wälsung (son of Wälse, the only name by which he knows his father), seeks refuge from a storm in the forest lodge of the warrior Hunding and his wife Sieglinde. Unaware that Sieglinde is his own twin sister, Siegmund feels drawn to her just as she responds first with pity,

then love. Her marriage, she confides, was forced on her. Siegmund thereupon woos her ardently and (incest, in prehistoric
times, being the rule rather than the exception, and highly regarded, too) persuades her to flee with him. Before leaving,
he recognizes his divine father's great sword Nothung (Need-
ful) deeply thrust into a tree trunk that holds up the roof of
Hunding's hut. Joyfully he dislodges the sword, a feat of
strength no one has accomplished before.

Act II

On a rockbound mountaintop where the *Walküren* (Valkyries, or warrior maidens, demigoddesses begotten by Wotan
and Erda) gather with their leader Brünnhilde, great anxiety
prevails. Wotan arrives in dark mood, for his wife Fricka, up-
holder of convention both in Valhalla and on earth, has demanded that the marriage vows of Hunding and Sieglinde be
respected. Himself a prodigious philanderer, Wotan reluctantly commands Brünnhilde to shield Hunding in the inevitable showdown with Siegmund. After the god departs, the
fleeing lovers appear and plead for Brünnhilde's aid, which she
cannot refuse them. In the Siegmund-Hunding duel that follows, the disobedient Walküre tries to interfere in Siegmund's
favor, but Wotan thwarts her at the last moment and causes
both fighters to die while Brünnhilde carries off the fainting
Sieglinde to safety.

Act III

In a forest shelter Sieglinde awaits the birth of Siegmund's
son, Siegfried, for whom Brünnhilde has salvaged the shattered
sword of his father. The Walküre then returns to Wotan, begging forgiveness for her defiance of his order. The god would
relent but for his wife's spiteful demands that there be retribution. Brünnhilde therefore is condemned to timeless slumber
atop the mountain, a prey to any man who wakens her. At this
indignity she pleads for worthier punishment, whereupon the
sentence is amended. He who awakens her must be a fearless
hero, willing to dare a ring of flames that are to surround her
rocky couch. Wotan beckons, and at his summons the magic
fire rises to envelop the scene.

SIEGFRIED

ACT I

Fafner, the giant, since becoming possessor of the Rhine's treasure, the Nibelungen Ring and the Tarnhelm, has used the witching cap to transform himself into a dragon. As such he dwells in a cave, guarding the glittering hoard.

Near by lives the Nibelung dwarf Mime, who saw Sieglinde die in the forest after the birth of her child Siegfried. The latter was reared by Mime in the hope that he might grow to manhood and slay the dragon, thus permitting Mime to lay hands on the treasure. In preparation for this the dwarf has spent years at his forge, trying clumsily to weld the broken sword he found at Sieglinde's side.

A youth now, Siegfried runs in from the forest, teasingly smashes Mime's handiwork as he is in the habit of doing, and asks to hear again the story of his own strange origin, only to lose patience and bound once more out into the sunshine. Meanwhile a wanderer arrives (the god Wotan, on one of his periodic visits to Earth) and engages Mime in an exchange of riddles during which he prophesies that the dwarf will die at Siegfried's hand. With the wanderer's departure the youth returns in high spirits. He picks up the sword fragments and, with much gusto and song, forges a perfect blade. The frightened Mime, however, is busy mixing a poisoned brew.

ACT II

Outside Fafner's cave the embittered Alberich lies in wait, for he knows his brother Mime's intentions. At dawn Siegfried arrives, led by Mime, and the dragon is roused from his lair. In the ensuing combat Fafner is slain and Siegfried anoints his body and touches his lips with the dragon's blood, which enables him to understand the songs of the birds. As Mime now steps up to offer a refreshing drink, the woodland voices warn Siegfried against the poison, whereupon he strikes Mime dead. The craven Alberich slinks quickly away.

Through the birds' song Siegfried now learns of the sleeping Brünnhilde on her flame-circled rock. He answers the challenge and sets out to liberate her.

ACT III

At the foot of the mountain Erda and Wotan debate the fate of the gods upon whom Alberich has put the Nibelungen curse. Siegfried passes by and Wotan tries to impede his path with a long wanderer's staff, but the lad shatters the staff and runs cheerfully on his way. The Tarnhelm hangs from his belt, the cursed Nibelungen Ring is on his finger; for the rest of the treasure he has no use.

Once atop the mountain, Siegfried steps fearlessly through smoke and flame, rousing the Walküre from her doom. Awakening, she greets the sun, then feels herself seized with an overpowering love for her rescuer who, unknown to her, is now subject to the fatal malediction. Siegfried places the Nibelungen Ring, in troth, on Brünnhilde's finger.

GÖTTERDÄMMERUNG

PROLOGUE

Below the Rock of the Valkyries sit the three Norns spinning the rope of Fate. It breaks, and they vanish with mournful wails. Darkness gives way to dawn, disclosing Siegfried and Brünnhilde emerging from a near-by cavern. Binding their troth, the hero has placed his ring on her hand, whereupon she gives him her horse, Grane, of great battle fame.

ACT I

In the imposing hall of the Gibichung clan, on a bank of the Rhine, the mortals, Gunther and his sister Gutrune, ask counsel of their half-brother Hagen (a son of the Nibelung dwarf Alberich), who is plotting to secure the magic ring for himself. To accomplish this he has lured Siegfried on a visit to Gibichung Hall, where Hagen now urges Gutrune to offer the guest a love potion and to win him for a husband, while Gunther is to wed Brünnhilde.

Siegfried arrives unsuspectingly and accepts the poisoned refreshment, which instantly blots out his memory and causes him to be infatuated with Gutrune. He likewise, unaware of what he is doing, promises to aid Gunther in winning the hand of Brünnhilde. Together the two set out to find her, while evil

Hagen remains behind, gloating over the success of his scheme.

Alone in her mountain dwelling where she awaits Siegfried's return, Brünnhilde is surprised by her sister Waltraute with a plea from Wotan: unless the Nibelungen Ring is restored to the Rhine the gods in Valhalla will perish. Brünnhilde, an earth woman now and deeply in love, refuses to yield the prized circlet. As Waltraute departs, two figures approach. One of them, Siegfried, now dons the Tarnhelm and thereby transforms his appearance to that of Gunther. He sweeps down and wrests the ring from Brünnhilde, then woos her stormily, soon making way for the real Gunther to take over.

Act II

At Gibichung Hall the waiting Hagen is haunted in dreams by his father Alberich, who prods him on to more aggressive action. Soon Siegfried arrives and Hagen realizes that it is time to prepare for a double wedding. Maidens and vassals are called to put things in readiness. And now Gunther comes, escorting the distraught Brünnhilde to the home he has promised her. At sight of Siegfried the erstwhile Walküre rejoices at what she presumes her rescue, only to find that he does not recognize her. Enraged by this apparent treachery, Brünnhilde is easily induced by Hagen to reveal Siegfried's one vulnerable spot, namely the middle of his back, where he could not anoint himself with dragon's blood.

Act III

A hunt has been arranged as part of the wedding celebrations. Siegfried wanders off from his companions to the Rhine, where the river maidens still mourn the loss of their treasure and beseech him to restore the ring. Hagen is at his heels, however, after the same prize. To shock Siegfried into lowering his guard, Hagen has prepared a second drink which revives memory. The hero imbibes and is confounded by the enormity of his sins, for, after musing briefly on his childhood, he recalls his first meeting with Brünnhilde and the love that sprang therefrom. As his head droops with remorse, the spear of Hagen finds the exposed spot. Siegfried dies with Brünnhilde's name on his lips.

On his shield the dead hero is carried back to the hall where

Gunther claims the ring, but before he can take it from Sieg-fried's finger he is slain by the savage Hagen. With victory all but in his grasp, Hagen is finally thwarted by Brünnhilde, who takes the ring and throws it back into the Rhine.

It is too late to stop the curse, however. The funeral pyre set for Siegfried's body, and into which Brünnhilde rides on her horse Grane, spreads its flames over the hall. The Rhine over-flows its banks and in the sky the heavenly castle of Valhalla is briefly visible before going up in flames. Flood and fire have cleansed heaven and earth. . . .

CHAPTER 4

AS THE musical form of the tetralogy progressed, Wagner no longer referred to his creation as the Nibelungen Saga. He had found a new title, *Der Ring des Nibelungen,* to be shortened, for working purposes, quite simply to *Der Ring.* On January 15, 1854, he notified Liszt: "Text, music and orchestration for *Das Rheingold* are finished. And so am I!"

In the same letter he permitted his friend, for the first time, a glimpse behind the scenes. He disclosed personal matters that heretofore had been carefully guarded:

> During recent months my work provided such an anodyne that I suppressed every urge for letter writing until completion of *Rheingold.* This is the first morning that frees me of further restraint. Let the piled up, choking miseries pour forth—I cannot hold them longer. . . .
>
> Not one of the past several years has gone by without finding me, again and again, in the near extremity of ending my life. Everything in my personal existence is so misdirected, so wrong! Due to a premature marriage with a worthy woman, who yet is a totally alien life partner, I am an outcast from normally happy human society. For a long time the spiritual desolation of my days found sublimation in ambitions and the striving for fame. Actually I reached the age of thirty-six before grasping the full depth of my inner loneliness. Until then two opposite yearnings struggled within me, the nobler of these finding fulfillment in art, while the other led to excesses in conduct. (You know my *Tannhäuser,* whose fundamentally vulgar dissipations I managed to clothe in poetic idealism!)
>
> Eventually, perhaps with *Lohengrin,* the unity of the spiritual and carnal urge became revealed to me in a concept of

completeness-in-love, such as my own life has never known. God, how I wanted then to scrap everything and escape, out into the world, naked, free, wanting nothing but the joy of loving and being loved! . . . Well, that is not to be. . . .

Ten days later, lifted out of himself by the impelling inspiration of his work, Wagner reported to Röckel:

The substance of *Der Ring des Nibelungen* is life itself in all its manifold variety, its abundance, its eternal renewal. Wotan himself soars to greatest heights only to bring on his own downfall. This is all we know of mankind's history, that we must seek fulfilment and then perish.

Creation's masterpiece is, then, the fearless, love-radiating soul, which I call Siegfried. This Siegfried (representing the lone human male) is not a complete being. He is a fragment, finding redemption only through Brünnhilde, and vice versa. None of us can do everything. Many are needed, and above all else the eternal feminine [*das ewig Weibliche*], wherein alone reposes love. In the person of Siegfried I am trying to embody the most nearly perfect being, full of candor, trust, and joy in action, whose failings spring from innocence (a fault, assuredly) rather than evil.

I perceive that my normal state of mind is one of exaltation, while calm serenity would in me be quite abnormal. Truly, I seem to feel well only when I am "beside myself," which is the only time when I am really "all there." . . .

The spring and summer months were spent with one final revision of *Das Rheingold* orchestrations. During April a note to Liszt made brief reference to this: "I have just gone down into Nibelheim [the netherworld of the dwarfs] with my orchestra." May 28, 1854, saw the script and partitura bound and put away. The work on the music for *Die Walküre* could begin.

In preparation for this task Richard gave himself over to serious reading. He rediscovered Schopenhauer, whom, in mid-December, he described to Liszt:

Alongside the—*slow!*—progress with my music I am exclusively absorbed in someone who, though only through literary channels, has penetrated my loneliness as a heaven-sent blessing. This is Arthur Schopenhauer, the greatest philosopher since Kant. For forty years our German professors have—wisely—ignored him, for he stands too far above them. His principal thesis is self-abnegation, in its highest sense, as the only road to salvation. This thought was not new to me, as indeed it lies dormant in all who meditate. But this philosopher has brought me clarity. . . . I now know that comfort against grief, pain or despair is to be found only in making friends with Death, with the final fade-out, with sublimation in the Eternal which alone brings redemption!

Of course I am not ready for that before the record of my young *Siegfried* is complete. *Die Walküre* has been very wearing; I am in the middle of the last act.

Also, since in my own life I have never experienced the magic of a great love, I am obsessed with an urge to glorify this most beautiful of human dreams with a monument that, from beginning to end, shall give this special kind of love full rein. In my head there is taking shape the legend of *Tristan und Isolde,* for which I am beginning to conceive the purest yet most full-blooded musical design.

Yes, he had been reading, and not Schopenhauer alone. The Irish saga of Tristram and Yseult, with its haunting Cornwall setting and stark drama, had captured Richard's imagination since early Dresden days. He had visualized it first as an adventure tale, with clash of arms and derring-do. But now, on second acquaintance, the element of mere action seemed to fade before the simple but profound emotional conflict. Brushing all nonessentials aside, he would concentrate on the inner tragedy alone. In his diary, later to be incorporated in the autobiography *Mein Leben,* these inchoate beginnings are given voice:

While studying Schopenhauer and continuing with the composition of *Die Walküre,* I lived in utmost seclusion, finding my only release in long walks. As so often, when steeped in prolonged musical effort, I felt a renewed need for verbal

(and poetic) expression. Most likely it was the solemnity
of mood, cast upon me by Schopenhauer, which drove me to
seek the most ecstatic yet elemental form of the *Tristan und
Isolde* tale. . . . Returning from one of my walks, I sketched
an outline in three acts, stripped of superfluities, condensed,
for future reference. In the last act I included a visitor to
Tristan's sickbed, the knight Parsifal—roaming abroad in his
search for the Holy Grail. The wounded Tristan, unable to
get well, yet slow to die, identified himself for me with the
incurable Amfortas of Monsalvat. But these cluttering arti-
fices I later removed.

On Christmas Day of 1854 the score for *Die Walküre,* in its
first nonorchestral draft, was finished. The following March
brought a surprising summons to London, where Richard was
offered a number of engagements with the Philharmonic. He
conducted the *Tannhäuser* overture in the presence of Queen
Victoria and the Prince Consort, both of whom applauded vig-
orously and received him in private audience.

During his absence he wrote Minna in contrite, tender terms,
for it was easier to speak with her on paper than in person. A
letter of March 6, 1855, ran:

Believe me, though we do not always see eye to eye, in the
most urgent crises of our lives you and I have mustered
enough patience and affection to sustain our union. What
harsh suffering you have undergone because of me! If I
could at last bring you some peace and pleasantness, I should
derive from it the deepest satisfaction. But it seems to be
my destiny to torment you with my incompetence and lack
of understanding, which, for your sake even more than my
own, I do deplore.

Minna enjoyed such repentant declarations and she responded with wifely alacrity. While Richard was away she
found time on her hands which could be put to use with sew-
ing. Did he wish for some special garment that she might
stitch and embroider for him?

He did. From early boyhood Richard had, in common with

many fair-skinned persons, suffered frequent attacks of erysipelas. Medical authorities knew nothing as yet about allergies,
but he himself had noticed that rough cotton weaves or heavily
starched muslins aggravated the incidence. He was too poor a
man to afford smooth, nonirritating silks, yet on a material
plane this was his most ardent desire. He replied forthwith:

Most excellent of wives! You ask what can you make for
me? Last winter you produced a splendid housecoat. Now
I should like a corresponding lounge-and-work costume for
summer. My extravagant imagination pictures a monstrous
delight: a loose jacket of velvet or heavy dull satin, not
quilted, but lined in silk foulard, with trousers to match. . . .
Unfortunately I have had many sleepless nights. On one occasion, in half slumber, I heard a nightingale sing in a near-
by park, imagine! It brought tears to my eyes. I now listen
to this endearing creature mornings and evenings. . . .

This was not all he did, however, for soon the unaccustomed
British diet, abounding in Brussels sprouts, upset his digestion.
He was forced to seek medical help and to keep to his room
except for rehearsals and concert appearances, which curtailed
what little sight-seeing he might have afforded himself. His
birthday came and went without celebration, but he sent Minna
a quatrain commemorating the date.

Im wunderschönen Monat Mai
Kroch Richard Wagner aus dem Ei.
Ihm wünschen, die zumeist ihn lieben,
Er wäre besser drin geblieben.

(Hatched in the merry month of May,
Richard Wagner came to stay.
But they who love him best will tell,
He never should have left his shell.)

During the summer he returned to Zürich and continued
composing. He had reached the Magic Fire scene of Act III
in *Die Walküre*. While working on this he was frequently car-

ried away by his own ecstasy. Needing an audience on whom
to try out the fabulous harmonies he hoped to achieve, Richard
trudged across town to the Wesendonk mansion. Mathilde
commented on these visits in her journal:

> Whatever he had composed during the forenoon he would
> rush over to us late in the day, trying it out on my grand
> piano and putting each measure to the severest test. It was
> usually between five and six o'clock. He called himself the
> Sunset or Twilight Man [*Der Dämmer-Mann*].

By March of 1856 the second "Ring" opera was finished, as
were Richard's London-earned funds. If work on the tetralogy
was to continue, he must seek a spare-time job or else find a
publisher willing to grant him an advance. Hopefully he wrote
the firm of Breitkopf & Härtel in Leipzig, submitting his first
two scripts for inspection and requesting a subsidy to permit
continuance of the task ahead.

An answer was soon forthcoming, followed in time by the
rejected texts. Breitkopf & Härtel thought the two operas "interesting but esoteric," and for the rest declared themselves
opposed to subsidies. Distraught, Richard unburdened himself
to his friends, whereupon Otto Wesendonk rose magnanimously
to the occasion.

"I don't know much about publishing," Wesendonk admitted,
"but I can hire a printer for you, besides furnishing an advance
on the work yet to be done."

Here was a godsend. Richard affected no false pride, but
unreservedly rejoiced in the offer. He wrote Otto an expansive
letter of gratitude, ending with the words:

> Should it come to pass that I may indeed one day amount
> to something in the world of art, you most certainly will
> share in those honors. It will be my sincerest and most
> deep-felt concern to gain you this recognition, unreservedly
> and with all my energies.

Money alone, however, did not solve Wagner's difficulties.
Living conditions at the lodging house were becoming more

intolerable by the minute. On September 22, 1856, he sat
down to draft the first musical scoring for *Siegfried,* when an
infernal clatter broke out across the street. A tinsmith and
kettlemaker had just moved in beside the ironmonger, whose
anvil already was driving the weary composer to near distraction. The new noises, added to the enduring racket of the music
students, exceeded all limits of tolerance. Under this bombard-
ment of decibels Richard fell into a frenzy that caused him to
forswear all further interest in sound. He would drop music
altogether and choose a silent profession, such as charcoal
drawing or painting. Better still, he would turn his back on
civilization and become a hermit.

Finding a place in crowded Zürich suitable to the needs of
hermits was, of course, problematic. While pondering the matter in agonized gloom Richard recalled an earlier impulse to
incorporate the pandemonium of his surroundings in some grotesque comedy scene. He now had a flash of enlightenment.
Here was the earsplitting cacophony to fit the dwarf Mime's
clumsy forging of the Wälse sword! Richard's own outcries
and expletives could well pour from the dwarf's lips as each
effort to weld a fine blade ended in failure. Madly, then, and
with nerves tensed to the utmost, the tormented composer rose
above his agony and captured it instead between bars of dis-
sonant, atonic measures. If he was to be spared nothing, then,
at least, let nothing be wasted.

But once the Hammering Scene in the Nibelung cave was
etched on paper, Wagner broke down. "I shall die," he wrote
Liszt, "or at least grow unfit for further work unless I find decent living quarters; that is, a small house, standing alone, with
a bit of garden, removed from all noise. . . . For four years this
has been my wish-dream."

Again the Wesendonks came to the rescue. The gardener's
cottage, once rejected by Minna, was occupied now. But near
it Otto was able to purchase an additional property which, after
some minor repairs, was put at the Wagners' disposal. This
time Richard gave Minna no chance to vacillate. His extremity
was such that he must seize the proffered straw (no straw, but
the noblest of prizes he deemed it!) or drown.

His gratitude, once more, was given testimony in pen and
ink. In January of 1857 he addressed the following lines to the
Wesendonks:

Oh, you kind, beloved persons! What shall I say to you?
As though by sorcery everything around me has changed.
All doubts are at an end. I now know where I belong, where
I can weave and create, where I shall find comfort, encouragement, strength and surcease—in the truest sense—at the
side of the most loyal and dear friends. Beloved ones, you
will not regret this, for I shall belong to you for life. Whatever my successes and joys, they will be yours as well and
made possible only by you. Ah, this is beautiful, and decisive
in many ways. If only I could describe to you the deep
peacefulness that enfolds me!

It was a wondrous peace indeed, but a peace of short duration, like the imponderable calm before a storm.

SURPRISINGLY, Minna this time had not the slightest objection to the Wesendonk hospitality. Her nerves were better than Richard's, but she too was near the breaking point, due to the intolerable conditions at the Abendstern. Furthermore, with the passing years her suspicions regarding the fair Mathilde had been lulled to rest. During April of 1857 the Wesendonks had been blessed with a new baby son, thereby further underscoring firm family ties and causing Minna to feel a trifle ridiculous. Whatever could she have been thinking of? Otto and Mathilde were proper and substantial citizens, pillars of society, and so rich! How lucky that Minna's earlier antagonism had gone unnoticed and that they, the Wagners, were being given a second chance!

Before the end of that same April the carpenters and painters had finished, and the move onto the Wesendonk property took place. Richard reported glowingly to Liszt, describing the rooms and every piece of furniture. He felt certain that this step was irrevocable, permanent. His worktable, piano, music shelves, all were placed just so, and not to be disturbed again until his death. Here in this idyllic setting, with a view across well-tended lawns and gardens to Lake Zürich and the Alps beyond, there would be no more interruptions, no more self-doubt, no more pangs. Tranquillity and inspiration, an artist's most poignant needs, seemed now assured.

Minna felt equally happy. On the morning of their arrival the Wagners had been greeted by Frau Wesendonk with an armful of roses and a housewifely admonition: "Put sugar in the water. It keeps flowers fresh much longer."

Minna looked from the bouquet to its gracious bearer. Somehow she hadn't remembered Mathilde as quite so beautiful as this. The younger woman appeared a shade too blond perhaps, but certainly alluring after her recent pregnancy. Very trim, too, and chic. It had been a long time since Minna herself had displayed so flattering a neckline and such engaging frills.

The roses disposed of, Mathilde skipped back across the path to the villa, only to return a short time later with a beribboned terrier puppy which she now placed in Richard's arms.

"I thought you ought to have a dog," she said hesitantly. "His name is Fips."

Wagner was enchanted. Minna, for her part, regarded this second gift as quite superfluous. Did it not exceed mere courtesy and establish a kind of bond? How odd that Richard should receive a living pet, while Minna was singled out for perishable blooms, destined to fade in a day or two and be thrown out! Instantly her guard was up. Those two bore watching. Her first instinctive distrust must have been right. After convincing herself that all was well she should have been the least convinced.

There soon were other developments to feed Minna's renewed suspicions. The cottage living room with its small upright piano was pre-empted at once by Richard for a studio. But the Wesendonks insisted that he avail himself also of their huge music salon at the villa, with its magnificent ebony Bechstein. Only against proper acoustics, they argued, could he judge the merit of his compositions.

This was incontestable. Accordingly the two families were soon gathering several times a week at the seignorial mansion for an evening's musical enjoyment. But things did not end there. Before long Richard found it necessary to scurry across the park at all hours of the day for the solution of some particularly tricky problem in harmonics. In vain did Minna try to keep up with him. If she scarcely turned her head to take up some household task, he seemed to be off, coattails flying.

During the hot weeks of summer, when windows were thrown open night and day, Minna made additional observations. On a terrace below the Wesendonk villa there was a hammock suspended under some trees. Here Mathilde spent a part of each day with her children at play or, when the latter were fetched away by their nursemaid, at reading. But she seldom got very far with this worthy pursuit. For as soon as Wagner sat down at his keyboard and the faintest sound of music echoed across the gardens Mathilde tossed her book aside and with an exultant cry leaped from the hammock. Breathlessly she ran toward the cottage, stopping only a short distance away and throwing herself on the grass where she lay—for hours, it seemed to Minna—listening ecstatically.

At first Richard was unaware of this. He crouched over the instrument, searching, improvising, pausing again and again to make notations on his manuscripts. During such stops the terrier, no longer a clumsy puppy, rose on his hind legs to put both forepaws on his master's knee. Richard caressed the animal, then went on with his work.

One day in mid-June the weather was particularly stifling and Richard found himself unable to concentrate. He stared unseeing at the score, as though his eyes were turned inward or, more accurately, looking out through the back of his head. He was restless, as if aware of a presence. Rising, he stepped from the piano and went, irresistibly drawn, to the French window. And now the "presence" became instantly clear as he beheld Mathilde stretched out amid a cluster of marguerites. There could be no doubt that his startled glance must have crossed hers in an unspoken but eloquent rapport.

Minna, at least, took this to be so. Surveying the scene from another part of the house, she hurried through the hall. Silently she opened the studio door and crept in on tiptoe. Not until she reached her husband's side and peered over his shoulder at the vision that still held him engrossed did she speak.

"Musical, isn't she?"

Richard veered round to meet his wife's eyes, agleam with spite. He found himself taking stock of her coarsening middle-aged shape, the faded hair, the face bereft of its long-ago prettiness, and he knew that he must swallow the sharp answer that rushed to his lips. He turned back to the piano while Minna, savoring the triumph of a woman who is allowed the last word, stalked from the room.

Her victory was not conclusive, to be sure. Biting remarks and innuendoes directed against a passively mute husband who at times also seemed to be stone-deaf left the disgruntled lady up in the air. What was worse, she had no way of striking at her whom she regarded as the real culprit—Mathilde.

With the passing months, as autumn chills approached, Frau Wesendonk's hammock was taken down. The garden faded and Minna observed with satisfaction that the ground grew damp and uninviting. But she rejoiced too soon. For now a new pattern developed which she was to find more difficult to countenance than anything that had gone before. Richard stopped work on *Der Ring des Nibelungen* with the *Wald-weben,* or "forest voices," in the second act of *Siegfried.* Instead, he appeared engrossed in a purely literary effort—the story, in blank verse, of *Tristan und Isolde.* This could mean only one thing: he was so smitten and bewitched by the Wesendonk vixen that his very lifework went by the boards. Not that Minna gave a fig for Valkyries, Valhalla and all that fiddle-faddle of which she could make neither head nor tail. But when Richard turned his back on an undertaking that for five years had occupied him night and day—as the Nibelungen tetralogy had done—in order to pen a three-act love poem, Minna needed no divining rod to interpret the signs. Like a moonstruck, romantic schoolboy, he was shockingly, shamelessly infatuated.

It galled her to arrive at this conclusion, yet she would not relent and ease her suffering by allowing that she might be wrong. If only she could catch those two in some compromising situation that would furnish proof with which Minna might confront the unsuspecting Wesendonk! Often enough, during late-fall afternoons, Mathilde called at the cottage, bearing some tidbit or a carafe of French claret for the Wagners' supper. If Minna chanced not to hear her knock, the lady slipped nonchalantly into the studio where Richard was fitting his stanzas to their corresponding measures on the piano. But now the instrument would suddenly grow silent, and for quite a time, too, until Minna's approaching footsteps aroused the composer to action. What chords and cadenzas Richard produced the minute his wife stuck her nose through the door! And how innocently that blond minx, Mathilde, sat in a far corner, well removed from the piano to be sure, drinking in the "divine" notes!

It was an eminently proper scene, this meeting of souls enraptured by the noble muse. Mathilde had unusual poetic gifts and she often submitted stanzas for Richard's approval and possible melodic adaptation. One such poem, entitled *"Träume"* ("Dreams"), was transcribed by him as a violin solo against a ten-piece orchestra accompaniment and presented at Villa Wesendonk on December 23, 1857, in honor of Mathilde's birthday. So well was it received that, with some changes in text, he soon thereafter incorporated the tune as a duet in the second act of *Tristan und Isolde,* assuring it immortality as the entrancing *"Oh sink hernieder, Nacht der Liebe!"* ("Ah, descend, thou night of love!")

This sort of collaboration, on however artistic a plane, failed to carry conviction with Minna. Or, rather, it convinced her only too well that something shady must be afoot. A man and woman drawn together by a passion for versemaking? Here was a pill too large to swallow; it simply would not go down.

In the midst of these mortifications Franz Liszt came to call. He was passing through Zürich on another of his few concert tours, made only in response to patriotic or charity appeals. He brought along his newly married daughter Cosima and the latter's talented young husband, the budding symphony conductor, Hans von Bülow.

Minna did not approve of Liszt. With the self-righteous primness of advancing age she frowned on the fiery Hungarian's amorous past which kept him still a subject for international gossip. Twenty years ago, nay, longer, Liszt had scandalized Parisians through his romance with Marie de Flavigny, Comtesse d'Agoult. This lady, known in literary circles as the novelist Daniel Stern, had left home and husband for the celebrated pianist. She bore Liszt three children—Cosima, Blandine and Daniel. The older girl had come into the world at Bellagio, on Lake Como, Christmas Day of 1837, and was named after the region's patron, Saint Cosmo.

More recently the Magyar artist's name had been linked with
Princess Karolyne von Wittgenstein, the wealthy Polish-born
patroness who had granted him his sinecure at Weimar. In
passing through that town on his flight from Dresden some
eight years ago Wagner had, of course, gained little insight into
the private life of the fabulous Franz. But he now remembered
a glimpse of the small Cosima, then a gangling, sharp-featured
adolescent with large dark eyes set in deep hollows. Like
Minna's poor Natalie, Cosima was downright ugly. Richard
had somehow always believed the fiction regarding the pronounced beauty of love-children. Natalie and Cosima certainly
knocked that fable into a cocked hat.

On meeting her today as a bride, Richard did not find Liszt's
daughter much improved. If anything, she was skinnier and
more owlish than before. But of course there was before him
almost daily the sight of Mathilde's ripe loveliness, against
which even Tannhäuser's Aphrodite would have paled.

During the Liszt visit the Wesendonk home threw open its
proverbially hospitable doors. There was much social activity,
which always made it difficult for Minna to keep tab on her
husband. Even with Liszt in competition, Richard became
easily a target for feminine attention. But jealousy can bide its
time. With craned neck and eagle eye Minna did what she
could to intercept not only Mathilde but all other flirtatious
poachers on her staked-out marital terrain. Richard might trade
smiles or warm glances while his wife's attention strayed elsewhere, but such derelictions were at best abortive and of fleet-
ing character. From her own anything but blameless past
Minna recalled two essentials for the consummation of even the
most trivial amour: opportunity and time. It was her job to
see that Richard found neither.

Oddly, it never crossed Minna's mind that, whatever bond
might exist between her husband and Frau Wesendonk, no
commonplace expedient was chosen by the supposed lovers for
realization of their desires. It would have been a simple matter for Richard to simulate a concert trip so as to keep a near-
by hotel rendezvous with the lady of his heart. Similarly
Mathilde, with a carriage at her command, could drive to some

remote part of town without fear of being spied on. How was the portly Minna, grown stiff with advancing years, to trot hither and yon after a still-nimble spouse and a young woman half her age?

Also, alert though she thought herself, Minna missed other straws in the wind that pointed in a direction she could in no way have held suspect. The Liszt sojourn in Zürich lasted several weeks and brought about a number of friendly meetings aside from the formal Wesendonk gatherings. Over afternoon coffee in the Wagner cottage Cosima's somewhat abrupt wedding was being discussed. Liszt shook a finger at Richard, declaring, "Actually my son-in-law has *you* to thank that Cosima accepted him!"

"Me?"

Young Bülow nodded. "Yes, indeed. As far as she was concerned I happened to be just another fiddler under her father's baton and a struggling music teacher on the side—until she found out I was a Wagner enthusiast."

Here was something that interested Richard far more than love's dawning between Cosima and Hans. Could it be that his compositions were being played often enough, somewhere, to result in so unbelievable a phenomenon as a Wagner enthusiast? He stepped past Cosima, ignoring the adoration in her eyes, and shook Bülow's hand. This young man had talent and perception! Despite the difference in their ages, Richard and the excellent Hans (who bore an aristocratic and politically illustrious surname) were going to be friends.

If Cosima's hero worship went unnoticed by both Richard and Minna, it did not escape the sensitive Mathilde, who saw therein only further justification for her own rapture. Up to now the poetically inclined matron had been singularly successful in spinning about herself a cocoon of self-delusion. She had convinced herself, and Richard as well, that the attraction between them was of a high, platonic order, possible only in persons of ethical worth and conscience. In a way this was borne out by a strict absence of routine trickery, of sordid assignations or other *sub rosa* romancing. They were not lovers pursuing an illicit affair on a gross physical plane. This was her honest belief. Yet an added degree of soul-searching would have revealed to both of them that they were playing with fire and, indeed, were about to find it a losing game.

Richard was the first to recognize the truth. In a letter to his sister Klara he confided:

> What has sustained and comforted me throughout these years of exile, especially in view of the dissonances existing between Minna and myself, is the love of this young woman [Mathilde] who with shyness at first and great hesitancy allowed herself to be drawn toward me. Since there can be no question—ever—of consummation, our deep feeling for each other has a poignancy and sadness that disdains vulgarity, seeking satisfaction only in the promoting of welfare and happiness, one for the other.
>
> From the first day of our meeting she has sought by the most tactful and courageous means to ease the problems of my life by arousing her husband's interest in me. He, in turn, could not but feel a stab of resentment at her complete candor and show of concern for a man who might well become a threat to their marriage. Yet such is her greatness that, by honesty rather than dissimulation, she not only retained his love but—in demonstration thereof—his full support of her good works in my behalf. Ultimately he did not want to lose the mother of his children, those same children who must remain the unsurmountable obstacle between herself and me.

It was evident from the above lines that, regardless of dialectic smoke screens, Richard and Mathilde had fallen desperately in love. Morally they bore as grave a responsibility as though they had been trapped *flagrante delicto*. The fact that Minna had not succeeded in thus trapping them did not by any means exonerate the guilty pair.

At the same time neither Richard nor Mathilde sought to augment their mutual guilt by reckless misconduct. They saw not the slightest chance of throwing off their respective family ties and obligations. For Wagner the dominant barrier lay in Otto Wesendonk's friendship. Also, despite the beastly life she led him, there was poor Minna—withered, disgruntled and lately troubled with palpitations. He could not see himself deserting the unhappy partner who had been—incredibly!—the delight of his younger years. As for Mathilde, she recognized even more keenly the futility of a forbidden passion. Besides her magnanimous and trusting husband, she had three children to whom she was answerable. Their honor, if not her own, must give her pause.

As a result of these prime considerations the relationship skirted the danger line of a routine love affair. It balanced along precariously on a conversational level, keeping less noble impulses in check. To excuse her occasional visits to the composer's studio Mathilde persuaded herself that she must further and inspire his career. Wagner supported such casuistic evasions by calling her his heavenly muse.

He was working full time now on the story outline of *Tristan und Isolde,* expanding its simple elements into a tremendous narrative poem. Set to music, one day, he hoped to make this Germanized tale of ancient Cornwall into a supreme apotheosis of love, the most overwhelming and tragic idyl of all time.

He was entranced by his subject. Into this music-drama he intended to pour all that was unattainable in his own life: the daring, the fear, the fire and voluptuous climax denied him in his adoration of another man's wife. If not in actuality, here, sublimated, he would live these things. But apology and contrition were there too, in the understanding of King Marke (the heroine's aged husband), the renunciation of Tristan and the love-death of the noble Isolde herself. That is, Richard did not in reality expect Mathilde to commit suicide for him, nor would he have cared to put Otto Wesendonk's tolerance to too severe a test. But in lifting the whole agonizing triangle onto a lyrical height he made an advance bid for Otto's pardon, while nonetheless bearing immortal testimony to the fatal cleft in Mathilde's heart. That he, Wagner, had never loved like this before nor expected so to love again was to be underscored in Tristan's own deathbed avowals. Yes, this was his plan. Few times, if ever, in the history of man were poetry, music and stagecraft to attain such summits of glorification, not of harmonic intricacies or plot, but of the all-dominant, all-consuming, delirious theme of love.

CHAPTER 6

THE libretto was finished September 18, 1857, and Richard made a notation in his diary, addressed to Mathilde, though not mailed. Here was evidence that, in a measure, matters were coming to a head.

> Today I completed the *Tristan* poem, and I brought you the final act. You led me to the chair opposite the sofa, where you embraced me and said, "Now I have no further wish!"
> On this day and in that hour I felt myself reborn. My past is gone, my future yet to arrive. But during that wonderful instant I knew the essence of living. . . . Do you know how I savored it? Not in violent and stormy intoxication, but with reverence and gravity, a warm sense of freedom and of eternity. I had for so long turned on the world in pain and negation, always rebellious and on the defense. Even my work was steeped in pain, for it contained only unfulfilled yearnings for affirmation, for a sense of belonging, of oneness, such as you gave me in that brief instant. . . . Loveliest of women, so timid and retiring, you found the courage to endow me with this glorious moment by uttering the words "I love you!" Thus you would die that I may live. Thus I shall live only to die with you. Together we have left the world behind. . . .

Unquestionably the scene referred to above gave Mathilde some bad moments. How could she have lost her composure, her very reason, to the extent of brazenly avowing her love and, worse, throwing her arms about Richard's neck? It was no use blaming the eloquence and power of his verses. She had surrendered to the wild impulse before the manuscript was in her hands.

For days thereafter she was in torment. On pretext of indisposition she retired to her rooms, receiving no callers. Fortunately the visitors from Weimar had departed, Liszt for Milan and the young Bülows to some Adriatic resort.

"But we'll be back through here," Cosima had promised, "on our way to Paris, to hear Papa play."

"Is that what you call retirement, Franz?" had been Richard's gentle taunt, to which Liszt replied with a shrug.

"Let's say I am tapering off." A wistful pause. "The open road still exerts a strong pull."

For Mathilde the guests' departure brought welcome relief. She somehow had not found Cosima a comfortable person to be with. The youthful Frau von Bülow appeared to be sharply analytical and observing. Her grave eyes had a way of resting steadily on people, as if to pry open their innermost secrets. Vaguely Mathilde felt that Cosima knew something of the emotional undercurrents that charged the atmosphere of both the Wesendonk villa and the Wagner cottage on the Green Hill.

Autumn weather came early that year and with it an unseasonable snowstorm. The garden lay buried in glittering white as a commodious sleigh drawn by two chestnut carriage horses waited at the Wesendonk door. A moment later Mathilde stepped out, in fur-trimmed coat with matching hat and muff. As she seated herself the coachman placed a robe across her knees.

"To the National Museum, Joseph." Her voice had its customary calm timbre, but inwardly she was excited, apprehensive.

"Yes, madame."

The ride was silent but for the soft thud of the horses' hoofs and the faint tinkle of their harness. It seemed only minutes before the dark silhouette of the museum loomed ahead. The sleigh halted and Mathilde hurried up the broad steps into the main hall. Here, half concealed by a group of statuary, Wagner was waiting. They greeted each other discreetly, though the building was not much visited during midday.

Richard's voice sounded grotesquely casual. "Good afternoon, madame. In here is the collection I spoke to you about—the finest collection of stained glass in the world."

They stepped into an adjoining and much smaller room where no one else could be seen. He led the way to a secluded bench.

Looking about her, Mathilde could not suppress a smile. "Nobody much interested in the world's finest collection of stained glass, is there?" She grew serious again, her anxiety returning. "We ought not to be here. I always said I wouldn't meet you like this. It's wrong for me to have come now."

"You mean that?" He took her hands in his. "Do you?"

"We are both married. We have binding obligations." She tried to pull away. "We're not cheap, frivolous people, yet this . . . this secrecy and hiding make us appear so."

He nodded. "I like it no better than you do." His tone took on a note of desperation. "But how else can I see you? Your servants turn away all callers. You have lost interest in my music, you never come to listen any more—even from the garden . . ."

Again a faint smile crossed her lips. "There's snow on the ground. Or haven't you noticed?"

"You used to come inside. The studio is never locked." His face lighted up suddenly. "I have the music finished for the whole first act of *Tristan,* an opera I am writing for you alone. Yet you give me no chance to play it for you!"

"You know I cannot. Not after our last meeting." There was a long pause. "Besides, I know I am not welcome in your house. She—Minna—is not a stupid woman. She understands that I must not be allowed under her roof."

"*My* house, *her* roof—when we are enjoying your hospitality!" He groaned at the impossibility of his position. "That's what makes everything worse."

She looked away. "You don't know how much worse. I myself have nothing. Before I married I was not rich. The property is all my husband's."

They had both grown increasingly uncomfortable. Rising, they walked among the display cases, back to the main hall.

"We must not go on with this, Richard. Two broken marriages—it doesn't make a pretty picture."

"No."

He nodded dejectedly, leading her to the outer vestibule. He bowed over her hand, then stepped back into the shadows, letting her go. "Good-by, my dear."

"Good-by."

Her eyes filled with tears as she turned from him. She walked toward the stairs, then stopped suddenly in her tracks, veered back and rushed wildly into his arms. They clung to each other in a passionate embrace.

He whispered hot, pleading words. "Don't let this be the end! Don't destroy both our lives!"

"That's what I am trying to keep from doing—destroying many more lives than just yours and mine."

Before her commanding reason he grew humble. "Yes, you are right. But let me have your friendship as before—please!"

She pressed his hand. "You shall have it, I promise. But I cannot come alone again to your studio. You must understand."

"I understand."

They parted quickly. Outside it was starting to snow again.

That evening Richard put the music score of *Tristan und Isolde* aside. His mood was melancholy and repentant. He scanned a sheaf of prose notations pertaining to projected future works. Among these was a paragraph written soon after his removal from the dreary Abendstern lodgings to the Wesendonk cottage. It concerned a drama of spiritual regeneration through contrition and purity, symbolized by the Holy Grail. The germination of this idea was related as follows:

On Good Friday [1857]—the little garden was green and the birds sang exuberantly—I sat on the roof of the tiny cottage in order to bask in the long-yearned-for and so blissful stillness. Enveloped by this calm, I told myself suddenly, "This is Good Friday!" and I remembered the same day, years ago, while I was reading Wolfram's *Legend of Parsifal*, which seemed to hold special significance for me. Since that time (during a short visit to Marienbad in July 1845) I had not occupied myself with this subject. But now its idealistic content seized upon me with overwhelming might. With Good Friday as a starting point I quickly conceived a complete dramatic design which, broken into three acts, I sketched in flying strokes.

He was sincere in turning over a new leaf. If the *Tristan* madness meant losing Mathilde altogether, he would harness desire and choke off all avenues to temptation. The Grail, not the white flesh of a loved woman, must become his goal, his all-absorbing creative preoccupation.

Vehemently he threw himself into the job of expanding the fragmentary notes. Before long, however, the habit of many months pulled at him. He was used to calling at the villa, when the day's work was done, to submit both dialogue and music texts to critical appraisal by Otto and Mathilde alike. Only by obtaining a listener's immediate reaction could he determine the value of what he had done. Lacking this long-accustomed "sounding board," to which his benefactors had faithfully lent themselves, the commendable *Parisfal* effort soon bogged down.

At length he could contain himself no longer. Risking Mathilde's displeasure, he penned a note in which he requested a resumption of the former harmless *status quo*. "My nights are torment," he wrote. "With daylight I pray to my guiding spirit, and my prayer asks only loving comprehension! This alone is my salvation. If I see you in the garden today, be warned that I shall join you for a word."

These were not well-chosen sentiments. If he wished to resume the friendly evening sessions in the Wesendonk family circle (the older children were allowed to stay up past their bedtime, occasionally, when the Wagners came to call), it was certainly unnecessary to importune Mathilde on her daily stroll through the grounds. Unnecessary and dangerous. For the above message fell into Minna's hands, providing her with what she deemed compromising evidence.

It happened less by accident than crafty purpose. For many months Minna had lain in wait for a chance to catch Richard at some devious machination. One day, watching the studio door, she espied the Wesendonk gardener's boy. He seemed to have been charged with an errand, for, some moments later, he set out across the lawn, bearing a thick envelope in his hand.

She intercepted the lad. "Good morning, Gustav. I was just on my way to the villa. Can I take that for you?" She reached for the envelope. "I know you want to get back to your pruning."

The boy stammered awkwardly. "Oh . . . why . . . thank you, ma'am." He surrendered the packet meekly and went on his way.

To save face, Minna continued walking in the direction of the Wesendonks, but as soon as she felt herself unobserved her fingers tore open the flap. At first there was nothing but a few manuscript pages—the morning's work on *Parsifal*, with marginal remarks here and there, "This is the new theme I am working on" or "Do you find the introductory scene too long?" A look, almost of disappointment, came over Minna's features. When one is trying to expose a pair of sinners it is aggravating to uncover what looks more like evidence of their virtue. Doggedly the embittered wife continued her search until, at last, a bit of note paper fell to the ground. She stepped behind a bush, certain that this was it. With gloating satisfaction she read Richard's reckless statement, "If I see you in the garden today . . ."

It was what she needed. True, something a bit more concrete would have suited her purpose better (poets did cover up their meanings in such garbled language!), but even so the message was most improper for a married man to send to the wife of a supposed friend. Tossing the manuscript pages away, Minna brandished the letter and headed directly for Mathilde's sitting room.

In doing so she cast a look back at the cottage, for she did not want Richard to catch sight of her. Ah, she could hear him plainly, trying out some sort of chime effect on the piano. Not very good, she thought, for hers was a factual mind. If chimes were wanted in this thing called *Parsifal*, why not make provision for the ringing of a bell?

She was about to proceed on her way when her attention was directed elsewhere. At the back door of the cottage the terrier

Fips had just emerged to find his drinking pan. At sight of the animal, Minna was seized with loathing. Mathilde's present, she thought. And what a fetish Richard made of the yapping creature! Nothing was too good for precious Fips; he must be fed the best things at table, not scraps, heaven forbid. Well, the drinking pan seemed to be empty, judging from the way the dog pushed it around. Minna's eyes narrowed with pleasure. A lot she cared! But wait a minute! This gave her an idea. Abruptly she turned on her heel and hurried back.

At the rear door to the cottage she picked up the dry pan. With the dog at her skirts she went into the kitchen, searching a cupboard for a small bottle marked RAT POISON. Yes, there it was, plainly labeled. She filled the pan with water, then realized that this would not cover the taste. She emptied it and now ladled out some soup from the kettle on the stove, blowing on it lovingly so the dog would not get burned. Next she poured the poison and set the drinking pan back outside in its accustomed place.

And now she was ready for her visit to Frau Wesendonk.

CHAPTER 7

IN A DOWNSTAIRS sitting room Mathilde was busy at a large needle-point frame. She looked serene and untroubled, having recovered her peace of mind since her meeting at the museum with Richard. They had come to an understanding, she was sure. Henceforth all would be well.

A slamming of doors broke the well-bred stillness of the villa (the older children were off to school, and the baby had been tucked in for his nap). That new maid Ella made far too much noise. She would have to be spoken to.

"Ella?"

Mathilde heard footsteps, but the person barging into the room was not Ella. Turning, she looked into the flushed face of Frau Wagner.

"Oh, it's you. Good morning!" Mathilde rose. "I'm sorry you weren't announced."

Minna wasted no time on formalities. Pulling Richard's letter from her bosom, she waved it before the other woman's eyes. "Here! What have you to say to that?"

Without reaching for the paper, Mathilde recognized the handwriting; but she did not bother to read. Her conscience was clear. Not regarding herself as either a wanton or a home-wrecker, she did not expect to be compromised by anything Wagner might have put into writing. Her only effort was to calm the overwrought visitor: "What have I to say? You are being very foolish. You have a husband, younger than yourself—" Minna winced at this, but the other went on, deliberately gentle—"a husband who is destined for greatness, yet who will never abandon you——"

"Ha! You mean *I'm* not giving him a divorce."

"I mean he has no intention of asking for one."

Minna was seething. "I suppose you're going to tell me you're not in love with him."

"In love?" Mathilde smiled faintly. "I am not a schoolgirl. But this you may believe: my love for Richard Wagner, and the love that generations still unborn will accord him, can't be dispelled simply because you forbid it."

Minna folded the letter. "I am not concerned with future generations, but with the disgraceful goings-on right now." She threw back her head defiantly. "We'll see what your husband thinks, when I'm through reporting to *him*."

"Don't bother," said Frau Wesendonk. "Where Richard is concerned, there are no secrets between my husband and me."

The visitor was somewhat deflated by this, as by her rival's poise, which only fanned her fury the more. Minna could not know, of course, that Mathilde's statement was a slight exaggeration. The Wesendonks did not see completely eye to eye on the subject of Wagner. Otto could not be expected to thrill to the artist's mere presence, nor did he (like Mathilde) toss through nights made wakeful by yearnings too cruelly denied. But the firmness with which Minna's threat had been parried left the latter confused. Unable to think of further intimidating measures, she snapped sulkily, "In that case I think we had better vacate the cottage." Without waiting for an answer, she stalked from the room.

She crossed the garden on the double-quick. A few minutes later the door to Wagner's studio flew open and Minna stood glowering on the threshold. Now she stepped forward and planted herself beside the piano, flinging out her challenge.

"Well, I've put an end to it. We get out of here tomorrow!"

Richard, scribbling a line of bass notes, was only half aware of the intrusion. "An end to what? Get out of where?" He tried to sort out what she had said. "Really, Minna, you're sometimes difficult to understand."

"I can't say it with poetic phrases, as you do in your pretty letters—" she tossed the incriminating paper on the piano—"but the affair with that woman next door is going to stop just the same. I've told her so."

"You—what!" Richard leaped to his feet, horrified. He took her by the shoulders, giving her a hard shake.

Now she was savoring her triumph. "So it means that much to you, does it? In that case I acted just in time. You'd better start looking for another address."

He was utterly distraught. "One of us must be insane." His first reaction had been emotional: the thought of Mathilde—and separation. But now a more transcendent issue rose before him—his operas, the unfinished *Tristan,* and the *Parsifal* outline which had been going really well. He looked about the room, shaking his head. "Furniture movers breaking in on my privacy, tearing everything apart. What is to happen to my work?"

Minna remained unruffled. "Should have thought about that earlier, shouldn't you?"

"What?" His distress was too genuine for her venom to come through. He tried to pull himself together. Surely this wasn't really happening. It must be some aberration born of Minna's neurotic tendencies. She had been short of breath lately, and Doctor Gertz had diagnosed a defective heart. Minna had been advised to lose weight in order to relieve that burdened organ. But, in the manner of most discontented and mentally idle women, she was a great eater. There was no sign of diminishing poundage. Perhaps this outburst then indicated an advancing of her cardiac affliction? In that case he must deal patiently with her. "Let's sleep on it, dear. You'll see things differently tomorrow." He touched her arm in a soothing gesture.

Just then the gardener's boy, Gustav, rushed in through the French doors, carrying a small furred thing. His voice was shaken. "It's Fips, sir, the little dog—he must have eaten something. He's dead."

Stunned, incredulous, Wagner looked at the boy. Then he saw Minna's knowing and pleased expression. He drew back in genuine horror. "*You!*" he gasped. "*You* could do this thing?" Then, hoarsely: "That ends everything between us."

"Oh, so you can run off and marry your Isolde, is that it?" She was screaming, unmindful of the servant's presence.

Wagner made a superhuman effort to restrain himself. "You

are talking nonsense. I don't want a divorce. I am not marrying anyone. I shall worry about the foolish creature that you are, and I shall provide for you as my legal wife, always." He exploded suddenly. "But for God's sake get out of my sight!"

He stood there, a figure of towering wrath. Minna shrank, retreating in terror. Now Wagner took the dog tenderly from the arms of Gustav and walked toward the French doors. "I shall have to borrow your spade, my boy."

While he dug the shallow grave his mind was in a turmoil. A marriage did not break up over a small dog. Besides, Minna was a sick woman who could not be held responsible—and she had not really admitted the deed. Over and over Richard told himself these things, without in the slightest veering from a decision that had been gradually and fiercely taking hold of him. He and Minna must separate.

Returning to the house, he heard her shuffling about upstairs, blubbering as she packed her trunk and satchels. A pang of self-reproach seized him. Yet, what he felt was pity rather than remorse, and so he did not weaken. Since Minna was not, like himself, a political exile, she could go back to Germany and rejoin her daughter Natalie. The latter, nearing thirty and almost certain spinsterhood, must be persuaded to look after her unhappy mother.

As for Richard's own plans, he would have liked to stay on at the Wesendonk cottage long enough to finish his *Parsifal* outline. But was this possible after the enormity of what had occurred between Minna and Mathilde? Even if Richard explained his wife's departure as occasioned by reasons of health, things would no longer be the same. For one thing, Mathilde would avoid him now more than ever, as the sensitive young matron's consciousness of guilt had surely doubled. Besides, what if the vengeful Minna were to complete her destructive work by unburdening her grievances in a letter to Otto Wesendonk? No, Richard must not expose Mathilde to this final calamity. His duty was quite clear. He, too, must leave.

It was in the midst of these events, and in fact just as Minna's trunk was being hauled downstairs, that the *clop-clop* of horses' hoofs was heard approaching and a carriage stopped at the

cottage door. From his studio window Richard recognized
Franz Liszt and the Bülows, obviously come to pay their promised return call. He hurried to the front door.

"Franzl"

"Well, Richard, here we are again. Only a short stop this
time, as we want to take in Paris before going home."

"Do come inside, and . . . er . . . please excuse me while I
call my wife."

Settling themselves in the studio, the visitors looked across
the garden toward the villa. Cosima turned to her father. "We
haven't time for another call at the Wesendonks, do we, Papa?
Why not suggest that they come over here?"

She had barely finished when the door flew open and Otto
burst in, with Mathilde, somewhat subdued, a few steps behind
him. Wesendonk headed straight for Liszt.

"Hello, Franz, you faithless vagabond! What do you mean,
stopping here before coming to my house? If my gardener
hadn't recognized you, I suppose we should have missed you
altogether."

"Certainly not! Cosima was just saying . . ."

There was a general exchange of pleasantries, during which
Minna entered, bearing a tray with coffee cups and the remains
of a *Guglhupf* cake. During the convivial *Kaffeeklatsch* that
followed, the men engaged in lively travel talk, but the observing young Cosima von Bülow sensed instantly that something
was amiss. It did not escape her that, after the merest nod of
greeting, Minna and Mathilde studiously avoided each other.
Wagner too seemed ill at ease. In fact, the afternoon proceeded
under a mounting tension, soon noticeable also to Liszt. Only
Wesendonk and Bülow conversed volubly and helped themselves to huge portions of the excellent *Guglhupf.*

It was before the final farewells that Liszt drew Wagner
aside. "What's happened here? You and Minna look on edge.
Is something wrong?"

Richard nodded. "My wife and I must separate."

"Separate? You mean divorce?"

"No. Minna is ill. I want her to go back home to take care
of herself."

"Without you?"

Wagner shrugged. "I'm still a political refugee, remember? There's that warrant out, in Saxony, for my arrest."

"Then what will you do—stay here?"

"No, not here. I've decided on that haven of struggling artists, Venice. By the end of this week I hope to leave for Italy."

"I see." Liszt paused near the piano where, pushed to one side, lay some pages of manuscript. He fingered these, then looked from Wagner to Mathilde. "You've reached the crisis between Tristan and King Marke, is that right?"

"Yes. Tristan loves Marke's wife, Isolde."

"But Marke is Tristan's friend." There was a pause. Then Liszt took Wagner's hand. "There's no choice for the lovers but to part, is there?"

"None."

On this note the afternoon ended.

The following day passed, and the one after that, with Minna dawdling over last-minute travel preparations. She had obviously experienced a change of heart and was hoping for a reconciliation. But there was no chance of this with Richard, who presently could not endure Switzerland another day. He packed his skimpiest necessities and planned his own departure for the morning of August 17, 1858. He described the final hours in his diary:

> The last night at Asyl [Wesendonk Cottage] I went to bed at 11 o'clock. My departure was set for the following morning at five. Before closing my eyes a vision recurred to me, with which I had often lulled myself to sleep, namely that here in this spot I would one day die. Here I hoped to stretch out, while you [Mathilde] stood beside me for the last time, openly before everyone clasping my head in your arms and receiving my soul in one last kiss! This death was my most blissful hallucination, and it had come to identify itself with this very room: the hall door would be locked, and you would enter from behind the studio draperies; your arm would enfold me as, held by your gaze, I ceased breathing. . . . And now? The fond illusion is no more. Where am I now to die? With these thoughts sleep at last overtook me. Then, out of

fitful slumber I was awakened, feeling clearly a kiss upon my brow and the breath of a sigh. This was so vivid that I rose and stared about me. All was quiet. I lighted a lamp and saw that it was almost 1 o'clock, the end of the ghosting hour. Had some spirit force visited me? Were you awake or sleeping at this moment? What were your feelings? . . . Now my eyes would not close again. I suffered torments, then gave up finally and got dressed, locked the last piece of baggage, and alternated between walking up and down or dropping on a couch till morning. Dawn came much later than on my many sleepless nights of last summer. With a deep blush the sun rose from behind the mountain. . . . I looked across the lawn, to you, a long time. Dear Heaven! I had no tears, but it seemed to me that the hair on my temples was drained to whiteness. This was good-by. I felt cold, and completely stony.

I went into the hall. My wife awaited me there, with tea. It was a dreadful, pitiful hour. She accompanied me. We walked down through the garden . . .

The parting was excruciating indeed. Till the last, Minna had looked for a patching of the rift and a resumption of the companionable, if not truly harmonious, marriage. From a practical angle she began to grasp what she was about to lose. The Wesendonk hospitality, her hatred of Mathilde notwithstanding, had many advantages which might never again be encountered. In short, Minna would have liked to set back the clock, a feat she thought could be accomplished by simply pushing back its hand. She was one of those unguarded people who fling about murderous language, then expect skies to clear simply by stating that they now are sorry. Words held no meaning to such shallow minds, hence their power to wound and ultimately to destroy human relationships—as surely as a fine crystal may be hopelessly shattered—was beyond comprehension. Unquestionably Minna had ample cause for provocation. But in choosing the tactics of an ill-tempered fishwife she had brought on herself far greater harm than on those who indeed had wronged her.

At all events, the crystal of her marriage had crashed to bits.

No chance now for application of even the best housewifely glue. Her own report of that last morning on the Green Hill in the Zürich suburb of Enge was to survive in a letter to her friend, Frau Schiffner:

Richard had no thought, no glance, no feeling left for me. As we walked down the garden path together, past the place where the Wesendonk house comes into full view, he stumbled like a blind man beside me, staring fixedly over there.... He paid not the slightest attention to my suffering, till I touched his hand and roused him with the words "Richard, please look at me."

CHAPTER 8

ON HIS way to Italy the unhappy Wagner stopped in Geneva, where, on August 20, 1858, he wrote his sister Klara:

> ... If I am today condemned by superficial critics, I am steeled against them. Minna never had a more compelling chance to stand by me and to give me the full strength of her love. But this kind of love was beyond her, since she preferred to let her fury prevail over all else. I excuse her since she is not well, but her sickness itself could be alleviated by a more mellow and gentle disposition. The many misfortunes which she suffered through me (without possessing my ability to find spiritual escape) do exonerate her, of course. But toward the last any thought of creative work was, for me, out of the question. As soon as I can once more recover the mood to continue with the music of *Tristan* I shall find my salvation. Truly, this is where I must seek help. I want nothing from the world save peace in which to accomplish the works that one day shall belong to it, the world! Therefore, let me be judged charitably!

To Minna, now en route to Germany, he also penned a few lines. He tried to ease her mind by reasoning with her:

> With you, one individual person must always be completely at fault. The complicated nature of things and of human fate itself remains outside your consideration, so that you are able to say, "If this one wickedness had not happened, all would be different." On such a premise we simply cannot talk.

He reached Venice on August 29 and found lodgings in an ancient residence known as the Palazzo Giustiniani, on the

Grand Canal, which had been converted into a rooming house.
Here, in a vast drafty chamber with high ceiling and enormous
undraped windows, he spread out his few belongings and prepared to dwell alone with his muse. But first he must have a
look at the town. He confided his impressions to the patient
diary:

> Riding along the Canale Grande to the Piazzetta, an im-
> pression of melancholy and somber mood; majesty, beauty,
> decadence, all blended together. St. Mark's Place is a magi-
> cal scene. This is a remote, an exhausted and spent world,
> eminently suited to my need for solitude. Nothing seems
> quite alive and real, but over all there is the quality of a
> work of art. This is where I want to remain. . . .
> My routine is to stay in my lodgings till five o'clock each
> afternoon, when I go out for a meal; then a promenade in the
> public park; a short sojourn on Piazza San Marco, which gives
> me a thoroughly theatrical stimulus with its very special
> quality and its completely impersonal and unreal crowds.
> Toward nine o'clock I come back by gondola, find the lamp
> lighted, and read a little before going to sleep.
> This solitude, almost nowhere possible to me, and here so
> sweetly possible, nurtures my hopes. Yes! For you [Ma-
> thilde] I hope to find myself again. To keep you within me
> is to salvage myself for my art. To live for my art, and
> thereby comfort you, shall be my purpose. This is dictated
> by my nature, my fate, my will power, and my love. Thus I
> remain yours, and through me you too will recover. . . . Here
> in this Venice *Tristan* shall be completed. After that, against
> a world of obstacles—and if you will let me—I am coming
> back to see you, to reassure you, and give you joy. This is
> my highest, most sacred wish. God speed, then, Hero Tristan,
> Heroine Isolde! Help me and my guardian angel! Here the
> wounds are to stop bleeding, and to heal and be closed. From
> here shall go out into the world a noble apotheosis of a su-
> preme love, and the deep sorrow of its agonizing bliss."

He was working again on *Tristan*. Like the mortally wounded
hero, fleeing to lonely Castle Kareol, Richard himself had had
to seek refuge far from the scene of his sufferings. Also, like

Tristan awaiting Isolde, Richard clung to the hope that Mathilde would somehow break with her past life and follow him. This was madness indeed, and he knew it. But was not a love such as theirs beyond all reason?

He soon was writing Mathilde every day, though she did not answer. He complained to the diary:

> Last night I lay sleepless for hours. My sweet child does not give me news of her. . . . The Canale is marvelously beautiful by night. Bright stars, last quarter of the moon. A gondola glides past. In the distance *gondolieri* call to one another in melodious voices. All this is extraordinarily lovely and uplifting. The deeply melancholy chants, sung with powerful and resonant voices, are carried from afar across the waters and their echo rolls back farther still. All this moves me profoundly. . . . Magnificent! [*Herrlich!*]

At last, early in September, he heard something about Mathilde's doings through a mutual friend. The diary reports:

> Today Frau Wille wrote me. The first news I have had about you. She says you are composed, serene, determined in your resignation for the sake of your parents, your children, your duty to your husband. How strange this sounds to me, who, where you are concerned, can give no thought to parents, children, duty! . . . I know only that you love me, and that all sublime things are paid for in unhappiness. To have you put labels on the reasons for our separation disconcerts me. I now see you in your splendid mansion, surrounded by those who can never grasp what is between us, and who, alien but physically close, watch fearfully to banish that which is far closer—our love. And I am seized with rancor that they who know so little of you and understand even less should have the right to claim you and to ask such sacrifice. . . . You hope, during the coming winter, to see me for a few hours in Rome? I'm afraid not. To see you, and then to part so as not to upset a carefully balanced domestic apple cart—I don't think I'm quite up to that just yet. . . .

Evidently, through Frau Wille, Mathilde made known to Richard that he was not adhering strictly to their bargain. How was renunciation, such as they had mutually agreed on, to be effective if he persisted in bombarding her with letters? She tried a small disciplinary measure which drew from him a yelp of pain, heard only by the diary:

> Yesterday I was quite sick with fever. In the evening a letter came from Frau Wille, containing, unopened, my last note to you—which you have sent back. This you should not have done. . . . How you have wronged me with such a rejection!

Mathilde followed with another effort to make him see reason. She did not write directly, but again expressed herself through their intermediary. This time she read Wagner's reply:

> I have been so depressed that I've even stopped making entries in my diary. Then your letter came today—that is, the letter you wrote Frau Wille. Of course I don't doubt that you love me! . . . And I can even understand your doing me an injustice, for it *is* an injustice to accuse me of importuning you. I would have thought that the immense wrench of pulling myself away from Zürich gave you proof of my honorableness and that any such accusation must offend me deeply.

A few days later Mathilde appeared to have apologized by direct mail. She also, wisely, directed Richard back to his work. Having learned from Frau Wille that he had no piano, she made arrangements for one. On September 16, 1858, Wagner replied in tones of highest bliss:

> How happy I am, how hale and hearty! I rejoice in your letter over and over. How thoughtful you are, how lovely and loving! Our personal, physical fate no longer matters, so long as we remain spiritually one. . . . In this frame of mind I await the piano, and shall steep myself again in work. *Tristan* will cost me much, but once finished I have a wonderfully certain feeling that a phase of my life will have reached fruition and I shall be at peace with the world, always knowing that my world is *you.* . . .

In everything Venice is of immeasurable help. Never have
I breathed air of such mellow softness. The magic quality
of the place keeps me enveloped in a melancholy yet pleasing
sorcery which soothes me unceasingly. When I set out at
night by gondola for the Lido there hovers about me an
exquisite sound, like the long-drawn-out note on a violin,
which I love so much and to which I once compared you.
Now you can measure what I feel under the moonlight on
this Adriatic Sea. . . .

A period of violent creative activity now ensued. With an
instrument once more at his disposal (Mathilde had sent a
grand piano, no less) Richard soon finished the musical score
for the second act of *Tristan*. He tackled the final portion with
even greater *élan*. Daily the housemaid Lauretta, who wielded
a lackadaisical duster in the dilapidated rental quarters of the
Palazzo Giustiniani, marveled at the strange sounds emanating
from the fair-skinned and blue-eyed artist's room. She thought
him very handsome, the Germanic gentleman *(il signor tedesco)*, though his musical idiom certainly differed from less
complex and more familiar Italian rhythms. He was currently
polishing an eerie, reedlike tune, the opening flute theme of
the shepherd watching for Isolde's ship, in the third act of
Tristan.

Possibly the poignancy of the notes, and indeed the whole
scene they would lead up to, tore suddenly across the frail
fabric of Wagner's painfully won composure. With Tristan's
agony his own returned. The maid Lauretta saw him grow
daily more dejected and gloomy, plainly eaten by some secret
longing. She knocked on his door one afternoon while he was
pacing up and down beside the keyboard. His work did not
seem to be going well. Hearing no answer to her knock, Lauretta let herself in. She was a handsome wench, barefooted and
appetizingly vibrant. She carried a bottle on a tray.

Wagner hardly looked up. "What do you want, Lauretta?"
he asked absently.

Her eyes brimmed with warmth. "Don Giocoso, the landlord, sends you this bottle of Chianti."

"Tell him I am most grateful, Lauretta, but I do not drink."

"It is a special Chianti, made in Toscana." The girl broke off, genuinely bewildered. "The *signor* drinks no wine, he touches no tobacco, and he does nothing else too." She stood expectantly, showing off her figure. "What kind of country does the *signor* come from?"

As Richard appeared lost in his thoughts, Lauretta shrugged her lovely shoulders and flounced from the room, taking the tray with her. But she did not get beyond the threshold, for a burst of organ-grinder music rose suddenly from the street. This brought her running back to the open window.

"Ah, the beautiful songs!" She leaned out, clasping her hands and emitting gay cries in Italian, then she reached into her blouse for a coin to toss into the street. This gave new impetus to the ambulant minstrel below. With great gusto he ground out a medley of hit tunes from *Rigoletto, Il Trovatore* and *Un Ballo in Maschera.*

Wagner paused in his pacing to listen. "Verdi," he said, nodding. "Your great Giuseppe Verdi—everything he touches turns to melody."

Lauretta turned eagerly. "He is here in town—it says so in the papers. Tonight he directs his opera *La Traviata* at the Fenice Theater." She smiled helpfully. "Don Giocoso can get you perhaps a ticket?"

He shook his head. "No, Lauretta. Thank you."

The organ-grinder had finished and moved on. Quietly the servant girl closed the door behind her. Alone once more with his visions, Wagner dropped into a chair. He was Tristan again, on the ramparts of his lonely home in Brittany, mortally wounded, calling for the lost Isolde. All at once he could stand it no more. He took up a music sheet marked Act III. With a few strokes he jotted down a melodic line, then under it the stanza:

> Isolde still, in sunlight . . .
> By day or night—Isolde!

Now he pushed this aside and pulled out from the table drawer a pad of cheap letter paper. On this he scrawled feverishly:

. . . It was all a mistake. We should never have parted. It is against all laws of God and Nature for such a love as ours to remain unfulfilled. You must come to me, you *must!*

He folded this second sheet, put it in an envelope, wrote Mathilde's address and sealed the letter with wax from a candle stub. Then, coming abruptly to his senses, he tore it to shreds. A new wave of despondency swept over him, but he fled from it to the pages of his diary. Here he poured out his woe:

The obsession is upon me to finish the one work that is most dear to me, *Tristan und Isolde.* . . . Yet I ask myself if this is not insanity—to tear out my own heart in this fashion and lay it before a public that can never know the suffering it cost me. . . .

He rose and returned to the piano, forcing himself to play. As he did so the merciful muses came to his aid, for his imagination conjured now a shining vision. On a far watery horizon Isolde's ship appeared, full sail, and at the gates of Kareol Castle the shepherd pipes changed to a merry tune. Isolde ashore, came running into the arms of the dying Tristan. And then her own last overpowering song, the *"Liebestod,"* brought dissolution for Isolde too.

As the music poured from his fingers the notes quickly took shape in ink. Consumed with desolation and grief, Wagner wrought the tremendous last act of *Tristan und Isolde* in a single and glorious sweep. Throughout the writing there lived within him the wish-dream of the adored Mathilde breaking away from home and duty to follow her innermost yearnings. He saw her image everywhere, silhouetted against the bare walls of his room, the golden Venetian sunset or the black Italian night.

But she never came.

To bear it and not to sicken with the pain, he brought Isolde to the ailing Tristan's couch, to die, herself, of that which could no longer be endured: her love.

When this, the final sublimation of his own agony in the searing music of the *"Liebestod,"* had been accomplished, he hoped to find a measure of peace. He might not be cured, perhaps he never could be, of his passion for Mathilde. But he must learn to live thenceforth, both with it and in spite of it.

He played on, seized with a madness and an intoxication that consumed him. As the music soared in ever-mightier waves, his face reflected the full ecstasy of his martyrdom. He finished at last, falling forward against the keyboard as he buried his head in his arms with a dry sob. He remained in this position for a long interval until a gust of wind tore at a rattling shutter and from a distance the returning organ-grinder could be heard, still giving forth his uncomplicated Italian tunes. Wagner raised his head to listen. Then he jumped up vehemently, grasped his hat and rushed from the room.

He was on the steps of the Teatro La Fenice a short time later, mingling with the eager crowd. With a standee ticket he climbed to the gallery in time for the opening measures of *La Traviata.* Below, in a brilliant spotlight, Giuseppe Verdi bowed after the overture, then held his baton poised for the opening curtain. The same age as Wagner, the Italian maestro had something his German contemporary lacked. Several somethings: good clothes, self-assurance, success. These, as yet, Richard could not match. As to the great Giuseppe's talent— and it was magnificent!—here the unknown standee upstairs felt himself capable of braving any challenge.

The first act of *Traviata,* packed almost to excess with surefire tunes, ended to salvos of applause. People embraced, kissed, screamed and danced with delight, leaving Richard dazed with amazement. Here was a manifestation of artistic triumph far beyond anything he had ever experienced. Here was proof of how far he himself had yet (if his genius sufficed) to go.

He felt discouraged. Humbly he fled from the theater and made his way home on foot. Crossing a bridge over a backwater canal, he stared down at the rippling waves. In the darkness they glistened with the reflection of an occasional street lamp. But he saw no lights. Everywhere his eyes were met by only one image, undimmed, unforgotten—Mathilde's face.

CHAPTER 9

IN TAKING flight from the Fenice Theater that night Richard Wagner was unaware that he had been in the presence of someone who would have an immediate bearing on his fate. Several tiers below his gallery place was the ceremonial box, occupied by the Viceroy of Lombardy and Venice, Archduke Ferdinand Maximilian of Hapsburg. Northern Italy, before the liberation movement led by Cavour, was under Austrian control. Though Maximilian personally was possessed of charm and a typical Viennese warmth that won him many adherents, the Irredentist cause seethed under cover with only one aim in view—the casting off of the foreign yoke.

To Wagner, immersed in personal problems, the political situation in Italy meant less than nothing. He had cast no glance at this young Maximilian, who, less than a decade later, was to die before a firing squad in Mexico after a short and futile dream of empire. Nor did he notice the Vice-Reine Carlotta (born Princess Charlotte of Belgium, now using an Italian name, which later she would change to the Spanish Carlota) sitting proudly beside her tall Hapsburg husband and sunning herself in the first blissful period of her honeymoon.

No, there was no bond between Richard and these two highborn strangers. Yet the Archduke's presence in Venice was to impinge on the composer's immediate future, for the arm of Dresden's secret police was long. Stamped with the special cachet of the King of Saxony, the edict of banishment against Wagner had gone out to all independent German principalities and to the Hapsburg Monarchy, with whom Friedrich August shared a treaty. A *Steckbrief*, or proscription list, naming a

272

half-dozen malefactors was sent also to Northern Italy, where it reposed in the chancery files of the Viceroy. The easygoing Maximilian had taken no notice of it. But one of his secretarial clerks, on viewing the customary report from hotelkeepers and rooming-house owners regarding their daily arrivals, came upon the conscientious Don Giocoso's listing of one Richard Wagner. He went with his discovery straight to the Archduke's desk.

"This man is dangerous, Your Highness. We are having enough trouble uncovering local conspirators and *agents provocateurs* sent by that tricky Cavour sympathizer, the Emperor of France, without adding a German anarchist to our hazards."

Maximilian gave a mild shrug, laying the report aside. "It says here the man is a musician. Surely we've nothing to fear from such as he."

The secretary made reference to international police protocol, quoting chapter and verse. "You are expected to take steps, Highness. It is the law."

"Very well." The Archduke smiled absently. "Give the man warning. But don't rush him, mind. If he's being hounded from pillar to post, he may have trouble finding a new place to go."

With this the brother of Austria's Emperor Franz Joseph dismissed the matter.

Richard was given a politely worded notice during late September, advising, in his own interest, that he make himself scarce. The message, however, at Maximilian's behest, was so innocuous and diffident (besides being in Italian, which Richard did not understand) that it fell unread amid the litter of papers on the composer's desk. Swinging back and forth from deepest gloom to dizzy heights of contrived optimism, Wagner was once more growing intoxicated by the power of his own dialectics. On October 1, 1858, he argued with his diary:

I have discovered that in seeking to avoid sorrow, one does not solve the human problem. Instead I find that suffering teaches sympathy and awakens an even nobler emotion, pity, for all mankind. This pity, then, I recognize as the highest moral value, and perhaps as the fountainhead of my art.

By October 12, after spinning out these meditations into ramified detail, he was able to make specific application of them to his relationship with Mathilde:

The world has been overcome—through our love and our suffering. It is no longer my enemy from whom I must take flight; in fact, I no longer have the urge to cut myself off in absolute solitude, for this was but a symptom of unceasing hunger, passion, desire. . . . All this I have now conquered by the realization that love's thirst can be slaked by its own greatness, so that there is nothing more to yearn for, nothing to expect. Nor must this be called resignation or despair. . . . It is rather the highest fulfillment that leads to noblest satiety. That is, the urgings and promptings of passion are willingly extinguished, for passion itself is now supremely satisfied. . . . Thus do I now regard the world, nature, the coming and going, the birth and growth and death of all things. I look upon it all objectively, as a creative artist bent on truth's elucidation, without further personal cravings and wants, even to material needs.

How is our future, then, yours and mine, to be shaped? Here is the sore spot, the sting of bitterness inflicted by those who stand between us without themselves gaining anything by it. It is for them, even more than for ourselves, that we must feel pity. . . .

In the midst of these philosophizings Richard did not lose contact with Minna. He wrote to her and kept her informed of his address. It was thus that during late October he received a warning from his wife's Dresden physician, Doctor Pusinelli, that certain expensive treatments were indicated for the patient's welfare. The letter concluded with an unvarnished demand for funds.

It could not have come at a worse time. As yet the Italian sojourn had not afforded the composer a single lira of income. He was living from hand to mouth off a residue of savings. The advance promised by Otto Wesendonk for the *Nibelungen Ring* had faded with the abandonment of that project, and in any case it would hardly have been fitting in the light of the existing

emotional triangle. Minna's request, through Pusinelli, for a
large financial contribution (in addition to the monthly stipend
she received regularly) threw Richard into consternation. He
scoured his resources, sold a pair of shoes and a suitcase for a
pittance, and ended by harboring thoughts of suicide. Testimony for this was given by a diary page on November 1, 1858:

> This is All Saints' Day! I am awake after a dreadful night,
> the worst that I have ever suffered. For a long time I stood
> on the balcony, looking down at the storm-swept black
> waters. One small jump, and I could disappear unnoticed.
> I would be free of all this torture. My hands gripped the
> railing, ready for the leap, yet I desisted. . . .

Like many a Hamlet before him, he found catharsis in literary expatiation on his own death and thereby resolved to keep
alive. Also, he remembered his good friend Liszt, to whom he
wrote:

> I have scarcely ten gulden left, which won't pay my rent.
> I can send nothing to my wife who, a fortnight ago, com-
> plained that she is in dire straits. . . . Perhaps you suspect me
> of living prodigally here in Italy? My good Franz, when you
> see the second act of my *Tristan* you will not deny me a
> sizable loan. I may be a wastrel indeed, but one day there
> will be something to show for it!

Liszt, of course, helped. Minna's medical requirements were
covered and Wagner saw himself, still among the living, well
into the new year. It was now that the authorities caught up
with him. A second message from the desk of the Viceroy, this
time less amiable and more to the point, set a deadline for
Richard's departure from Venice. On February 6, 1859, the
hounded composer described his plight in a note to Liszt's son-
in-law, Hans von Bülow:

> I have just been notified by the police of my banishment
> from Venice. Saxony, I see, gave Vienna and the House of
> Hapsburg no peace. . . . What troubles me much more than

the immediate problem of finding a new refuge is the unbelievable heartlessness of mankind. I, who through gruel-
ling pain and want have only one purpose—to live creatively
—am persecuted without letup. To me this remains an everlasting riddle!

He was given a generous leeway of several weeks to wind up
his affairs, of which he hadn't any. Most of this time was spent
in some poignant correspondence, for he had just learned the
reason for Mathilde Wesendonk's long silence. Tragedy had
struck at the villa on the Green Hill. The elder Wesendonk
boy, Guido, aged three, had died during early winter, throwing
the household into bitter gloom. A belated Christmas message
from Otto reached Wagner now, apprising him of the loss.
There was also a note from seven-year-old Myrrha Wesendonk,
eldest of the children. In sending his condolences to the be-
reaved parents, Richard penned a special answer to the little
girl. It was dated March 10, 1859, and read in part:

My dear Myrrha!
   That was a beautifully written letter you sent me, far better and more legible than I can produce, for I am already too
old. . . .
   You are right in not doubting that I have wept with you
over the beloved little Guido. When you bring him your next
present of flowers please give him my tenderest greeting. I
am so glad that your baby brother [Karl, two years old] is
growing so fast. Of course he doesn't have the same face as
Guido, but you must love him like Guido with—well—another face. . . . Believe me, it is the same in the world of
grown-ups: we are all really much alike but we have different faces and therefore we look at things out of those
different faces and become confused, each thinking that his
view is the right one. But that passes. When we laugh or
cry we all make the same face. And when we go where Guido
has gone, it is a particularly peaceful one, a face for God to
look upon.

This difficult task accomplished, Richard packed his few belongings and set out for Switzerland by way of Milan. He was

not headed for Zürich but for the smaller city of Lucerne, where
he hoped to find quiet and composure for the final revisions on
the music score of *Tristan und Isolde*. It was from Milan that
he notified his friends Liszt and Bülow of his purpose: "I have
said farewell to dreamlike Venice. . . . The dream which I there
set to melody will one day be heard by all of you."

Despite his wish to avoid the Wesendonks, word reached him
en route that they would be offended if he did not pause in
Zürich. With considerable misgivings, for he did not trust the
containment of his wild heart, Wagner relented.

The visit proved short, ill-advised and painful. All were ill
at ease, except the children. Otto, who had been the determin-
ing factor in this reunion, hoped to restore the bonds of a formerly harmless friendship by ignoring all *sub-rosa* implications.
Mathilde, for her part, still burdened with a mother's grief, appeared doubly strained in the presence of the man whose impact on her senses had so nearly torn her whole life from its
moorings. Only Myrrha and the baby Karl (who was just beginning to speak) welcomed "Uncle Richard" with unabashed
delight.

He left as quickly as possible. From Lucerne, on April 4,
1859, he wrote Mathilde, but only in the secrecy of his diary:

> So—we have seen each other again. . . . Yet were these
> hours in your house comparable to that sweet vision I cher-
> ished of our eventual reunion? The vision actually is stronger
> than the fact. It does not seem to me that I saw you; a fog
> lay between us, through which even your voice scarcely was
> audible. Nor do I think that you truly saw me, but rather
> only a ghost that entered your home. Did you recognize me?
> Ah, Heaven, perhaps this is it, the road to redemption, when
> reality itself becomes unreal: the senses fail, the staring eye
> is blind, the willing ear grows deaf. When we are both pres-
> ent we do not see each other; yet apart we live forever, un-
> forgettably defined, in each other's hearts. . . .

He had made a discovery. "The noble mind seeks happiness through inner resources; only a fool depends on outward
things." With this for a motto, he plunged anew into the work

on *Tristan*. Before the end of April he reported on this to the Wesendonks, from Lucerne:

> This *Tristan* is going to be catastrophic, especially the last act! I am afraid the opera will be either forbidden or else unmercifully parodied. Only a mediocre performance can save it, because a superlative interpretation will drive audiences mad. What a dilemma to get myself into!

Otto did his best to answer this incomprehensible outburst, while Mathilde sent Richard a book of Friedrich Schiller's letters and a volume of Shakespeare. With characteristic impetuosity he devoured them at once, sending his reactions back to Zürich:

> How I have laughed with Schiller! He is very witty, more so than Goethe. Thank you again for these *Letters*—I love reading the intimate records of other people. . . .

He made Shakespeare his companion for midsummer. Of the Bard he reported in late June:

> My favorite occupation: to associate, through the medium of reading, with the world's great. This helps us over all of life's misadventures. How wonderful is Shakespeare's fine mockery! This godlike scorn of human foibles! Here is really the highest level of spiritual composure, attained only by genius—or by sainthood, and saints don't even need a sense of humor!

In July he thought he needed some exercise to counteract the long sedentary labors on *Tristan*. He recklessly and without prior training signed up with a group of mountaineers bent on climbing the snow-capped Rigi. The first day's hike led, fortunately, only to the alpine foothills and a cozy log cabin where the party settled for the night. The next morning's events are described in a note, dated July 9, 1859, to Minna at a convalescent home in Dresden:

The Rigi adventure managed to be of profit to my *Tristan.*
. . . On the morning of the actual climb we were awakened
by a peasant guide blowing on his alpine horn. It was 4:00
A.M. I jumped up, saw that it was raining, and went back
to bed. In my sleep the droll tootling of the reedlike horn
came back in a lively and gay rhythm, which I have now
incorporated in the flute theme [of Act III] when the shepherd warns joyfully that Isolde's ship is at last sighted. The
effect is surprisingly winsome and naïve.

To Mathilde he wrote the same day:

Just think, the cheery tune of the shepherd's fife [announc-
ing Isolde's coming] has led me beyond *Tristan* and back to
my unfinished *Siegfried.* . . . I have been looking over my
manuscripts and I find a clear relation between the forest
sounds or murmurs [*Waldweben*] in *Siegfried* and the shepherd call in the present work. Am I not to believe in patience,
then, and in the great teachings of Buddha?

Magic was pouring from his musical pen. Few passages in
opera or symphony repertoires would equal the caressing throb
of the *Waldweben,* with its undulating breezes and the whispering rustle of leaves, punctuated by the brightly piercing
call of the bird: "*Hei! Siegfried erschlug nun den schlimmen
Zwerg!*" In sheer luminescence it would be approached one
day only by the tone painting of Richard Strauss in his scene
of the Silver Rose Presentation in *Der Rosenkavalier.*

As for the alpine horn and its effect on the shepherd delineation in *Tristan,* it would have a pedantic interest for future
musicologists bent on painstaking tracery of Wagner's methods
of composition. But more significant and enlightening, in its
revealing disclosure of an inner transformation, is a small philo-
logic factor—small but by no means trivial—appearing for the
first time in the above-quoted letter to Frau Wesendonk. The
locution *Denken Sie* replaces the intimate address of Richard's
previous correspondence. He has changed from the second-
person singular *thou* to the second-person plural *you,* which
hereafter is to be encountered in all writings to Mathilde.

This did not mean that he had succeeded in tearing the beloved woman's image from his heart. But the change of language, from poignant ardor to controlled formality, was evidence of a long-fought struggle for emancipation. He had won his battle at last. However long the ache of memory might yet endure, the pain had ceased in Richard's heart.

CHAPTER 10

THE partitura, or full orchestration, of *Tristan und Isolde* was finished on August 27, 1859. The year was memorable in that it marked another finish, more noteworthy to contemporary historians: the defeat of the Austrian armies at Magenta and Solferino, by Cavour and his ally, Napoleon III. The days of Hapsburg rule in Italy were done. Maximilian and Carlotta, like Wagner a bit earlier, were forced to pack and make hasty farewells. They repaired to the vacant castle of Miramare, near Trieste, Austria's prized seaport on the Adriatic, for some years of genteel boredom pending materialization of a new and suitable royal job.

Richard too was casting about for concrete employment, now that he had laid his manuscripts aside. He hoped to find some German opera house outside the Saxon kingdom willing to hold a tryout performance of *Tristan*, to be followed by a world *première*. To this end he wrote the leading impresarios of Brandenburg, Bavaria, Westphalia, Württemberg and Baden. None but Baden bothered to answer, and the answer was negative.

Since he could not remain at Lucerne without prospects of earning a living, he set out for Paris, where at least there were always copyist's and arranger's jobs available with his old boss, Monsieur Schlesinger. He would mark time once more at this earlier niggardly occupation until some prominent French producer finished reading the glorious *Tristan* text and made him a correspondingly magnificent offer.

It is doubtful that any leading Paris impresario took more than a cursory look at the submitted opus. To begin with, it was in ponderous German, an insurmountable obstacle where Gallic ears were concerned. But even if, language difficulties

aside, the odd symphonic music line had pleased a potential
sponsor (it definitely hadn't), there was the handicap of the
composer's near anonymity. Who outside Dresden and the
neighboring Weimar had ever heard of Richard Wagner? True,
he had concertized in London, but only because an inexpen-
sive off-season conductor had been sought to permit the regular
baton master an annual holiday on the Riviera. No Wagner
opera had as yet achieved production in Britain. As for Richard's professional rating in Saxony, it was thoroughly over-
shadowed by the dubious political reputation he had earned.
Paris producers were suspicious of his work.

Nothing, to be sure, could have been less concerned with
politics than *Tristan und Isolde*. The opera was built around
the simplest of plots, with a minimum of physical action. Richard had aimed at a deliberately static form, in contrast to all
his other past and future works. Normally he followed Goethe's
admonition for the dramatic presentation of *Faust*—"Let things
happen on stage, if you would not drive audiences to sleep"—
but with the tragic story of *Tristan und Isolde* Wagner meant
to give far more than mere entertainment. He wished to build
a lyric monument to the noblest of human passions—everlasting
Love. For this he wanted few motions or gesturings on stage,
and preferably no stock appurtenances such as a prancing ballet or romping chorus. The cast was to be kept as small as
possible and costumed in noble robes of an "ageless and timeless" character, befitting the subject's heroic mood. Finally, the
music, wedded and interlaced with the powerful story, represented Wagner's faith in the peak of tonal and visual art: the
sublime music drama.

In synopsis form the tale itself is short, though filled out with
its orchestral substance the opera is four hours in length, a record in almost any repertoire. Much of the plot involvement
precedes the action on stage and is made known only through
narrative dialogue. There is, then, more to hear than to follow
with the eye, though visually Wagner's stage directions call for
settings of majestic color and beauty. Against these the love
story takes immortality unto itself.

TRISTAN UND ISOLDE

Act I

After a mood-setting overture the curtain rises to disclose the deck of a sailing vessel whose stern looms up behind great draping sails that hide a flight of steps toward the helm, due center. In the foreground, protected by the draperies that form a chamber on deck, two women travelers are seen, the Irish princess Isolde and her maid Brangäne. They are defiant and bitter, for the princess is to be joined in loveless wedlock to the widowed and aging King Marke of Cornwall. It is Marke's young nephew Tristan who commands the ship and has been entrusted with escorting the bride to her waiting groom.

Since marriages of state are notoriously unhappy, Isolde's mother (a queen with knowledge of ancient magical devices) has supplied her daughter with a cruet of helpful potions, designed for most varied purposes, from swift extermination of an enemy to welcome balm that will render an unwanted marriage bed more bearable.

These ought to take care of Isolde. But she is proud and angry at Tristan in particular, for he is the killer of the knight Morold (Isolde's former betrothed) during a raid made by Morold on Cornwall to collect tribute for Ireland. In Tristan's presence now, Isolde plans to poison herself, thereby escaping from Marke and thwarting Tristan's mission in behalf of his king. Sternly the princess orders her maid to pull aside the center curtain leading to the ship's helm and the quarters of the crew.

On Tristan's appearance before her mistress, Brangäne is overcome with horror at Isolde's purpose. Surreptitiously the frightened maid exchanges the suicide philtre for the nearest flask, which turns out to be the hymeneal love potion. Isolde meanwhile has decided to kill Tristan as well as herself, a maneuver which requires that he be invited to join her in a goblet of refreshing drink. To this he innocently agrees, whereupon Brangäne brings on the prepared tray. Unwittingly now the two hostile protagonists imbibe the love potion and are seized with flaming passion toward each other, just as the ship nears the coast of Cornwall where King Marke waits ashore, surrounded by his court.

Act II

As preordained, Isolde and the King are married, while the
stricken lovers bear their longing in secret. When Brangäne,
however, confesses to her mistress what occurred aboard ship
Isolde realizes that it is useless to fight the power of the love
potion. She agrees to a meeting with Tristan in the palace
garden under cover of night. The lovers trade ecstatic vows
to the melodies of *"Nacht der Liebe"* ("Night of Rapture") and
the watchful warning of Brangäne from her outlook in a near-
by tower—*"Habet Acht!"* ("Take heed!").

An ambitious rival of Tristan's at court, the knight Melot, has
long sought a chance to ingratiate himself with the King. He
has divined Tristan's love for Isolde and is spying on them
patiently until this fatal hour. Now he leads Marke (back from
a pretended hunt in the forest) to surprise the trysting lovers.
Gently the old king berates his nephew for such treachery—
"Sieh ihn dort, den treu'sten aller Treuen" ("Behold, most loyal
was he, to me, of all"). But Melot is not satisfied with such
tolerance and forbearing. He draws his sword and runs it
through Tristan, who falls gravely wounded. While Isolde
drops, fainting, into Brangäne's arms, Tristan's servant Kurvenal drags his master away. The King plans no revenge, but
Tristan goes into voluntary banishment to his forsaken an-
cestral castle Kareol, in Brittany, where—he hopes—Isolde will
join him.

Act III

Almost no action marks the closing of the drama, for it concerns itself purely with Tristan's hopeless longing and Isolde's
arrival soon enough only to join him in death. Yet music and
lyric text are on so high a plane that the noblest thrill is im-
parted to the listener.

The curtain rises on the ramparts of Kareol, where the hero
lies on a bearskin-covered couch, with Kurvenal in devoted attendance. Near by, from a jutting turret, a shepherd plays
sadly on his pipes while looking out to sea. Intermittently
Tristan, though delirious, inquires, "Is there a ship?" And Kurvenal, interpreting the melancholy piper's tune, shakes his head.
Stubbornly Tristan insists, "Isolde will come—she *must* come!"
But still there is no ship.

Then the shepherd's pipes change to a new note, a glad, bright, joyous lilt that causes Kurvenal's anxiety to fall from him. The ship must be in sight; the master's beloved is on her way; now all will be well. Tristan too hears the changed music. In an ecstatic frenzy he rises from the couch, tearing the bandage from his wound as he runs toward Isolde, who at length has come ashore. But the long wait has been too long. Life has been drained from him in endless hours of uncertainty, and the reopened wound claims his last heart's blood. For an instant only he sees Isolde's face, then collapses lifeless in her arms.

A clash of swords is heard now beyond the ramparts, and King Marke is seen arriving with his men. Kurvenal, ready to defend his master's castle, rushes forth to do battle. But he has misunderstood the royal purpose. The old king is not following his wife in wrath, but out of insight and magnanimous renunciation. He has come to pardon Tristan and to give the lovers his blessing.

It is too late. Isolde, transfixed beside the still form of Tristan, pours out the fullness of her passion in the "Love Death" theme. Softly the epic measures begin—"*Mild und leise, wie er lächelt*" ("Mild and calm, behold him smiling")— growing by slow intervals and in a rising sweep, mounting, swelling, repeating and piling up ever-new shadings of an insistent, violent, overwhelmingly triumphant love call. Orchestrally the music soars with equal vehemence, ravishing the listener's ear and drowning his soul in glory.

At the end Isolde's own dissolution is audibly manifest. Up to a climactic point she and the orchestra are one. But at the zenith she begins to stray from the melodic line, her voice rushing off in a race with itself, farther, farther, beyond reach. Before the orchestra's concluding measures it has been made vocally, transcendently clear that Isolde is no more.

A few loose ends are disposed of in peremptory Shakespearean fashion. Melot, the villain, has been killed by the avenging Kurvenal, who in turn prefers to fall on his own sword rather than face life without his loved master. But, mercifully, the casualty list ends here, for Wagner was less thorough than the Bard. As the curtain falls there is no doubt but that King Marke must return to his royal duties in Cornwall, while the bungling Brangäne (who started it all by playing at destiny with a pair of poison vials) is presumed to be setting out in search of a new situation.

Symbolically, the opera was heavily weighted with meaning, for it had been born out of Richard Wagner's real-life predicament, the triangle involving himself and the Wesendonks. Since in actuality that drama did not play itself out as his yearnings dictated, he shaped his plot in conformity with the wish-dreams of his heart. In this connection he permitted himself a degree of overstatement. The character of King Marke, for one, was overdrawn to the point of patriarchal senescence, which hardly befitted his virile prototype, Herr Wesendonk. Also, while the good Otto displayed remarkable forbearance and tact in the face of extreme provocation, he did not relinquish his wife, nor did he follow Richard to Venice and apprise him of any such intention.

Similarly Isolde was not Mathilde drawn from life, but Mathilde as Richard sorely wanted her to be. The wife and mother who was hedged in by prosaic domesticity, social convention, the "proprieties" and, last but far from least, the legal aspects of matrimony made a pallid heroine for a blazing romance. Frau Wesendonk's response to Richard's wooing, if closely scrutinized, revealed a series of guarded concessions—none of them daring or even remotely scandalous in nature—which at no time jeopardized the secure pattern of her life. But despite high-flown and noble protestations to the contrary, Wagner would have been delirious with happiness if she had done just that. Subconsciously he tried to shame Mathilde for not tossing her cap over the windmill and walking out on home, husband and children to share the Venetian love nest he hoped (but did not have the money) to prepare for her. In delineating Isolde he showed what a woman in love ought really to be. For here was a Queen of Cornwall, braving a stormy sea to rush to her lover's side, ready to trade the splendor of worldly position for love in a very dilapidated Breton castle (stage directions called for Kareol to be "a desolate ruin," much meaner, in short, than the rented room at the Palazzo Giustiniani).

The figure of Tristan, on the other hand, was Wagner at his

handsomest and amorous best. Since there had been no real-
life villain (unless perhaps Minna) to keep Richard and Mathilde apart, the wicked Melot was again a dramatic necessity
to embody the cruel force of fate. The wound of which Tristan
would die was nothing more than the composer's unrelieved
suffering from the pangs of an impossible desire.

Lastly, to lift the entire matter beyond the realm of puritani-
cal values, the element of sin was disposed of by resorting to
metaphysical exposition. Such human passions as anger, jealousy, hatred or love lay outside the powers of will and conscience, attacking their victims with the same savage impact as
any dread disease. In short, they were a poison, evil or divine,
administered by some guardian angel (Brangäne) in a moment
of unguarded folly. Once the fateful potion worked its magic,
for good or ill, there was no halting it. King Marke himself,
informed by the maidservant of the bottle business, hastened
to declare Tristan and Isolde innocent.

Richard and Mathilde, though Otto Wesendonk made no
public proclamation to the effect, were innocent too.

CHAPTER 11

ARIS in 1859 was a city throbbing with growing pains. An architect named Haussmann was mapping out a pattern of vast modern boulevards to replace the network of crooked alleys that for centuries had formed the medieval inner town. Behind the promotion and financing of this estimable project stood the Emperor Napoleon III, currently at the peak of his spotty political career.

He had guessed right, the crafty little monarch who must needs live up to a grandiloquent name: in lending support to an Italian uprising that proved successful he saw the tentacles of a potent neighbor, Austria-Hungary, neatly pruned, with a share of glory accruing to the armies of France. Great was the clamor with which news of the battles at Magenta and Solferino had been received. In a flower-garlanded and flag-draped carriage Napoleon and Eugénie drove through their capital to accept the homage of their jubilant subjects, while fashion designers rose to the occasion by launching a new color in ladies' gowns, *le rouge magenta,* "to commemorate the sad bloodshed, *mesdames.*"

It was a trying period for Austrians abroad. But European diplomacy during the second half of the nineteenth century prided itself on meeting the most delicate contingencies with virtuosity. Thus, barely after their homeland had been humbled by the Bonaparte-Cavour axis, the Austrian ambassador to France, Prince Metternich, and his wife Pauline, restored amicable relations between the Hofburg and the Tuileries. After centuries of practice, war—to the Continental mind—was somewhat like a game of Rugby: the contesting sides fought savagely for either goal, with impassioned supporters screaming invective across the field. But passion spent and a decision reached, the crowd went amicably home, quick to lay aside reasons for rancor.

During crisp autumn of that fateful year the Austrian Embassy, then, threw open its portals for a formal and grandiose reception. It was really Princess Metternich's idea. This lean and homely but very brilliant lady, an Eszterházy by birth, had discovered the presence in Paris of her Magyar compatriot Franz Liszt. What better pretext for resuming the diplomatic niceties than a gala fête honoring one who stood above international issues—an artist?

The guest list was dazzling. It included, besides the Emperor and Empress of France, such notables as the Duc and Duchesse de Gramont, Count and Countess de Castiglione, Monsieur Prosper Mérimée, Lord John Russell and a stream of lesser names. In the ballroom under the tinsel-bright chandeliers Pauline Metternich aided her somewhat glum husband in meeting this first and vital postwar test. She stood erect, wearing her hair piled high above a neck bolstered by a choker of diamonds. She was not young, not beautiful, but very arresting because of her infectious smile and bursting vivacity. With Liszt's arrival she knew the evening's triumph was assured.

She greeted him with affectionate reproofs: "Franz, you miserable wretch! At last you give us a chance to see you again."

Liszt bowed gallantly. "I made a special detour from Switzerland to greet my Paris friends again before returning to Weimar."

"Weimar, that sleepy, forsaken hole! Why must you bury yourself in the German provinces when here you could be the idol of the music world?" She slapped him with her fan. "Don't tell me. I've already heard that the Grand Duchess of Weimar is a raving beauty."

"My friend, you forget that I am a family man. I have grown children."

"Family man, bah!"

"Besides, what has a merely beautiful Grand Duchess to compare with your charm?"

Pauline was pleased. "For that, my dear Franz, you shall sit

on my left at dinner. On my right, you understand, I am forced
to have an emperor."

Soon thereafter the assemblage gathered in the glittering
banquet hall, where the dinner opened with a toast to their
Majesties and a gracious response offered by *L'Empereur*. Conversation sparkled in all directions as everyone strove to banish
reminders of the "recent unpleasantness" which, historically
viewed, left scarcely a ripple in the sea of world strife.

During the lively plash of voices the Princess turned to
Napoleon. "Oh, Your Majesty will love this!"

"Yes, madame?"

"Franz here tells me that Paris really has been missing something by not performing German opera."

"German opera?" The French sovereign's eyebrows rose in
condescension. "There *is* such a thing?"

The remark caught Liszt's ear. He broke in. "There not only
has been for some time, Your Majesty, but a star of phenomenal
magnitude is rising in the operatic heavens. A man who is his
own librettist, composer, stage manager and conductor."

With obvious doubt Pauline interpolated, "His name is Richard Wagner."

The Emperor swallowed a shrimp. *"Comment?* Vag—
Vag—?"

"Vaguenaire, Your Majesty," the Princess gallicized helpfully.

"Thank you, madame. This Monsieur Vaguenaire, what has
he done?"

Again Liszt leaned forward. "His latest work, *Tristan und
Isolde,* has just been completed. There is also one entitled
Tannhäuser, which I would especially recommend." He turned
to Pauline. "Since you are always eager to support struggling
artists, here is a cause worthy of your best efforts."

Napoleon's lips moved pensively. *"Tann—Tannés—Hussards,*
a tongue twister, eh?" Suddenly he appeared to make something out of it. "Ah, it is the cavalry troupe, the Tanned Hus-
sars!" He looked pleased. *"Eh bien,* why should not the Paris
Opéra put on such a spectacle? Especially to please a lady."

He bowed to his hostess, winking confidentially. "This Monsieur Vaguenaire, you have a special interest in him, no?"

"Not at all." The Princess shook her head vehemently. "I have never seen him."

Napoleon was clearly flabbergasted. He put down his knife and fork. "What! A woman takes an interest in a strange man only because he makes ze *musique?*" He stroked his tuft of beard in a pensive fog. "And people go to the opera for the same *raison? Parbleu, c'est épatant! C'est formidable!*"

Liszt looked up. "Your Majesty attends for a different reason?"

"But of course, *mon ami*. The ballet!" Suddenly the imperial brow darkened with suspicion. "This German opera you speak of, it has a ballet?"

"I confess, Your Majesty, I do not know. But the work has already been played in several cities without complaints in this regard." In Wagner's interest Liszt was toying with the truth.

"Ah, *bon!*" Napoleon was reassured. "Let Monsieur Vaguenaire come here. We shall applaud his show."

Liszt did not mention that his friend was already in France. He got in touch with Wagner the next day, assuring him that with the Emperor's backing a performance at the great Paris Opéra could be counted on. This happy prospect hinged, however, on whether *Tannhäuser* contained a traditional dance sequence.

Alas, here was something Richard had not thought of! The story of his pilgrim knight called for no pirouettes, no acrobatic leaps, no revealing ballerina flounces. What was more, the opera had survived several tryouts beyond German borders—at Riga (1853), in Zürich, Antwerp and Strasbourg (1855), and New York (1859). None of these cities had clamored for choreography. Wagner himself was at a loss as to the placement of a dance routine. Furthermore, he had prospects of a conductor's job in Brussels which, considering his chronically empty pockets, he could not afford to overlook. He was leaving for the Belgian capital that week. In short, any work on *Tannhäuser* was out of the question.

The conductor's job did not materialize, but Richard stayed on in Brussels with the hope of arranging a few concerts. This was finally accomplished after a winter of dickering and a stint as a private music teacher to keep alive. He gave an account of these events to his friend Hans Richter:

In March [1860], three Brussels concerts were signed for. I was to receive half the box-office revenue, after deduction of hall rent, programs and other costs. The seats were sold out. But after the second concert I had to withdraw from the third because the management's mathematics left me not only without any profit, but I had hotel and travel bills to cover from my vanishing funds. . . . Yes, these are strange conditions, leaving one to struggle for no reward other than honor. High honor it is, nevertheless. At least, I was told that even to be thrashed by the press here is something.

He came back to Paris somewhat chastened. Perhaps the *Tannhäuser* project could now be put in motion. Liszt had gone home, but he had referred Richard to Princess Metternich for further dealings in the matter. The Princess unequivocally stated Napoleon's dictum: "No ballet, no Paris *première*." When Frenchmen went to the theater they wanted something to look at as well as listen to. Let that stubborn Monsieur Vaguenaire reconsider.

Richard did so, out of dire necessity. He persuaded himself that the French point of view had merit. Some tentative rehearsals were set, attended by Pauline Metternich herself.

"I will help you," that well-meaning lady promised.

As the Pilgrim's Chorus moved solemnly on stage early in Act I, the Princess had a flash of inspiration. This fustian and somewhat heavy-footed episode was just the spot for a lightening touch. From her first-row seat behind the podium she plucked Wagner's shirt sleeve. "What did I tell you? *That* is where one puts the ballet!"

Richard stared at her aghast. "But that's impossible! Your Highness is joking!"

She wasn't. "Never, never, *never* have I seen a man so thick-

headed! One must compromise, Herr Wagner, in the interest
of the opera's success." She threw up her arms in despair.
"*Ach,* always the German stubbornness! In Vienna and Budapest we are not so. We do not beat our brains against stone
walls! Why can you not put in the little bright touches, the
gaiety—" cajoling, she jumped up to illustrate—"the gavotte?
Our Mozart, he has done it."

Richard pointed to the venerable, bearded pilgrims. "This
is a religious procession, madame, coming back from a penitent
journey to Rome."

Pauline conceded the point after brief reflection. She studied
the sandaled feet of the holy wanderers and shook her head.
"You are right. They cannot be made to dance." For a moment
her brow furrowed dejectedly. Then a new idea dawned. "I
have it! You are a man of imagination. Can you not write a
special scene around this hero Tannhäuser while he is inside
the magic mountain?"

Richard caught his breath, inspired. The Venusberg! Of
course, that was it! A bacchanal inside the grotto of the goddess—what could be more fitting?

"I will do it!" He leaped down from the podium to kiss
Pauline's hand. "Madame, you are a genius!"

Revisions were started at once and, within a few days, the
prologue to the opening act of *Tannhäuser* had been expanded
to double length by interpolation of the "Bacchanal." Hereafter, instead of a static though undraped goddess of Love who
engaged in ardent melodic dialogue with her earthly guest, a
whole brigade of prancing maidens, nymphs, fauns, satyrs and
other fanciful creatures injected some rousing action into the
tableau. Napoleon was notified of the improvement, whereupon he ordered the Paris Opéra put at Wagner's disposal for
a *première,* on March 13, 1861.

The date being far off, there was ample time for the training
of dancers. But now a new hitch developed. Information
leaked out to the newspapers that the ballet sequence took
place at the beginning of Richard's opera rather than, as was
customary, during the second act. This meant that a large portion of the Paris public, particularly a group of male epicureans

belonging to the Jockey Club, would be discommoded. Ordi-
narily these gentlemen, most of whom kept pet ballerinas, never
bothered to show up at the theater until it was time for the
ladies in pink tights. If this absurd new German composer had
his way, however, a lot of people must eat their evening meal
an hour earlier or miss the best part of the show.

"Not likely," said the members of the Jockey Club.

A deputation was sent backstage at the next rehearsal to confront Wagner with a vigorous protest.

The hard-working composer, sufficiently harassed with language difficulties aside from a conductor's routine woes, despaired at the enormity of the Jockeys' request, or, rather, their
ultimatum: "The ballet goes into Act II or we sabotage your
opera, with stamping, whistling, catcalls and a fruit-and-vege-
table volley!"

He had no answer for this. It was impossible to explain to
lay listeners, who knew nothing of the Tannhäuser legend or
of the opera's structure, that the second act (opening in the
great hall of the Wartburg, with Elisabeth singing her noble
aria *"Dich, Teure Halle"*) must not be marred with a frivolous
dancing interlude. The castle's real-life counterpart, still standing in Saxe-Weimar, was more closely associated with memories of Martin Luther than with terpsichorean endeavors.

To add to Wagner's distress, Pauline Metternich barged in
again on the scene. "Wrong, wrong, *wrong!*" she shouted in
her splendid baritone.

With a sigh Richard put aside his baton. *"Now* what is the
matter?"

She had not heard about the earlier deputation. She had
come independently to plead the cause of the Jockeys. "Ah,
my friend, I should have warned you—fashionable Parisians
dine late and do not come to the opera before the second act.
That means they would miss your beautiful ballet." She smiled
brightly. "It is quite simple. You put the ballet, this Venus
Bacchanal that you have made, into the second act, no?"

"No!"

His answer was incomprehensible to her. "What? Again the
German mulishness?" She changed tone, as if talking to a small

child. "My foolish friend—this Paris public is something you must learn to understand, especially the members of the Jockey Club."

"The Jockey Club! The Jockey Club! What makes its members so important?"

"They are a group of men, the richest in France, and the most spoiled."

"What have they to do with music?"

"With music?" The Princess floundered momentarily. "Why, nothing."

"Ah—" Richard was trying his best to understand—"I see. It is the ballet they love."

"Well, not exactly. That is, most Jockey Club members have lady friends *in* the *corps de ballet.*"

Now comprehending fully, Wagner let his anger rise. "Then it is neither the music nor the dancing that interests them, but only the sight of their favorite ballerinas' legs?"

Pauline was delighted. "Now you have it." With relief she returned to her opening request. "The Bacchanal goes into the second act, no?"

"No!"

"How is that again?"

"My opera is not a vaudeville extravaganza, with interchangeable acts. Let people dine earlier or after the last curtain, if they want a complete performance."

Wrapping a feather boa about her throat, the Princess rose. "You do not know Paris, my friend."

Wagner was adamant. "Paris does not know me." He picked up his baton and resumed rehearsal while the Princess stalked furiously from the theater.

This did not, however, end the argument. Director Royer of the Opéra now put in an appearance. Politely he advised Richard that some sort of compromise was highly desirable. Most of the Jockey Club, it appeared, were wealthy stockholders on whose favor depended Monsieur Royer's job. Since they held a predominant number of boxes, year in, year out, *Les Jockeys* exerted a powerful influence. *Alors,* they were never known to show up at the theater before 10:00 P.M., hence such craftsmen as Meyerbeer, Gounod, Berlioz and Auber had long ago learned to shape their operatic efforts accordingly. Surely a German newcomer, with neither name nor fame, could do likewise!

Wagner could not.

Through one hundred and sixty-four rehearsals he stood his ground, preferring to cancel the contract rather than permit further mutilation of his work. Already he had expanded the opening scene of *Tannhäuser* with the Bacchanal, strictly a concession to French taste. More should not be asked of him.

The unresolved contest continued till the actual day of the *première*. Twenty minutes before curtaintime Director Royer made one last effort. Dabbing his moist brow with a handkerchief, he drew Wagner aside. "There is still time, monsieur, to change your mind."

Richard shook his head. "What you ask is an absurdity. The second act takes place in a medieval castle, the Wartburg, where Martin Luther once was imprisoned. Can you imagine a ballet in such a setting?"

"I have no interest in Monsieur Martin *Lutaire*," said Royer sharply. "I know only that Gounod or Meyerbeer, *they* would find a way."

"I do not doubt it. But I am Richard Wagner." Wearily he reached for his coat and hat. "You wish me to go? As you have said, there is still time——"

"Impossible! The Emperor and Empress will enter their box at any moment. The performance cannot be called off." Royer was alternately wringing his hands and tugging at Wagner's lapel. "One thing, however, Maestro. I must insist that you do not step on the podium but permit our assistant conductor to take over. Otherwise I cannot answer for the consequences."

"Consequences?" Richard paused, baffled, then smiled wryly. "Very well. I shall provoke no blood bath."

Royer sent a call boy to fetch the assistant conductor.

CHAPTER 12

MINNA was in Paris for the *Tannhäuser première.*
Her presence came about through an access of pity
that overwhelmed Wagner after a spate of woeful letters with which she pelted him. Patiently he had responded
with arguments and soothing advice, stressing the wisdom of
their separation. But her laments continued until at last they
wore him down. When the first whisperings reached him regarding the Emperor Napoleon's interest in a command performance of *Tannhäuser,* the financial outlook appeared promising enough to fulfill Minna's expensive wish. Richard sent her
the fare to Paris. In a letter to Hans von Bülow he explained
his action:

> I am taking back my unhappy wife. She is in somewhat
> better health, but needs nursing and tender care. She tells
> me I am the only one who can provide these for her and that
> she depends on me for both. Plainly my duty is hereby
> indicated.

Despite her manifold aches and complaints, Minna was no
invalid. She sat in the theater now, primly corseted and attired
in her Sunday best, awaiting the wonders to come. Personally
she did not think much of *Tannhäuser* or any of Richard's odd
creations, but if a French sovereign took an interest in the present undertaking there must be some virtue in it.

Her first disappointment was, of course, not seeing Richard
on the conductor's podium. When he turned up unexpectedly
beside her, in the stage box reserved for the Opéra's management, she thought at first that her watch was wrong and he
had some time to spare before the curtain. But Richard soon
disabused her with the sad truth.

297

She could not hide her disillusion. Was he destined to be forever second-rate? This sort of thing would certainly never have happened to Meyerbeer! She was about to say so when she thought better of it and checked the cutting remark. Richard seemed tired of hearing about Meyerbeer.

Minna now turned her attention to the house. Aha! There were a lot of empty seats. Paris *première*, fiddlesticks! Here was no moneymaker. She might as well go back to Dresden before the hunger and wretchedness of her first French sojourn set in again.

Her appraisal was right. The *Tannhäuser* performance took place before a scanty audience, as the theater had been boycotted by a large segment of the Paris elite. Yet, to Wagner's supreme satisfaction, the Emperor and Empress had come. This fact alone sweetened for him the hostile comments of the next morning's press.

As a matter of fact, Napoleon and Eugénie enjoyed the show. They expressed the hope of seeing a second performance, which was promptly set for five days later, March 18. The news spread across Paris with fire-alarm speed, and it did not sit well with the Jockeys. What! Was a boycott not enough to put that upstart foreign composer out of business? Well, more effective measures would be taken. The original threat of sabotage had failed in its effect, hence it must be backed up with something more: the threat would be turned into action.

Director Royer's nerves grew increasingly tense as the new date approached. Again he warned Wagner at curtaintime of possible disaster. But Richard's optimism was not to be quelled. With the French sovereigns themselves in his camp what was there to fear? He tried to calm the director's pulse by indicating a peephole in the stage draperies.

"Look, Monsieur! You think this time no one at all will come? You are too pessimistic. The theater is filling nicely."

Royer peered cautiously, then made a deprecating gesture. "The gallery, yes, where the music lovers sit. And the family stalls of the culture-conscious *bourgeoisie*."

He was right. As was the case with opera houses throughout the world, the cheapest seats were solidly packed with a nameless, eager and always punctual tribe of music devotees. An equally prompt herd of middle-class patrons, less starry-eyed perhaps but purposefully bent on getting their money's worth, took over row upon row of balcony and orchestra.

"But the boxes, my friend," Royer lamented, "they are empty. The people who *matter*, where are *they?*"

It was true. In the plush-fringed boxes could be seen only a trickling of aristocrats, the tall figure of Princess Metternich in elegant robe (with pearl choker, and a cluster of aigrette plumes in her piled-up hair) prominent among them. Farther forward, in the management box, sat Minna, plainly bored with the proceedings. It had taken considerable persuasion on Richard's part to bring her to the theater this night, for she felt truly that her capacity for absorbing *Tannhäuser* was exhausted. She leaned back in her chair, heavy of body, her chest heaving in short breaths. Her feet tingled, for the ankles were puffed from advancing heart disease. In short, she would far rather have been in bed than attending still another of Richard's dreary fiascos.

Under somnolent eyelids Minna observed the bright proscenium. Lighting facilities having been greatly improved, the house was well illumined, in contrast to the theaters of her youth. She saw the substitute conductor appearing gingerly on the podium, holding his musicians in readiness for the flourish that must greet the arrival of the Emperor and Empress. All eyes were fixed on the Imperial Box. A breathless hush, and now from the far end of the theater an attendant waved a signal to the waiting orchestra. A fanfare was sounded and the audience rose, as the attendant called out: "Their Majesties!"

In the fleur-de-lis-carved box of the Bourbons, now damask-draped with the gold-embroidered Bonaparte Bee, Napoleon III and Eugénie appeared with their entourage. The sovereigns inclined their heads in gracious response to the acclaim, then settled into their seats. The house lights were doused, the conductor's baton tapped faintly, and the first measures of the overture soared through space.

Royer and Wagner were still standing in the wings. The director looked acutely unhappy. "You see," he whispered. "The boxes remain empty. Our best subscription patrons, they are not here!"

Richard smiled sardonically. "Quite so. The house is full of unimportant people."

The grave, churchly harmonies of the Pilgrim's Chorus had given way to the Hörsel Mountain theme, evoking the enchantments of the Venus Grotto, with melodic shadings from the coming love duet between the goddess and the minstrel knight. And now the curtain rose on the subterranean realm itself, where Venus sat enthroned—or, more accurately, reclining in voluptuous languor on her couch—while, 'round about, the fabulous creatures of her court engaged in their galvanized gyrations.

The spectacle cast rapture on audience faces. At the ballet's conclusion, and before the surfeited Tannhäuser begged Venus to allow his return to Earth, the listeners broke into spontaneous applause. The subsequent scene outside the grotto, with pilgrims marching by and Tannhäuser breathing the sweet air of the Thuringian countryside, likewise cast a palpable spell. The curtain descended, and in the intermission that followed there was a buzz of enthralled comment. People voiced unrestrained approval of the daring new harmonies, the rich scenic devices, the translucent orchestral effects.

In the Imperial Box the Emperor nudged his consort: "A far cry from your Spanish bullfights, my dear, is it not?"

Eugénie's lips curled in a slight pout. "Oh, we like something besides toros in Spain," she assured him, then turned to her ladies. "This music, it is intoxicating—like the wine from my grandfather's lands in Málaga!"

The lights were going down again. Full of anticipation, the audience returned to its seats, awaiting the wonders of Act II. On stage Mademoiselle Marie Sax, as Elisabeth, now sang "Dich, Teure Halle," followed by the magnificent procession of the Wartburg guests. And it was at this point that in the theater foyer, simultaneously, a different kind of processional was taking place. A stream of late-comers was pouring through the doors, silently creeping toward the vacant boxes. They were the Jockey Club contingent, composed of bachelor *bons vivants* of all ages, monocled, mustachioed, pot-bellied, skeletal, myopic, bald, or with trumpet hearing-aids. Having dined, and primed themselves with vintage wines, these tardy patrons could not refrain from heralding their entrance with hiccups and belches, as well as audible mutterings against whatever they expected to see. All carried horns, police whistles, rattles and other noisemaking devices of less decorous nature. They were spoiling for a fight, though not at once.

Their battle maneuver was well planned. For the moment, as soon as seated, the newcomers started playing card games or dominoes across the railings of their boxes, glancing only now and then at the events on stage. They had missed the beautiful Fortunata Tedesco's Venus, and they took no notice of the Elisabeth aria which ought to have given even the most rabid anti-Wagnerian cause for plaudits. The subsequent alternation of voices during the assembly of guests in the Wartburg atrium brought cries of "Bravo!" from the gallery and salutes in the direction of the Metternich box, as though the Austrian diplomat and his wife had themselves turned a hand in the creation of such melodies. But with the middle of Act II, and the start of the Minstrel Contest, the critical moment had come. This was the traditional spot for the ballet, which made opera bearable to the habitués of the Folies Bergères by letting them view their favorite chorines cavorting in leotards and crisp *tutus*. With nothing but tenors and baritones in the spotlight (the Wartburg song tourney was not fought by ladies) disappointment gripped the balletomane element. Whistles and catcalls issued suddenly from the boxes, while loud thumping of feet punctuated the mockery that greeted the struggling singers.

In the wings Royer glared furiously at Wagner. "The Jockeys! There you have it, Maestro—the result of your obstinacy."

From the circle of boxes came wild shouting. "What's this? No women? We want the ballet! We want the ballet!"

Royer gasped frantically. "This is a catastrophe! We must ring down the fire curtain before they start throwing fruits and vegetables!"

"No—wait!" Wagner stopped him. "My singers have good lungs. They will top the noisemakers." He pleaded. "Do give them a chance."

From the side lines he waved to the healthy baritone and the basso, Morelli and Cazaux, not to give up the fray. With blood in their eyes the artists expanded their chests and sang above the tumult until the rioters were overwhelmed. Triumphantly, with a maximum of bellowing on stage, the disturbance was drowned out. A trifle off key, the act ended in a draw.

During the second intermission a council was held backstage to weigh the merits of closing the performance. Princess Metternich arrived in consternation, seeking out Royer.

"Call off the show!" she cried. "The Jockeys are in a savage temper. They have sent out for reinforcements. There may be shooting!"

"That settles it." Royer waved to a stagehand. "We cut Act III."

A number of singers rushed up to Wagner. They were gesticulating in protest against such a decision. Richard shrugged helplessly. "I am only the author, not the director."

They turned on Royer. "Don't give in! Let *us* fight it out. You'll see. We can win."

Against his better judgment, the harassed man bowed agreement. Act III opened, once more in the green valley of Thuringia, with Elisabeth praying at a roadside shrine. For the duration of her orisons there was silence in the house, though of a lowering sort. Next, Wolfram's stanzas to the "Evening Star" passed muster and there was a cautious round of applause from pro-Wagnerites. On stage the singers smiled hopefully at one another. However, the scene of the returning pilgrims was now at hand. In dusty rags, weary from their long journey to Rome, the hallowed wanderers shuffled across the stage. At this point the bored *boulevardiers* could take no more. Whistles and taunts were directed at the bearded figures in their monkish garb: "Pull up your skirts! Let's see some pretty legs!"

As the procession, undaunted, moved off in orderly pattern, Tannhäuser (played by Albert Niemann), also in garb of penitent, appeared alone. A burst of guffaws from the Jockey circle greeted him. "Hey, fellows—" a shout followed the earlier crew of singers—"you lost a pilgrim!"

Now pandemonium broke loose. Roaring laughter shook the house until even the Emperor found himself unable to keep a straight face. The balletomaniacs whipped one another into a frenzy, climbing from box to box, breaking up chairs and cracking the pieces over the heads of outraged Wagnerians.

On stage the tenor Niemann forgot the weariness of his purported hike from Italy. Straightening up in full vigor, he hurled his pilgrim's hat and wanderer's staff into the brawling crowd, promptly receiving a shower of tin horns, whistles and a couple of orchestra seats in return.

At the height of the melee the police arrived. The brave gendarmes quickly formed a cordon through which the Emperor and Empress tripped carefully to make their exit, followed by a crestfallen Princess Metternich.

Needless to say, Paris newspapers the following morning had a field day. The detailed accounts of the night's hullaballoo made absorbing reading that kept readers buzzing for weeks. Twice that same fortnight Wagner stubbornly put on *Tannhäuser*, for the benefit of disappointed patrons who had missed the end of the plot. But the power of the Jockeys was too strong. In the face of such opposition the work had to be pulled from the repertory.

Tannhäuser did not reach the French stage again until a full generation later.

CHAPTER 13

THE Paris fiasco was too much for Minna. She packed her
satchels and departed for Dresden, certain that Richard
Wagner had no future. This conviction was shared wholeheartedly by her downcast husband. Richard too resolved to
leave France.

He did not know where to go. But while gathering up his
music scores backstage at the Opéra he found himself confronted suddenly by Pauline Metternich.

"Your Highness!" he exclaimed, deeply embarrassed. "I'm
afraid I brought you no honor." He laughed harshly, mutter-
ing to himself rather than to her, "I've proved a triple loser—as
artist, husband and businessman."

Pauline made a gesture of protest. "My friend, you must not
blame yourself! I was at fault. I should have known what to
expect from a Folies Bergère audience." She touched his shoulder. "I am *very* sorry."

"Do not worry about it, madame, or my shame will be only
the greater." He kissed her hand, then looked up puzzled. "But
what are you doing here in all this backstage dust and disorder?"

"You ask too many questions, Maestro." She peered into the
shadows. "Is there a place to sit down? Ah, here are some
boxes." They pulled up a pair of low packing cases and settled
themselves on them. "Now listen carefully. I have a wonderful
new plan."

Alarmed, he shook his head. "Not for *Tannhäuser*, I hope.
I've lost faith in that opera. I think I shall tear it up."

"Nonsense! Paris isn't the world."

"Theatrically it is."

She brushed this aside. "I owe you some form of apology.

No, more than that, some *practical* restitution—and in Vienna
this will be possible. Austria, the Danube lands, there is the
true center of music!"

Wagner smiled doubtfully. "Of operetta, madame. But not
of opera."

"Never mind. Give me a chance to prove you wrong. I have
already written Director Heinrich Esser—or is he Conductor
Esser?—at the Hofoper."

"The full title is Hofkapellmeister of the Court Opera."

"Thank you. Anyway, I'm sure I can persuade him to take
an interest in your work. What is that opera Franz Liszt was
telling me about, which he put on with such success in
Weimar?"

"Madame means *Lohengrin*, perhaps?"

"Right. You have a score with you?"

He hesitated, then nodded. She held out her hand in a commanding gesture. Silently he reached into a voluminous brief
case and brought out a manuscript. Pauline seized it, leaned
back on her seat, discovered somewhat shocked that there were
no cushioned back rests on stage packing cases and resumed
her upright position. With intense absorption she began to
read.

The upshot of this conversation was a definite commitment
on the part of Vienna for a *Lohengrin* performance during May
of 1861. Richard received a much-needed advance, which
would permit him to mark time until that date and also to re-
establish Minna in another Dresden apartment. He reported
these developments to Liszt, receiving a congratulatory reply
that contained a postscript about Cosima. All was not well in
the Bülow household, it seemed. Liszt's high-strung daughter
appeared restive, a victim of nervous tensions that bespoke
some inner conflict. As Wagner thought well of the gifted Hans
von Bülow, he wrote a sympathetic note to the perplexed young
husband:

Paris, April 4, 1861

My dear Hans—

You probably don't need to be reminded that Cosima's
temperament is her worst enemy. This springs, of course,

from her too extraordinary origin, and means that she is difficult to protect (against herself). . . . Tell her how fond I am of her, and how it would please me to hear that she is behaving herself and showing good sense, which now and then she appears unable to do!

Some time later he again showed an interest in the couple's welfare:

. . . I should be most happy to have some news from you and Cosima. If only that incorrigible girl would watch her health! She is a wild, reckless child, I must repeat. But she comes of great and noble stock. This nobility you must appeal to in trying to tame her willfulness.

Such minor concerns did not, to be sure, absorb Richard's full time. While awaiting Vienna developments he busied himself with an experiment in an entirely new field—namely, comedy. A plot outline occupied him, dealing with some merry doings in the medieval town of Nürnberg. For a hero of the piece he had chosen a historic character, a bluff and hearty cobbler named Hans Sachs, noted in his day as a rhymester and singer. So engrossed did Richard become with this subject that he approached a new publisher, Franz Schott of Mainz, about it. Schott did not share his enthusiasm.

At last the *Lohengrin* rehearsals started and Richard left France for Austria. And now, for a welcome change, a gratifying experience awaited him. The Hofoper performance proved a rousing success, leading to the management's immediate interest in some further work by the composer. Diffidently Wagner suggested a world *première* for his *Tristan und Isolde*.

"By all means!" agreed Conductor Heinrich Esser, quickly immersing himself in the vast libretto. On his recommendation the management of the Imperial Opera House took an option on the work and launched into elaborate production plans. It looked as if this city, long synonymous with romance, would prove an ideal setting for Wagner's symphonic glorification of love.

In the midst of these preparations, which Richard had reported faithfully to the Wesendonks, there came a gay note from Zürich. Otto and Mathilde were on their way to Italy for a winter holiday, and they would be in Venice during early November. Could Wagner join them there, even if only for a few days?

He could not really spare the time just now. And yet the unforgettable Mathilde had added her signature to that of her husband, stressing the fact that Richard's knowledge of the picturesque Adriatic city would greatly enhance his friends' sight-seeing plans. No, it would be graceless to refuse. Making a special effort, he managed four days in Italy, from November 8 through 11. The experience closed—once and for all—the great romance of his life. For, to his profound discomfiture, he found the wedded pair in high spirits and as blatantly happy as though embarked on a second honeymoon. Not only that: Mathilde was once more pregnant.

Somehow this seemed the cruelest indignity a loved woman could have heaped on him. The fact that, being married, she found herself again with child was certainly not something Richard had a right to take amiss. But her indelicacy in summoning him to her side at such a time as this did border on a callousness of which he could not deem her capable. Mute, but inwardly outraged, he turned away. Let her perform her wifely function, since she must; but there was assuredly no need to flaunt the gravid consequences in his face. No, now at last he was done with it. Never again would he, voluntarily, set eyes on Mathilde.

Shaken and sick at heart, Richard returned to Vienna. Here a major calamity had been shaping up. It exploded at just about the time of his arrival, during a full-scale afternoon rehearsal of *Tristan*. On entering the theater Richard found Esser in shirt sleeves, surrounded by musicians, stagehands and singers, all engaged in altercation. Especially wrought up was a florid figure, the famous tenor Ludwig Schnorr von Carolsfeld, who, on being introduced to Wagner, instantly broke out in a flood of reproaches.

"Aha! *You* are the creator of this amazing extravaganza! Let me tell you, sir, this so-called music of yours is a disaster. It is beyond the range of human vocal cords!"

To prove his point he intoned a passage from the "Love Duet" in Act II. His voice, splendid in quality and range, broke. At the same time a soprano stepped forward in vehement support of Carolsfeld. She was manipulating a throat spray and could hardly speak above a whisper.

"Only a—a—monster," she gasped, "could write such impossible crescendos!"

Orchestra members arose to join the general protest. The violinists waved their instruments. "The arpeggio line is too drawn out. There are too many chromatic chords. It's the devil's own work!"

Harpists and cellists tossed sheets from the music racks. "Fireworks, musical acrobatics—such stuff was never meant to be played!"

Only the piccolo player sat smugly happy amid his supply of small reed instruments and pipes. He expressed himself, wide-eyed and unworried: "I *like* the Shepherd's solo." In demonstration of this fact he ran through some gentle, tootling rhythms. But loud shouts from the scene designers drowned him out.

"It was bad enough, bringing a swan on stage in *Lohengrin*— and then, the set for *Flying Dutchman,* which called only for the prow of a sailing vessel. But this *Tristan,* in the opening act, must have the deck of a whole ship!" Spitting and grumbling, they stamped off stage.

In the semidarkness of the auditorium Richard had had enough. He was still too aware of the *Tannhäuser* drubbing in Paris to take issue, apart from the fact that in vocal debate the victory went necessarily to the opera personnel's greater lung power. Richard told himself, furthermore, that Vienna was the recognized operetta capital of the world, where weightier forms of art did not rule supreme. The gay and frolicsome city could hardly be expected to meet the requirements of a pretentious new hybrid called a music-drama.

Dejectedly he left the theater and hied himself to his quarters in the suburban home (at Penzing) of a Doctor Josef

Standhartner, a bachelor physician who customarily sublet his house when he had a mind to go on holiday. An adjunct of the establishment was Doctor Standhartner's niece, a pleasant young woman named Serafine Mauro, who served as house-keeper to a series of lodgers. Fräulein Mauro, like others be-fore her, had found the Wagner personality irresistible. She fluttered and cast adoring eyes on the moody artist who was too troubled and downcast to notice her. But today when, after the humiliation of the Venice meeting with Mathilde, he must face also the possible cancellation of the *Tristan* project, Serafine wept with him. Not in love but in pain he put his arms around her.

No serious romance blossomed, possibly for lack of time. The following morning Richard was informed by the Hofoper management that rehearsals must be temporarily suspended due to general loss of voice among cast members—unquestion-ably occasioned by the shouting of the previous afternoon. Wagner was free to occupy himself with something else.

His immediate impulse was to leave Vienna. In this con-nection he was influenced by an item in that day's newspaper. It concerned Germany, where a political giant, Otto Eduard Leopold von Bismarck-Schönhausen, was coming into promi-nence with an ambitious plan to unify the Reich. In keeping with this purpose, conciliatory gestures were being extended to-ward exiled liberals. A general amnesty had just been granted, permitting their return to the Fatherland. This did not assure Richard Wagner a pardon in his native province of Saxony, but he could at least set foot elsewhere on German soil. The art center most accessible from Vienna was Munich. To Munich he would go.

Leaving a sadly palpitating Fräulein Mauro behind, he donned Tyrolean hiking clothes and set out by the most eco-nomical travel means, on foot, with no more than a rucksack for baggage. On the Austro-Bavarian border he showed his identification papers to the sentry on guard, then stepped joy-ously across onto German soil.

He reached Munich on an extraordinary day. The Bavarian capital was draped in mourning as its principal streets filled with spectators watching the funeral procession of a Wittels-bach ruler, King Maximilian II. By the church calendar it was also Good Friday, a date that lent additional solemnity to the occasion.

Wagner, the ardent patriot who had suffered exile for his democratic principles, was hardly impressed by the panoply of royalty, whether alive or dead. From personal experience he knew the pinch of hunger and want. His eyes shed no crocodile tears as they looked on the casket bearing the mortal remains of one whose days had been spent in luxury and ease.

Since there was no way of crossing the roped-off Karls Platz in the center of town, Richard decided to dodge the crowd by heading for one of the Isar River bridges. But before doing so his gaze was caught by a striking apparition. It was the ap-pearance, in the funeral procession, of the tall, handsome eight-een-year-old heir to the throne, Bavaria's new king, Ludwig II. This incredibly poetic figure, aloof and resplendent even in mourner's garb, cast a sudden spell on Wagner's imagination. Here in this hardly more than adolescent prince was the physi-cal embodiment of knighthood, a figure from Arthurian legend, made visually manifest. This untouched youth with the clear brow and noble features conjured up images of Perceval, Lan-celot, Galahad and all the idyllic community of the Holy Grail.

In Wagner's breast this theme of the Grail had long burned as a living flame. While working on *Lohengrin,* whose hero was the son of Monsalvat's King Parsifal (the English Sir Per-ceval, of the Round Table Brotherhood), he had been gripped by a mystic urge. He wanted to portray, in the sublime form of a music-drama, man's pain-ridden and perilous quest for good. To this end he must have a Christlike central character, and for a time he actually labored on a script entitled *Jesus of Nazareth,* and on another, *The Feast of the Apostles.* But both had been laid aside as too theological to blend with the pan-theism inherent in Wagner's love of nature.

Actually *Tannhäuser* and even *Tristan,* as well as the still unfinished Siegfried story of the *Nibelungen Ring,* constituted no departure from the road-to-salvation motif. In the first two the heroes were gallant men, bedeviled by temptation but rising in the end to true chivalric stature. Siegfried, not yet fully shaped by the artist's creative magic, dwelled in Wagner's mind as a symbol of youth and innocence whose valor sprang from ignorance of evil and of its concomitant, fear. But the world of Siegfried was superdimensional, peopled with gods, dwarfs, dragons, mermaids, and endowed with a rainbow bridge leading to Valhalla, a castle in the clouds. As yet Richard did not feel quite at home in such an extramundane climate. More plausible and more realistic, because based on folkloric memory, was the figure of Parsifal. Remote enough to stand outside the confining grip of Church dogma, the Knight of the Holy Grail encompassed Christian piety with metaphysical introspection. He was of this world, yet able to reach beyond it.

In Ludwig II a certain romantic unearthliness seemed equally apparent. The young king was the scion of an ancient but spent and neurotic line. His had been a lonely, isolated childhood, free from ordinary cares, from ugliness and strife. His face bore the Siegfried bloom of innocence and the Parsifal mist of melancholy, both instantly recognizable to Wagner's searching eye.

What the composer did not know, there in the crowded Munich street, was that the passing monarch happened to be an ardent devotee of opera and particularly of its new Wagnerian form. Only recently Ludwig had attended a performance of *Lohengrin,* which left him entranced and eager to meet the author-composer in person. He could not have guessed that the same Richard Wagner, to whom he felt himself inwardly bound by a strange unity of thought, was at this moment looking at him out of the multitude.

A period of official mourning had, of course, set in for all Bavaria. This threw a pall over things theatrical. Music halls and other entertainment centers were closed, while rehearsals of planned productions met with cancellation. Wagner's hope of finding a Munich sponsor for one of his works was dashed in the first hour of arrival. He decided not to bother looking for lodgings but to continue on his way.

Unable to return to Saxony, he hardly knew where to go. France, after the *Tannhäuser* scandal, held little attraction.

England was too far away, considering his limited funds. But were there not untold regions of Germany unknown to him, which could be reached economically and on foot? He resolved to do just that. Beginning with Bavaria, he would hike across the map at a leisurely walking pace. Here and there he would give a few music lessons or hire himself out to some village band, so as to earn a night's lodging and a meal. Thus he would learn things about people and places not to be found in books.

Tightening the straps of his rucksack, he headed for the edge of town and the open road.

CHAPTER 14

THROUGH scenic Bavaria Richard Wagner made his way. He beheld the mountain splendor of Garmisch-Partenkirchen and the great heights of the Zugspitze, Germany's most picturesque peak, before heading northward into more gently sloping country. While resting on a wooded knoll he saw a road marker identifying the next town: Bayreuth. The name meant nothing to him, yet his eye lingered lovingly on it, on this land, this sky, as though he could not absorb enough of either.

Some hours later, after having taken in the sights of the quaint hamlet, he moved on. His attention halted on every valley, every meadow, as though his were the craft of landscape painter who must take mental note of all the eye could absorb. Soon, however, his footsteps brought him to the Saxon border and it behooved him to turn back. He swung southward again, this time in the direction of Nürnberg, home of the historic cobbler-poet Hans Sachs. As the turrets of the medieval city came into view, Wagner stopped to rest at a roadside inn beyond the ancient town gates. He took a simple meal under a wide-spreading oak, then pushed aside his plate and started writing at the table. The *Meistersinger* text had come to life again, with newly inspired stanzas to expand the original draft. He was ardently at work when the innkeeper came to clear away the dishes. Looking over the guest's shoulders, he nodded appreciatively.

"That is a song you are writing?" He stroked his apron, preening himself. "I am a musician too."

Wagner nodded in a happy, gracious mood. "We are fortunate indeed, are we not?"

"I play the zither," the innkeeper said proudly. He peered

313

again at the guest's scribblings. "Your song, it will be good for the zither?"

"Well, not exactly. You see, I am writing an opera . . . er . . . something that is intended for many instruments."

"Ah—" there was disillusion in the other's tone—"sad stuff that is. People dead all over the place." With a great clatter the innkeeper gathered up plates and cutlery, then slapped a dust cloth across the table. "Such things I do not play on my zither."

Wagner murmured a reply, more to himself than to the stranger. "This will not be sad. It is a comedy—my *first* comedy." He held up a page containing a line of dialogue by Hans Sachs, reading aloud:

> *"Verachtet mir die Meister nicht,*
> *und ehrt mir ihre Kunst!"*

> ("Scorn not artist or artisan,
>   but through them honor Art!")

Looking up for a response from the good innkeeper, he observed that this worthy fellow had long departed. Cheerfully Richard packed up his notes and continued on his way.

He reached the Rhine Valley a few days later. Here, while encamped on a sunny hillside, he watched vintners at work far above the rushing stream. Beside him lay a sketch pad with drawings, and a whole new set of notations. His fancy had been caught by a fresh theme, or, rather, an unfinished old one, for the notations were headed by the caption "Siegfried's Rhine Journey."

Again some days later Richard entered the city of Mainz, where he headed straight for his publisher. Herr Schott received him cautiously. "You are bringing me *Die Meistersinger,* as promised in your last letter?"

"The orchestration is not completed. But you shall have it in another fortnight."

"Oh." The publisher's manner cooled noticeably.

Richard paused to gather his nerve. "I have walked and

begged rides all the way from Vienna. My funds are exhausted.
I wondered if you might find it possible to——"

"Give you an advance? Certainly not!" Herr Schott never
minced words. "I buy no pigs in pokes. There will be cash
when you bring me a finished manuscript. Good day!"

Considerably disheartened, Richard set out again, this time
without direction. He had no goal whatever, let alone funds
for transportation, but his vagabond's luck continued to hold.
Along the riverbank peasant carts moved westward, their humble owners always willing to give a weary wanderer a lift.
This meant also the sharing of a bit of provender, consisting
usually of delicious dark country bread spread with goose fat,
or a chunk of smoked bacon. Thus, in hit-or-miss fashion, Richard found himself ultimately once more on the border of Switzerland and headed for Zürich. He had no intention of getting
in touch with the Wesendonk household, but in his plight he
turned to the near-by suburb of Mariafeld, where his and Mathilde's friend Frau Wille lived. No one here expected him,
and indeed raised eyebrows greeted his arrival. However, he
was given shelter and a very welcome warm meal.

In the days that followed, Richard unburdened his worries
to the Wille family, emphasizing his usual bankrupt state. This
elicited his hosts' sympathies to the point of facilitating a longer
stay, during which he worked feverishly on the *Meistersinger*
score. Before long the opera was sufficiently rounded out for
submission to Herr Schott, who reacted with the longed-for
monetary advance. Promptly thereupon Richard gave thanks
to his kind hosts and relieved them of his company. He knew
that the Wille household had undergone a period of strain
throughout his stay, as Otto or Mathilde Wesendonk might at
any moment have put in an appearance. In deference to his
hosts he knew he ought to make himself scarce.

Once more on the road, with no place to go, he headed back
for the Rhine. Some revisions of *Die Meistersinger* being his
immediate concern, he decided on the environs of Mainz for
a goal, so as to be close to the publisher Schott. Before reaching that city, however, he came through the small river town
of Biebrich, which was far better suited to his pocketbook.

Here he found comfortable lodgings in a sunny cottage, within easy commuting distance of Mainz and the firm of Schott—which led directly to a minor complication in his life. For, during a business conference with his publisher, Wagner made the acquaintance of a legal counselor named Maier and the latter's very susceptible daughter Mathilde. Whether the young lady's romantic temperament was responsible, or Richard's subconscious response to her Christian name, a sentimental interest soon blossomed between the middle-aged composer and the eager Fräulein Maier. On Wagner's part the emotional response was dictated by loneliness rather than erotic enthusiasm, but the young woman's feelings were unequivocal. She fell madly in love and deemed the world well lost for her life's great passion.

Wagner explained his situation to her. A natural spendthrift, forever borrowing from friends and struggling to catch up with his debts, he must practice strictest economy, for he had an ailing wife to support. Indeed, he had lately fallen behind on Minna's monthly allowance which at best, with the aid of her daughter Natalie's earnings, barely kept the unhappy woman out of the poorhouse. Having made clear these circumstances, as well as the fact that marriage would be out of the question, Richard left no doubt that Mathilde Maier's favors were nonetheless welcome. This was all the impassioned girl needed to know.

Into this idyl Minna crashed unexpectedly. Through the resumption of regular payments she had been able to ascertain Richard's address. On realizing that he was back in Germany, and no farther away than the Rhineland, her wifely feelings reasserted themselves. Life with a spinster daughter was dreary and not always congenial. Also, Richard's prospects appeared to be looking up. Decisively, Minna packed her wicker satchel once again and purchased a third-class train ticket. On a bright April day she appeared on Richard's doorstep in Biebrich.

"I've come to keep house for you," she announced peremptorily. Then, taking stock of his neglected appearance: "My, you certainly need looking after!"

This was true. Mathilde Maier's visits to his lodgings did not include domestic pursuits. If anything, the young woman contributed to the general disorder of his bachelor rooms. He really missed the comforts of a regulated home life, and he could do with a little mothering, which was all that the aging Minna had now to offer. He was a conscienceless blackguard anyway, he told himself, encouraging the infatuation of a girl who might be his daughter or even his grandchild. He ought to make an end of it and straighten out his life. Once again the delusion that his marriage could be saved took hold. In short, he welcomed Minna in.

She took over the reins at once, quite as though there had never been a separation. When, that same week, Richard was summoned by Franz Schott for a business conference—which was to include a reading of *Tristan und Isolde* for possible production by the Mainz Opera Company—Minna insisted on going along. Richard tried to dissuade her, but without success.

The consequences were regrettable. No sooner had a select gathering of listeners been seated in the Schott drawing room, and Isolde's first speech begun, than Minna realized she could not endure it. This was the work inspired by that Wesendonk woman! Not only that. Minna remembered distinctly that her hated rival had once urged Richard to try his hand at comic opera, a suggestion leading to his only effort of this kind, the *Meistersinger* work likewise currently under discussion.

On both counts the injured wife felt herself outraged. She forgot that she had returned unasked to her husband's side and that her presence in the Schott home was on sufferance, to say the least.

Her supply of tact and good manners had never been great. She now dispensed with all vestige of either as, reaching toward a near-by serving table, she snatched up a bit of pastry and threw it in Richard's face.

Consternation gripped the assemblage as Wagner broke off in mid-sentence. He stiffened, biting his lips, then folded his manuscript. With a bow to his host he left the room and disappeared into the night. The reading, and the precarious marital reconciliation, were over. That same week Minna returned to Saxony.

On March 4, 1862, Wagner confirmed this in a short letter to
the poet and composer Peter Cornelius:

> It is now settled. I cannot possibly again live with my
> wife. You would not believe all that is covered by those few
> words. My heart bleeds, but I recognize that soft impulses
> must be conquered. There is salvation only in firmness and
> honesty.
>
> I have been taught quite graphically that my wife is in-
> finitely better off far from me than at my side; indeed, I
> recognize plainly that she harbors for me no real feeling of
> love. She acknowledges only the wrong that has been in-
> flicted on her, and is utterly without capacity to forgive it,
> ever. That's the way it is. In all of us lies only that world
> which we choose to accept. . . .

Once again Richard Wagner was ready to pull up stakes. But
the musical score of *Die Meistersinger* (the libretto had been
finished in January of 1862) kept him in Biebrich. Also, during
early summer, Hans and Cosima von Bülow came to the Rhineland on holiday, counting on a visit under his roof. Unless he
wanted to take precious time from his work to broadcast the
latest of his domestic skirmishes, he had better contain himself
and welcome his friends as if nothing had happened.

The Bülows brought with them a breath of worldliness and
excitement that helped dispel Richard's gloom. They asked to
hear passages from the opera now before him and from the still
unfinished *Nibelungen Ring*. He rejoiced at this, sunning himself in their warm praise. How wonderful it was to receive
tribute and encouragement when self-doubt gnawed so relent-
lessly at his soul! Richard wanted to embrace Cosima and Hans,
shouting exultant thanks for the healing balm their presence
furnished him. As it was, his gratitude manifested itself in long
hours of playing whatever they begged to hear, day after day,
until—to everyone's amazement—the Bülow visit stretched into
eight full weeks.

Throughout this time, with no housewife in attendance, Richard was put to considerable expense in providing his guests
with food and home comforts. Having no steady servants, he

managed to obtain a cleaning woman who doubled in marketing and cookery, while the carefree visitors had no inkling of
the economic havoc they were causing. Within a fortnight
Richard was out of cash and heavily in debt at the baker's and
greengrocer's. In panic he addressed himself to the only person who had never yet turned him down, Otto Wesendonk. It
was preposterous, to be sure, in view of the aggravations Richard had once brought on the Wesendonk ménage. But there
was still a semiprofessional arrangement between himself and
Otto regarding ultimate publication of *The Ring* operas, in
connection with which a loan might not be too far out of order.

In pleading for aid Richard thought it unwise, however, to
mention his house guests. He used poor Minna for a convenient
peg whereon to hang a persuasive argument. He wrote:

MY DEAR OTTO!
You will readily understand that only in utmost extremity
would I have the indelicacy to approach you once again for
help. Truly I don't know how I can meet the ever-growing
responsibilities that are heaped upon me. An immediate
crisis has arisen, particularly with regard to resettling my
ailing wife in Dresden and providing for her during the next
several months. . . .

The letter ended more succinctly with the naming of a sum
that would accrue only slightly to Minna's benefit and very
substantially to defraying the cost of playing host to the airily
guileless Bülows. Nor did Herr Wesendonk turn a cold shoulder on his friend. He sent the required amount, with a polite
inquiry as to the progress made thus far on the Nibelungen
tetralogy.

Richard gave effusive thanks but an evasive answer. As
soon as his house guests departed he picked up not *The Ring*
but *Tristan und Isolde* for renewed polishing. Perhaps this
opera, already in completion, could at last be launched and
counted on to wipe out some of its creator's debts.

He reopened negotiations with the Hofoper in Vienna. Politely he inquired whether the protesting singers had recovered
from their mass attack of laryngitis and might be amenable to

a second go at the controversial work. They had, and they
were. By return mail Richard was invited to the Austrian capital. He set out in October, high of hope and courage; but the
triumph he counted on was not yet. After a month of strenuous
rehearsal the same chorus of protest arose from orchestra and
cast: the music was too difficult, both for instrumentalist and
singer. In addition to anger, however, another reaction now
set in. A number of Vienna critics attended the new production
tryouts and found the proceedings irresistibly funny. The leading musical authority, Hanslick, referred to the unconventional
melodic soaring of the *Liebestod* as "screeches and caterwaul-
ing," which in turn encouraged lesser journalistic colleagues to
unleash a torrent of epigrammatic abuse.

Since these tirades concerned themselves with rehearsals
and not with a full-fledged performance, they did no lasting
damage. But their weight fell heavily on the Hofoper's distinguished conductor, Heinrich Esser, who could not stomach
ridicule. Under the sting of Hanslick's taunts the sensitive
Hofkapellmeister laid down his baton and wrote a letter to
Wagner's publisher, Schott, warning him against bringing out
the worthless *Tristan* in print. In Herr Esser's words:

> My ears are currently being subjected to a noisy calamity
> by one Richard Wagner, entitled *Tristan und Isolde,* a re-
> hearsal of which ended yesterday with a nervous headache
> for all concerned. I really don't know whether I can cope
> with this vastly complicated and thankless job. It is my mis-
> fortune not to be able to remember the endless chord se-
> quences that make up this so-called opera.
> Wagner told me confidentially that you look with ill favor
> on the payment of an advance on doubtful works. You are
> very wise to close your purse where this incorrigible wastrel
> is concerned. . . .

The latter remark was perhaps uncalled for on the part of an
orchestral director, whose responsibility ought to have been
confined to musical values. But Wagner had indeed embarked
on an interlude of reckless spending. So certain was he of
achieving a successful *Tristan première* this time that he again

rented the Penzing home of Doctor Standhartner and, capping optimism with sheer folly, plunged into a frenzy of interior decorating. Over the staid landlord's simple draperies he ordered velvet portières hung from thick brass rings, while cabinet makers and upholsterers were summoned to replace prosaic chairs and high-backed benches with cushioned sofas of far more luxuriant texture and design. How was all this to be paid for? With the *Tristan* profits, of course.

So blind and deaf was Richard to the signals of impending disaster that he took time off from rehearsals, which—he felt confident—were proceeding very well without him, to fill some concert engagements in Russia. For this purpose he wrote a quick note to Hans von Bülow, asking if in the latter's circle of acquaintance there might be someone from whom a fur coat could be borrowed for the trip. A foot warmer (fur-lined bag worn on sleigh rides) would also be welcome. Richard promised to return both articles promptly and "saturated with fame."

In high spirits he dashed to St. Petersburg and Moscow, reporting some of his impressions to the sentimental Fräulein Maier back in Biebrich:

> Well, here I am in Asia, truly Asia, my child! As yet I have seen no signs of Muscovite magnificence. All I can say thus far is that I find myself in an enormous, sprawling village with a palace (the Kremlin) and a number of Boyar mansions rising from its center.

It was in Moscow where news reached him that Hofkapell-meister Esser definitely had tossed *Tristan* from the Vienna Opera's repertoire, after a total of seventy-seven expensive rehearsals. The reason given was vocal fatigue among the top singers, but Esser's own earlier expressed antipathy unquestionably served as a contributory factor.

Heavy of heart, Richard returned to Austria, where not only humiliation awaited him but an impressive pile of debts. The rugs, draperies and furniture of his Penzing lodgings would have to be returned, of course, with payment for their temporary use, plus wages due the upholsterer, the carpenter, the moving-van agents. In short, the rubles earned in Russia covered less than half the outstanding obligations.

Fortunately, thanks to Bülow's intercession, another group of concert engagements materialized in northern Germany. Richard accepted with alacrity, but he had to leave Vienna in secret, for his creditors had little faith in the penniless composer's promise to make good his remaining commitments by mail.

He arrived in Berlin during the fall of 1863 and was warmly received by the hospitable Bülows. A glimpse of family life and ordered domestic patterns aroused in him a painful realization of his own unsettled and lonely existence. Children's voices rang through the well-appointed home, for Hans and Cosima were parents of two small girls, Daniela, aged three, and Blandine, a baby six months old.

Hans von Bülow too sensed the contrast between his own good luck and the dreary misfortunes that dogged his friend. He exerted himself endlessly in Richard's behalf, striving to obtain additional professional appearances for him and likewise urging Cosima to put aside all personal interests so as to concentrate on the welfare of their beloved guest.

This was something Cosima did not have to be told twice. Her girlhood adoration of Wagner had carried over, undimmed, into marriage and even motherhood; it burned still with an incandescent flame. To see the incomparable one again, under her own roof and plainly in need of spiritual and material solace, stirred up fires never banked in the young wife's breast. With eyelids lowered to conceal the intense gleam of joy that lighted up her pupils, she listened to her husband's instructions. Ah, yes, they would be followed to the letter, and beyond. Hans could rest assured.

It was in November of the same year, while Bülow hastened to an afternoon orchestra rehearsal of his own, that Cosima took Richard on a carriage drive through Berlin's beautiful Grunewald forest. Outwardly she was performing no more than the gracious duties of an exemplary hostess. But the man at her side was no becalmed and settled husband, lulled into contentment and assurance by the routine of matrimonial habit.

He was a storm-beaten outcast, sensitive to every gust and blow, a stranger to happiness and peace. Also, long unattached to any woman, save in the lightest of amorous dalliance with accidental and almost anonymous quick loves, he bore within him a volcano of passion, smoldering and unspent.

Whether Cosima recognized this elemental threat in him, or he responded to the unmistakable vibrations set off by her unfulfilled and ardent being, the Grunewald ride led to a fateful revelation. In terms of action, nothing happened, since the Bülow coachman was a silent witness to all that might have gone on. Yet, just the same, in silence and without need of slightest gesture, everything happened. In Richard Wagner's diary the moment was forever captured:

> We stared, mutely, into each other's eyes, and a violent desire for truthful admission seized us. There was no need for words with which to confess the boundless misfortune that henceforth would weigh upon us. With clouded gaze and choked breath we gave testimony of belonging each irrevocably to the other. . . .

In consequence of this grave interlude Richard shortened his Berlin stay. It had been understood, and so proposed by Hans von Bülow, that Richard should remain for an indefinite period after the brief round of concert dates was filled. But, though Hans was kept blissfully unaware of any reason for an upset of this plan, it was obviously out of the question. Quickly, almost gruffly, Richard bade his friends farewell.

"Ungrateful sort of fellow, isn't he?" Bülow complained to his wife.

Cosima smiled cryptically. "Your favors burden him."

Richard, meanwhile, had hastened blindly on his way. He did not know where he was heading, but ultimately he turned up in quiet Mariafeld, the Swiss mountain retreat of his friends the Willes. Here he was always certain of shelter and unbroken respite for creative work. But what was there left for him to create, when everything within him was in a turmoil of hopeless confusion? From Mariafeld he wrote to Peter Cornelius, on April 8, 1864:

I have nothing more to give, nothing! A light must strike me now, or some luminous human being to lend me support and energy while I still have my powers to reward such help. . . . Or maybe it is already too late! Yes, deep inwardly I feel that I am finished. Only a truly beneficent miracle can save me, otherwise it is all over. Strangely, the frightening paralysis within me seems to promise, somehow, that such a wondrous miracle is indeed on the way. . . .

Instead of magical solutions an angry message came from Doctor Josef Standhartner, in whose Vienna house Richard had wrought some unpaid changes. The good doctor was being dunned by diverse merchants and handymen, wherefore he saw himself obliged to demand immediate settlement.

Wagner counted these economic headaches among the lesser of his ills. In high-flown language he answered Standhartner, on April 12, much in the same vein employed toward Cornelius:

At present I can do nothing whatever toward settlement of my affairs. There is only one who can help me—not many, but the *right one*. He exists, I know it. But how to find him? There must be a way to find him. . . . For the rest, the world will have my works—let it forget my sins. That is all I ask in exchange.

This was no help to Standhartner, who had been left holding an irritatingly large bag.

PART III

The King

CHAPTER I

LUDWIG II of Bavaria had little taste for kingship.

During his adolescent years he had disappointed his royal father by showing no pronounced qualifications for the role of crown prince. His leanings were literary and artistic. Statecraft bored him.

Nevertheless, since the spring of 1864, Ludwig had had the job of ruling Bavaria. Daily he must sit in council with government officials, learning from them the routine of his kingly duties. At night he retired to the cold emptiness of the Munich Royal Palace or the labyrinthine vastness of Nymphenburg Castle on the edge of town, while his thoughts drifted to a happier setting on Starnberg Lake, where he had spent his childhood.

If at least he might have some music! But, owing to the official period of court mourning, there was no opera season this year. He would have to get along with the banal small talk of his ministers or a lonely alternative—silence.

Not caring for either, he contemplated a possible third choice. Since protocol permitted him to attend none but solemn state functions he decided to circumvent such strictures. If he was forbidden to seek out pleasure, let pleasure come to him. He yearned in particular to satisfy an inborn hunger for music, abetted by a recent experience, just before his accession to the throne. He had attended an opera entitled *Lohengrin*, by one Richard Wagner of whom people were beginning to talk. What sort of man was this Wagner? And where could he be found? Ludwig felt himself gripped by an obsession to meet the artist face to face.

Scarcely a month after assuming kingship Ludwig translated

his impulse into action. Among the secretaries left behind by the defunct Maximilian II was an officious Baron von Pfistermeister, who appeared most suited to the young monarch's purpose. Ambitious, oversolicitous and always getting underfoot, Pfistermeister was also secretive and could be entrusted with a delicate mission. His mission would be to locate Wagner and invite him to Bavaria for a visit with the king.

Where was the search to begin?

"That, my dear Baron, is your worry," said Ludwig. "But a promotion awaits you if you succeed."

Pfistermeister pondered the matter and arrived at a logical conclusion. He would make the rounds of Munich music dealers and go through their operatic files. If this fellow Wagner had a publisher, it should be easy to call on the latter and uncover the composer's address.

As surmised, the trail led, via Schott & Co., to Biebrich near Mainz. But Richard had long vanished from there, following the deplorable food-throwing scene enacted by Minna at the Schott home. Which way could Pfistermeister turn next? He consulted again with Herr Schott, revealing his identity this time as well as the high nature of his employ. This information caused a considerable stir in the publisher's office, where some time earlier Wagner had requested further loans on his *Meistersinger* and had been turned down. If royal favor beckoned in the offing, it behooved Schott & Co. to join the search and get hold of the neglected *Meistersinger* script for immediate publication.

Fate intervened at this juncture. Doctor Standhartner and the coterie of Vienna creditors had managed to track down Wagner to the Wille home at Mariafeld. Discreet threats were reaching the composer with each morning's mail, promising action on the part of the Swiss police if a deadline for payment was not met. Richard borrowed from Peter to pay Paul; that is, he accepted several loans from a scholarly admirer, Herr Wendelin Weissheimer. But there was a limit to the Weissheimer resources. In the end Richard was faced with the dilemma of bringing humiliation on his hosts, the Willes, or taking French leave before the situation grew more acute. He took the latter course. A well-practiced refugee, he abandoned Switzerland and resumed his earlier hike along the Rhine, this time heading upstream. If his slim cash reserve sufficed to cover food and drink, it was his purpose to reach Mainz and throw himself on his publisher's mercy. The revised score of *Meistersinger* was finished. He would surrender it for a decent bed to sleep in and a month's undisturbed lodging at some quiet hotel.

The reception accorded him at the Schott offices hardly coincided with such humble thoughts. The firm's entire staff rushed forward to greet him.

"Ah, good morning, Herr Wagner! We have been waiting for you. Where have you kept yourself?"

"Not where but *how* would be nearer the mark," said Richard.

The well-rounded and balding Schott stepped forward. "But of course! By the way, since you have been traveling you may not have heard the news: Meyerbeer is dead." In the same breath Schott went ahead, hands reaching out eagerly: "That parcel under your arm is, I trust, the new manuscript? We promise you our very best publishing job."

Richard was struck dumb at the Meyerbeer news. Mechanically he handed over his bulky script. His thoughts were far away as the happy Schott rambled on. "Well, you seem to be getting somewhere, my friend! We've had your stuff . . . er . . . works on our shelves for years, with no sign of their moving. And now, all at once, we can't keep enough in print. The enthusiasm of the King——"

"What king?"

"Ludwig II of Bavaria. He is supplying every theater and orchestra in his realm with Wagner texts. Didn't you know?"

Richard shook his head. "I have talked to no one. I have read no papers."

"That is a mistake. You should realize that young Ludwig— he is only nineteen, mind you—loves music, and particularly operas. *Your* operas." Schott rubbed his hands contentedly.

Wagner frowned. "I don't like that word, opera. My works are music-dramas."

He came through here, eight or ten days ago, on his way to Stuttgart."

Pfistermeister followed the trail to the mountain-ringed Württemberg capital. He spent some time making a tour of its inns, taverns and hostelries. And now at length he caught up with his quarry, for the name of Wagner appeared on the register of an obscure back-street hotel.

Drawing a crested visiting card from his pocket, Pfistermeister wrote a message in behalf of his master, the King. But the unknown boarder upstairs, submerged in one of his melancholy moods, received no callers. He sent back the visitor's card instantly and unread.

This did not deter Pfistermeister, who had spent too many years in royal service not to have learned patience and perseverance. He simply took a room at the same hotel and waited till morning. The following day he knocked in person on Wagner's door and presented his credentials together with the framed portrait of King Ludwig, an envelope containing His Majesty's invitation, and the diamond-encrusted ring.

Richard could not believe his eyes. Wild fantasies and extravagant daydreams were nothing new to him. But surely his mind must be deranged to conjure up anything as fantastic as this! He slammed the door with a bang. Perhaps that meddlesome stranger—or was it a spook?—would go away.

But Pfistermeister proved himself no goblin. He knocked again. "What answer, sir," he inquired, "am I to give my master?"

Only now did Wagner grasp the miracle unrolling before his eyes. Could this be the supernatural intercession of which he had written Cornelius and Standhartner, in half mockery and despair, as his only salvation? Confused but fascinated, he asked the visitor inside.

The royal emissary came straight to the point. "How soon can you travel with me to Munich?"

No question had ever been easier for Richard to answer. After a second glance at the royal photograph and the jeweled circlet he reached for his hat. "Right now!"

"Very well." Pfistermeister stepped from the room. "I shall make all arrangements."

Later that same day, on May 3, 1864, the travelers left Stuttgart and on the following evening the composer and the King
held their first meeting. Ludwig received Wagner at his favorite home, the rustic chalet of Berg on the shores of Starnberg
Lake. Here he had arranged for a suite of rooms to be put at
his guest's disposal, then thought better of it and chose a small
independent villa on the royal estate.

"Have you a family or other ties?" the monarch asked. "If
so, bring them here and let me care for them. Let me provide
all your needs, so you will have nothing to do but to compose,
compose, compose!"

Here was an artist's dream come true. Richard wrote Wendelin Weissheimer:

> The young King is a wonderful grant to me from Destiny.
> An instant devotion has sprung up between us, such as is
> possible only between pupil and teacher. . . . There is in him
> such beauty, such spiritual depth, that our daily contact
> becomes a solace which opens up for me an entirely new
> life!

Herr Weissheimer could only rejoice at such news, as he had
over the years helped Wagner in many a crisis and "lent" him
considerable amounts of money. With royal patronage now
furnishing an income, Richard might get around to paying off
some of those debts.

A letter to the Wille family at Mariafeld, dated May 4, 1864,
also described the happy change in fortune:

> I would be an ingrate if I did not tell you at once of my
> boundless blessings. You may have heard that the youthful
> King of Bavaria has called me to his side. I met him for the
> first time today. Unfortunately he has such beauty of intel-
> lect and spirit, and is so sublime a being, that I fear his life
> will be shattered like some evanescent and divine vision in
> our vulgar world.

The premonition contained in the above lines would before
long prove only too true. But for the moment Wagner's star
rode high.

NO SOONER had Richard been established at Starnberg Lake than Ludwig summoned him to Nymphenburg Castle, and later the Royal Palace in Munich, for a tour of the Wittelsbach domain. "I want you to see my private theater," said a note from the King, "where all your past and future masterpieces are to be played."

Again Wagner traveled by regal equipage, and on his arrival at Nymphenburg he was awaited by his host atop the castle steps. Now, eagerly, the monarch came halfway down to meet his guest, and Wagner marveled anew at the highborn youth's extraordinary good looks. No words were exchanged as the King and the composer walked arm in arm through the great portals.

A long tour of inspection followed, with treasure upon treasure unfolding before Richard's eyes. Particularly impressive was the collection of priceless porcelains for which Nymphenburg was famous. And then, with this sight-seeing expedition finished, there remained a visit to the *Residenz,* or royal town house.

It was this latter, the Munich Royal Palace, which revealed to Wagner that his kingly patron was rather more than a music enthusiast: he was unquestionably an eccentric. For, in a manner highly flattering to Wagner yet at the same time alarmingly excessive, the King had tampered with traditional décor by burdening his rooms and salons with operatic touches. More significantly, he seemed obsessed with but a single Wagner theme, the swan emblem of *Lohengrin.* It appeared on andirons and mantels, on doorknobs, keys and tableware.

"I have discarded the coat of arms of my Wittelsbach an-

cestors," Ludwig explained proudly, "in favor of a nobler symbol—Lohengrin's swan!" In testimony he waved at the carved
baldachin above the throne, the gilt canopy over the royal bed,
the bell pulls, water carafes and bathroom fixtures.

They entered the court theater. Swans spread stucco wings
across the proscenium, while cygnets adorned the alabaster rail
of loge and royal box. "Everything must have the mark of your
resplendent hero," Ludwig repeated.

Now they had reached the carriage house and stables, where
Richard was astounded to see swan images embossed on every
piece of harness, including the coachmen's cockades. There
was even a swan-shaped sleigh.

"And I believed myself scorned, friendless, my work unrec-
ognized!" Wagner gasped. He looked at the King as though on
a vision. "This can't be real. You, Sire, are Lohengrin himself.
No, you are that most exalted figure of Arthurian legend, whom
the English call Sir Perceval—our Parsifal."

Carried away, he saw himself once more on a crowded Munich street during Holy Week when, as a lone traveler, he had
first beheld this same Ludwig whose features even then had
evoked before his inner eye the flawless Knight of the Grail.
There seemed indeed to be a mystic bond between this benign
monarch and himself, woven by destiny for a purpose of loftiest
design. At this moment Wagner did not think Ludwig at all
eccentric, but a wondrous intelligence of vast enlightenment,
perception and dedication. The *Lohengrin* monomania was
neither laughable nor odd. It was the ultimate recognition of
an essence, a substance, an aesthetic value in art that Richard
himself identified as Wagnerian. Liszt, Bülow, the Wesendonks had variously and individually hailed his creative efforts,
but had they really understood the extramundane cosmos his
music no less than his pen had tried to build? No, none had
had the sweep of imagination to follow his soaring flight, none
but this anointed youth on a worldly throne. If Ludwig, in
short, had been sparked by contact with Richard Wagner, the
reverse was now equally true. Wagner was ecstatically aflame
after exposure to Ludwig.

One of the King's immediate and most magnanimous gestures toward his idol, after providing the composer with a home and a more than ample salary, was to settle with the waiting array of Wagner creditors. At short intervals Richard traveled to Vienna, Zürich, Paris and even Dresden (for the Saxon amnesty had at last been granted); in all these cities he paid up such debts as he remembered, though some were undoubtedly overlooked as he did not keep accounts. It was characteristic of Richard that he lacked a sound appreciation of money. When paying a coachman or tavernkeeper he never waited for change, even out of a disproportionately large bill.

"Am I to hold out my hand for coppers from someone who is worse off than I?" he asked in disbelief.

By the same token, however, he now helped his royal benefactor to dip into the state treasury and spend with both hands. First, Ludwig's bounty financed the hitherto unproduceable *Tristan und Isolde*, which, by royal command, made its first appearance at the National Court Theater of Munich on June 10, 1865. During the long months of rehearsal there were frequent moments of despair as singers complained that, after memorizing the ultradifficult music of one act, and its text, they promptly forgot both while taking on the next. But in the end all obstacles were conquered and the production took form. The two outstanding vocal artists, Ludwig Schnorr von Carolsfeld and his wife Malwine Garrigues, who twice before had given up *Tristan* as hopeless, carried off the title roles with signal success. Mitterwurzer sang Kurvenal, Zottmayer delineated a noble King Marke, and a Fräulein Deinet made much of the lesser Brangäne. Carolsfeld, in those pre-Caruso days, had the reputation of being the greatest tenor ever appearing on European boards.

The opera proved a sensational triumph, not least because Wagner had persuaded the King to summon Hans von Bülow to Munich as Royal Conductor. The gifted son-in-law of Franz Liszt brought to the *Tristan* music a depth of understanding which the Viennese operetta-minded Esser had totally lacked. All the same, earlier protests to the effect that *Tristan* was too much for human voice or frame appeared in the end to have been right. A brief time after the performance the great Carolsfeld collapsed from overwork, and a month later he was in his grave. By popular request *Tristan* disappeared from the repertoire. Not until new generations of singers learned to train for the gigantic demands of Wagnerian opera did this musical tour de force return again to life.

To offset the damaging effect of Carolsfeld's death and the immense impact of the tragic Cornish love story over which hung so ill-fated a star, Wagner did a sharp turnabout. He believed the time had come for a try at a lighter theme. Why not confound those critics who damned his work as too gloomy and morose by presenting them with the only comedy effort of his career, *Die Meistersinger?*

This opera was tailored, quite unintentionally, for Bavarian audiences. Utilizing the singing-contest idea from *Tannhäuser,* but in a homespun rather than an aristocratic setting, it presented familiar popular figures—tradespeople, tanners, goldsmiths, bakers, cobblers and other craftsmen of medieval Nürnberg—in an amusing battle for the prized minstrel's crown. The plot was simple and in the tradition of accepted *opéra bouffe,* even including touches of slapstick. Its synopsis runs as follows:

DIE MEISTERSINGER

ACT I

Following the overture which introduces the outstanding thematic patterns, the action opens in the Katharinenkirche (Church of Saint Catherine) of Nürnberg. While the congregation is at prayer in the background, a young Franconian knight, Walther von Stolzing, attracts the eye of young Eva, daughter of the prosperous goldsmith Veit Pogner. Eva is accompanied by her nurse Magdalena, who in turn has amorous intentions toward David, the boy-apprentice of the cobbler Hans Sachs.

As the church empties, Walther contrives to beg Eva for a tryst, but she whispers that her father has promised to give her in marriage to tomorrow's winner of the singing contest, in which Walther therefore decides to take part.

Several townsmen arrive to rearrange the church pews for a

final rehearsal of the vocal contestants under direction of the pedantic Sixtus Beckmesser, who embodies fanatical worship of rules. Hans Sachs, gentle and philosophic, invites the stranger, Walther, into the circle and bids him open with the first song. Hereupon Pogner, who has just reiterated that his daughter is to be the winner's prize, wants to know where Walther learned to sing. The youth replies with the short and lovely "*Am stillen Herd zur Winterszeit*" and a reference to the poet, Walther von der Vogelweide. This fails to impress the hidebound listeners. During the song that follows, Beckmesser noisily chalks up on a blackboard all the technical mistakes he detects in Walther's "*So rief der Lenz in den Wald.*" A general dispute breaks out and the assembly disbands, while Sachs alone has praise for the singer.

Act II

It is evening. A street winds between two opposite houses, of Pogner and Sachs respectively, with interiors partially visible. Eva stops by the cobbler's window to inquire about the probable outcome of the contest, revealing her love for Walther. The middle-aged Sachs, himself in love with the girl, hides his own feelings and determines to do what he can to further the young romance. Beckmesser meanwhile stops under the Pogner balconies and serenades the absent Eva with an outrageously academic composition that illustrates all precious rules. The apprentice David, believing that the singing is intended for Magdalena, rushes out and gives Beckmesser a sound trouncing in which a few spectators soon take part, then other passers-by, until a general brawl results. Abruptly all tempers calm down again and everybody goes home, to an orchestral accompaniment of pointedly placid music and the disarmingly peaceful toot of the town watchman's horn.

Act III

SCENE 1: Morning sunlight pours into the cobbler's home on the Feast of Saint John, which is the date of the contest. Walther, whom Sachs has taken in as his guest, now tries out his "Prize Song" while Sachs writes down music and words. Then the two retire to dress themselves in special finery for the event. During this interval the wily Beckmesser, still black and blue from his beating, sneaks in to learn what sort of competition he must meet on the part of his younger rival. He sees the scribbled text and steals it. After Beckmesser departs, Eva enters, ostensibly to have a shoe repaired, just as, clad in their best finery, Walther and Sachs reappear. The lovers embrace and Walther instantly improvises another stanza for his "Prize Song." Now David and Magdalena too arrive, and all five set out merrily for the festival.

SCENE 2: A meadow on the banks of the Pegnitz River outside the walls of Nürnberg. With banners and pomp the various workers' guilds march up, followed by townspeople and a bevy of costumed village girls who perform a rustic dance. After an opening address by Sachs the contest begins. Beckmesser pushes himself forward and attempts to render the stolen song, which he had not had time to memorize properly, aside from not knowing its tune. His performance meets with ridicule and scorn.

Now Walther mounts the flower-banked knoll and sings out in clear tones "*Morgendlich leuchtend im rosigen Schein*," easily winning all hearts and the day's prize. Eva herself steps up to place a wreath of laurels and myrtle on his brow, since he is both victor and bridegroom-to-be.

Hans Sachs winds up the proceedings by singing the praises of art in his apostrophe "*Verachtet mir die Meister nicht*," before the curtain falls.

In writing and composing *Die Meistersinger* Wagner departed from the special design that distinguishes his work from that of all other opera creators. He chose here a cast of simple human beings in place of other-world creatures belonging to legend and myth. *Rienzi* too might be listed as an exception, were it not a typical beginner's effort, imitative, pastiche and therefore unfit for comparison within the true Wagnerian output.

Throughout operatic literature a gallery of stock characters has been shuffled and reshuffled into standard situations: the brave soldier, the kindhearted courtesan, the cursing gypsy, the noble savage, the wronged maid, the fortuneteller, the jealous princess, the cynical rake, the Oriental doll and the sad clown. These hoarily familiar protagonists roam unremittingly through such respective librettos as *Andrea Chénier, Manon, Il Trovatore, L'Africaine, Cavalleria Rusticana, Carmen, Aïda, Rigoletto, Madama Butterfly* and *I Pagliacci.*

Wagner alone left this obvious company behind, for the unobvious denizens of mankind's dream world: the Elysium, the Hesperides, the Valhalla, the Nirvana of the Ages. Even as his music patterns were spacious and soaring beyond the limits of previously accepted form, so his pen chose loftier material to clothe in language that transcended—except in *Die Meistersinger*—the needs of straight entertainment.

Only with *Die Meistersinger* did he accord a salute to the functional theater.

CHAPTER 3

THE *première* of *Die Meistersinger* took place in Munich on June 21, 1868. Again leading singers of the day studded the program, while Bülow rose to his usual excellence. Critical reception was warm, despite the opera's employ of almost rudimentary folk tunes and archaic music forms to fit the naïve spirit of its medieval setting. By far the most telling assessment of the performance, and of the opera's lasting worth, was given by the philosopher Friedrich Nietzsche in a group of dissertations under the heading of *Jenseits von Gut und Böse (Beyond Good and Evil):*

Right from the start of the overture in Richard Wagner's *Meistersinger* one is forced to recognize that here is grandiose, ancient art which pridefully demands for its understanding that two centuries of music patterns be assumed to be still alive. All honor to Germans everywhere that this proud assumption was not wrong! What sap and strength! What seasons and points of the compass are here mingled in richest confusion. . . . We find these happenings on stage now old-fashioned, now foreign rather than homely, and again bittersweet, youthful, pompous with adherence to tradition, yet not seldom prankish and more often crude and rough—there is fire and courage, and at the same time the slightly aged texture of late-ripened fruit. . . . All this pours out in breadth and fullness, with uneven moments of puzzling hesitation, of change in tempo and mood, as in a dream or nightmare—but quickly the great stream of pleasure and contentment returns, a satisfaction with old and new joys, including the artist's own revealed pleasure in his art, which he is at no pains to conceal, for he is himself astonished at having found the means to give expression to such things.

341

All in all, here is not prettiness nor the fair brightness of
southern skies, no grace, no dainty dance (save for the lusty
hopping of some village maids) and certainly no great plot
issues. A certain clumsiness of pattern is actually underscored, as though the author meant to emphasize: "This is
my purpose!" The costuming too is heavy, willfully gaudy
yet worn with dignity, a blend of academic authenticity and
lacy flitter. Here is Germanism in its best and worst sense:
a Teutonic showcase of variety and excess, of overpowering
might and glutted symbolism, unafraid of expressing itself
in an antiquated medium—and indeed appearing there to be
fully at ease. For it is a mark of the German spirit, this com-
bination of youthfulness and age, of brittle decline ever ready
for the upswing to a richer future.

Long before the above testimony confirmed Ludwig's belief
in Wagner's greatness, the King had heaped further favors on
his guest and friend. In addition to the pleasance on Starnberg
Lake, the artist was provided with an elaborate Munich villa
in Renaissance style, with numerous balconies and terraces as
well as a spacious garden surrounded by an iron grille. The
address was Brienner Strasse 21.

All this, in conjunction with the court-sponsored Wagner
premières (for which Ludwig furnished stage, orchestra, sets,
costumes, props and salaries), proved a heavy drain on the
state treasury. A day of reckoning was bound to come when
both the dreamy artist and his reckless royal master were faced
with grim reality. The awakening blow was dealt by a candid
report from the Bavarian Ministry of Finance, which showed
a shocking deficit. Similarly a private review of the King's personal coffers revealed a yawning insolvency. The Royal Cabinet thereupon called for a detailed accounting of all official
expenditures, including His Majesty's private charities and
grants.

It now came to light that Ludwig's passion for art arose from
something deeper and more sinister than aesthetic inclination.
There was a pathological base, linked to generations of dynastic
inbreeding, plus early twists in personality and emotional development. The latter included a cowed childhood under the

dominant force of a disciplinarian father, causing the young prince to grow up with a sense of total inadequacy. To compensate for this, Ludwig had taken refuge in a world of his imagining: the paradise of poetry, music and their offshoot, opera. Here he could identify himself with heroes of his fancy, who boasted the freedom, authority and gallant prowess that were beyond his own reach.

On attaining kingship Ludwig's situation suddenly changed. He now could turn fairy tales into reality and live to the hilt his visions of a world of chivalry and beauty. But the beauty and chivalry he had in mind derived only from books and belonged to ages long past. In mid-nineteenth-century Europe people no longer walked about in satin panniers or breeches, their heads topped by powdered perukes. The machine age was on its way, with its industrial pressures that would affect transportation, architecture and every phase of human life. These sobering facts the romantic king was not prepared to face. He would oppose the encroachment of modernity by clinging obstinately to the past.

First, he would raise the magic world of opera to theretofore unknown eminence. Then, to counteract the dull classicism of Munich's public buildings (erected by his father and grandfather with an eye to progress), he launched a construction program of his own by blueprinting a series of stupendous castles to be scattered across the Bavarian countryside. Each of these would embody a particular royal fancy. The magnificently devised palace of Herren-Chiemsee was to be a brilliant sequel to Versailles; the enchanting Linderhof a miniature Potsdam or Trianon; the lofty turrets of Neu-Schwanstein would represent Lohengrin's legendary Monsalvat or Castle of the Grail as well as a glorified Wartburg for Tannhäuser. In the last project the King's obsession with Wagnerian imagery expressed itself in repetition of the swan motif, carried over presently into the décor of all objects pertaining to his private life.

Slipping from mania to mania, Ludwig soon lost all contact with his century or, for that matter, with any actual century before him. Even before meeting the idolized Richard in person, he sank into a pseudohistoric limbo of Wagnerian drama, a Venusberg from which there was eventually no escape. In keeping with his operatic mood the King took to costuming himself in highly original style. *Lohengrin* had been the first of Wagner's works to come to his attention, hence the one to make the greatest impact. He soon saw himself as a reincarnation of the *Schwanen-Ritter*, son of Parsifal, come from a land beyond the ken of ordinary mortals.

Needless to say, the trappings of delusion were outrageously expensive. The cost of launching experimental new operas and the liberal subvention of their composer might be borne by a state budget that allowed for cultural pursuits. But the erection of needless castles, architectural freaks too inaccessible and outlandish for habitation or any other use, called for sums the shocked Finance Ministry could not pay.

It was inevitable that the blame for the King's excesses must be shared by Richard Wagner. Until the composer's arrival in Bavaria, Ludwig had been a dreamer and rhapsodist whose harmless eccentricities played themselves out on a small scale. But nothing could ever be small scale with Richard around. The prodigal effusions of his genius seized on everything that might serve the purpose of creation, including the precarious stability of the King's mind. The end was bound to spell twofold disaster as the Wagnerian sorcery threw the state treasury out of balance and the royal reason as well.

Richard's first confrontation with the King's ministers took place at Nymphenburg, as he was strolling with Ludwig through the porcelain museum. A group of gentlemen with portfolios under their arms came down one of the corridors, apparently on urgent business. At sight of the King they bowed ceremoniously, then paused in expectation. But Ludwig waved them away.

"I am sorry, gentlemen, no audience today. As you see, I am busy with our new Opera Director, Herr Wagner." He completed the introduction by turning to Richard. "Allow me to present my unbending taskmasters, the Royal Ministry."

As Wagner exchanged nods with the solemn gentlemen he suddenly recognized among them a familiar face which gave him a jolt and a vague sense of impending doom. It was the

face of Von der Pfordten, his Dresden enemy, who had been
instrumental in obtaining the decree of exile against him. A
thought flashed through his mind. "I shall not last where this
man is present!"

Pfordten too reacted to the introduction. His eyes narrowed
and his face hardened into faintly concealed menace. Ludwig
sensed something as, looking from Wagner to Pfordten, he
asked, "You two have met before?"

"Indeed." Pfordten nodded significantly. "Herr Wagner and
I had . . . er . . . dealings, during my years of service at the
Saxon Court."

Ludwig smiled, relieved. "Ah, charming! Then you are able,
my dear Baron, to appreciate his great worth." Happily he put
an arm about Wagner's shoulders.

"Completely, Your Majesty." Pfordten did not smile as he
kept his eyes on the silent Wagner, who walked on now with
the King.

A few days later, in an anteroom of the *Residenz,* the same
Pfordten and two colleagues paced the floor impatiently. Obviously the Baron had chosen not to hold back his secret longer
but to reveal the revolutionary record of the King's new protégé. Von Lipowsky and Von Dollmann, the ministers of Finance and Education, respectively, made horrified protests.

"You are quite sure it's not a case of mistaken identity?"

"False accusations are dealt with severely by our laws."

Pfordten sneered. "Mistaken identity, false accusations, bah!
I tell you, I myself drove that Wagner fellow out of Saxony.
He is a dangerous radical, a firebrand who'll bring the mon-
archy crashing down over our ears."

The others exchanged troubled stares. Just then a door flew
open and Pfistermeister entered. His manner was apologetic.
"I am sorry, gentlemen, but His Majesty is receiving no one
today."

"What—again?" The Minister of Finance held up his portfolio. "But I *must* have an audience! The national budget must
be approved."

His colleague pushed forward to gain Pfistermeister's attention. "And *I* want authorization to go ahead with the new

school and orphanage project at Straubing. I know His Majesty favors this matter, but we still lack the official word."

The Royal Secretary shrugged. "It is useless, gentlemen. His Majesty is attending a rehearsal of *Tannhäuser.*" He bowed and made his exit.

A smile of grim satisfaction spread over Baron von der Pfordten's face. "There you have it, my friends. Affairs of state can go hang while the King listens to his favorite minstrel's music."

"But that's impossible!" cried the others in unison.

"Not at all. The royal house of Bavaria leans toward . . . er . . . shall we say, eccentricity." Pfordten paused significantly. "A special reason for alertness on the part of the Cabinet, don't you think?"

His listeners were plainly distressed. "Yes. Yes indeed, but . . ."

Pfordten now pulled from his brief case a folded paper and spread it on a table for his companions to see. "Here, gentlemen, is something else our rattleheaded sovereign is planning. You are looking at an architect's drawing for a palatial building to be called the 'Richard Wagner Theater.' It's to be constructed right here in Munich, at government expense. And the designer, one Gottfried Semper, happens to be none other than a revolutionary from this same Wagner's Dresden circle." Again Pfordten let the words sink in. "Take a look at the specifications. They're a passport to national bankruptcy, since not only a theater is asked for but a whole 'Wagner City' and its government-paid upkeep for generations to come!"

The Finance Minister gasped. "But our treasury is already strained by the cost of the King's string of castles! Where are we to raise the money for such an absurd project as—" his hand slammed the table—"as this?"

Pfordten remained casual. "According to Wagner, everything must be sacrificed for Art. When people need food, give them opera. If they want clothes, wrap them in symphonies." His tone changed sharply. "I tell you, we must run that mountebank out of town!"

The Minister of Education had misgivings. "Wait a minute. I must confess that, for a long time now, Munich has needed a first-class theater. Not only would it enhance our reputation abroad, but the effect on our admittedly rustic Bavarian character might prove highly beneficial." A withering glance from Pfordten caused him to clear his throat momentarily, but he stood his ground. "Yes, I would deem it a civilizing factor."

"In that case," came an acid challenge, "are you prepared to pay for this 'civilizing' enterprise out of *your* budget, sir?"

The Finance Minister was on Pfordten's side. "That's right, Herr von Dollmann. How about a cut in your allotment?"

This was more than the latter had bargained for. "Oh, I didn't mean to go that far," he cried aghast. "The need of the schools is too great."

"Then you no longer favor the Wagner project, if your department must help foot the bill?" inquired Pfordten.

Lamely the answer was given. "I—I suppose not."

"Good." Pfordten rolled up the paper. "Thank you, gentlemen, and allow me to compliment you on your wisdom in recognizing that this adventurer, Wagner, is a corrupting influence on our young and far too high-strung king." He tapped the table with the scroll. "And now, regarding this fantastic theater plan, do I hear a veto?"

Lipowsky spoke up. "By all means. You may put my name on the record."

Pfordten nodded. "That makes two of us." He turned to Dollmann. "What about you, my friend?"

"I was thinking, we could perhaps . . . er . . ."

Lipowsky gave his colleague a brusque nudge, adding *sotto voce:* "Budget!"

At this the hesitant Dollmann gulped and made up his mind. "I was just going to say I am in complete accord. We veto."

"Agreed." The tension on Pfordten's face relaxed. Without further words he snapped his brief case shut. Then, after silent handshakes, the three men left the room.

Once again the mills of the gods had been set in motion, and their grinding would bode Richard Wagner ill.

EVER since his son-in-law, Hans von Bülow, had taken the post of Royal *Kapellmeister* with the Munich State Opera House, Franz Liszt had promised himself a visit to Bavaria. He was fond of Hans, of whose talents he held the highest opinion. But this was not why Liszt decided to go to Munich. An odd notion had taken root in his sharp Magyar mind, regarding his daughter Cosima and that unpredictable firebrand, Richard Wagner.

He had nothing on which to base any suspicions. Nothing, that is, except his own flagrantly amorous past, about which, nowadays, the graying Franz did not like to think. He was middle-aged, well over the half-century mark, and sobered in outlook. The autumnal Liszt no longer brooked any nonsense, and if there *was* any "nonsense" afoot between the imprudent Cosima and his friend Richard he intended to put a stop to it.

The Bülow marriage had always troubled Liszt. Hans was a model husband and son-in-law, but from the start there had been signs of incompatibility on the young bride's part. It was no love match, that was sure—at least on Cosima's side. Even in preadolescent years that foolish child had known only one obsession: Richard Wagner. Liszt held himself responsible for this. His own boundless enthusiasm had nurtured the fire in his daughter's breast, unaware of the conflagration it might lead to. Well, his Wagner worship had dimmed with the years, since he and his old friend had been long out of touch. Liszt was only an anxious father now, and a grandfather to boot, concerned with the welfare of his loved ones.

He arrived in Munich during the peak of the musical season. Bülow was at his busiest with a second performance of *Die Meistersinger* in rehearsal and a concert version of *Tristan und*

Isolde set for the very night of Liszt's coming. There were only the most cursory greetings before the visitor found himself ushered into the royal box just as the theater lights were dimmed.

In the half-light Liszt was able to study his environment. He saw the introvert, romantic King of whose strange caprices all Europe had begun to talk. Ludwig's profile, flawless in line, was reminiscent of another Wittelsbach—his cousin, the beautiful and almost equally eccentric Empress Elisabeth of Austria. A close friendship linked those two, though since childhood their paths had crossed only seldom and the exchange of letters had taken the place of personal contact.

Next to Ludwig sat Wagner, flushed with success and glory. He looked like a man in his prime, not in the late fifties which he must certainly be. The blond hair at his temples was scarcely fading into gray, while face and figure remained taut, virile, surcharged with life. He was a short man, below average in stature, at least among Nordics. But he bore out a theory associated with Mediterranean peoples regarding the vigor and sheer durability of the smaller, firm and thick-set frame as against long-limbed, loose-jointed lankiness. Liszt's own experience supported this. Scarcely older than Wagner, his lean and towering limbs ached in every joint, while the once scandalously rampant Magyar lover had long turned to ways of continence. Indeed, he was seriously thinking of entering some religious order, a sure sign, for the phenomenal Franz, of all passion spent.

Though matters might be thus with him, Liszt clearly saw that they were not so with his daughter. Now grown to full womanhood, and having twice become a mother, Cosima was still no beauty. But there was a radiance about her, an arresting quality. Her large eyes, luminous and piercing, fixed themselves not on the happenings across the footlights or even on the silhouette of her husband on the podium but solely on him who had been the idol of her childhood, youth and maturity—Wagner. She was intoxicated with his poetry, his music, his physical presence. Her fixation, like some potent drug, was Wagner.

Liszt would have liked to concentrate on what took place on stage. Comments regarding *Tristan und Islode* had reached Weimar at intervals, arousing his curiosity to highest pitch. He was impatient to discover for himself the worth or inadequacy of this controversial work. But now his mind refused to obey; his ears were deaf to opera. Only one question absorbed him: What was happening between Richard and Cosima? With growing alarm Liszt watched his daughter. Only occasionally did he cast a glance of approval—and sadness—in the direction of his former pupil, Bülow, who was acquitting himself in so musicianly and creditable a fashion while about to lose a wife.

As for Wagner himself, he seemed totally remote and untouched by his immediate surroundings. He was absorbed in nothing but music. Perhaps the *Tristan* melodies were bringing back the torturing love of his life, Mathilde, in memory pictures of a Zürich garden or a museum rendezvous. Now, on stage, the *Liebestod* was being sung—that soaring cry of heartbreak which had been wrung from him at the peak of his sufferings, in Venice. He sighed as the music ended and the curtain fell to the echo of a rousing audience ovation. Almost absently Wagner stood and thanked the public, then accepted the congratulations of his companions in the royal box.

Cosima was the last to touch his hand. She gave him a penetrating look. "You haven't forgotten your Isolde, have you?"

Missing the reproach in her voice, Richard was astounded anew at the depth of Cosima's understanding. How well she read his innermost thoughts! He stared at her, speechless, then shook his head as though he were only now confiding a grave secret to her, yet one which her perspicacity had guessed so long ago.

The rest of the evening, following the concert's end and the King's retirement to his private chambers, was given over to Franz List. Both Wagner and the Bülows were eager to have news from family and mutual friends, as well as to hear the visitor's own immediate plans.

"My plans?" Liszt shrugged casually. "I leave for Budapest tomorrow noon."

"What is this, another 'farewell concert' tour?"

"No, my virtuoso days are definitely over." An apologetic smile crossed the haggard, bony features. "I don't like speech-making, but they trapped me into making the inaugural address at the new National Conservatory. For some years now I have spent part of my time in Hungary, teaching."

The following morning Liszt tried to see his son-in-law alone, to ascertain whether Hans truly liked working in Munich or would welcome help in being transferred to a different locality. The interview was unsatisfactory, taking place during rehearsal of a sequence from last night's performance. There was grumbling backstage. The singers, it seemed, were demanding a fortnight's respite before taxing their voices anew. Liszt's ear caught some of the complaints.

"The whole idea of 'Wagnerian Opera' is insane!"

"Who ever heard of top-range bellowing for almost five hours? And yesterday was only a concert version!"

"No wonder Carolsfeld dropped dead."

"That's what'll happen to the rest of us if this nonsense isn't stopped. We ought to scratch Wagner from the repertoire and call in a sensible Italian like Rossini or the great Verdi."

"Not Verdi, for heaven's sake! They say he's been bitten by the same bug, trying to out-Wagner Wagner."

Liszt approached the podium where Bülow was sorting out some scores. "Well, my boy, how are things going?"

The younger man appeared entranced with his work and quite unaware of the mutterings backstage. "Spendidly! We are going to do great things here, thanks to the patronage of a music-loving king." In his typically self-effacing way, Bülow now nodded toward the foyer. "I suppose you are looking for Richard? I saw him outside a moment ago with Cosima."

Liszt realized the futility of interfering where dedication was so absolute. His eyes narrowed quizzically as he bade Bülow farewell. Then, frowning, he strode through the empty theater toward the lobby, where he came upon his daughter and Wagner sitting halfway up the carpeted stairs. They were talking excitedly, without thought of being overheard.

"You must weed out the malcontents and hire some new leads," Cosima argued. "I tell you, as I came through the wings just now the prima donna was calling you a slave driver and despot."

Richard waved his hand with *élan.* "Of course I'm a slave driver and hard to work with! Of course I ask more of performers, and musicians too, than anybody else! I am trying to do something new in a field that has grown stereotyped and barren. I want opera, first and last, to be a *show.*"

Cosima's face lighted up. "Like a play?"

"Exactly. That's why I can't repeat often enough that I must have singers who can *act* and instrumentalists who can identify themselves with the happenings on stage. I want theater, not song recital or symphony concert. There must be movement, action—things must *happen.* That's why in the *Tannhäuser* meadow scene I have cowbells, and in *Die Meistersinger* a cobbler hammering on his shoes."

"I understand." Impulsively Cosima had reached for his hand and clasped it to her. Wagner paused in his expostulations. No matter how pressing the things he had to say, he must halt and drink in the adoration on the young woman's face. There was a long silence before both became aware of someone stepping from the shadows.

"Ah, Richard, there you are!" Liszt tried to be casual. "I've come to say good-by." He turned severely to Cosima. "I looked for you, my child, at your home."

Cosima met the veiled reproof. "But you know, Papa, that I always come to rehearsals."

"Are you sure that's it?" Liszt's voice had an undertone. He let her feel his disapproval as he turned ostensibly to Wagner, while all his words were clearly meant for Cosima alone. "When my Budapest visit is behind me I am going to Rome. I have decided to take religious orders."

"What?" Richard had jumped to his feet. "First you turn from a top pianist's career to that of composer, and now you want to be a priest? Unless you are joking, Franz, forgive me, but that—that is sacrilege."

"I am not joking. Oh, I can't be fully ordained, I know. My life has hardly been impeccable enough for that." Liszt glanced

sideways at Cosima. "But worldly success, of which I have
had a fair share, has left me weary of selfishness. Believe me,
I want nothing so much as a return to obscurity—and peace."

Wagner was still incredulous. "You, the most celebrated
performer of our century!"

"When next we meet I shall be simply the Abbé Liszt." He
turned to his daughter. "What are your thoughts, Cosima?
Does my decision impose any . . . er . . . restrictions on you?"

With concealed defiance the young woman answered brightly. "Why should it, Papa? It's you, not I, who are taking the
cloth." Now her manner changed. She was kitten-soft as she
rose to kiss him sweetly. "Come. I'll ride with you to the
station."

She waved gaily to Wagner, then took her father's arm and
strode with him through the hall. Richard remained behind,
shaking his head in surprise and delight at her spirit. With
such a champion on his side, plus the conspicuous support of a
ruling sovereign, did he have anything to fear? Surely the time
was here at last when his artistic mission would come into fullest flower, without further blight from the reactionary forces
of intolerance and economic stricture. At peace with himself
and the world, Wagner ambled through the empty theater and
joined his friend Bülow on the podium.

The reassurance that filled him was ill founded. Royal favor
and the blind adoration of Cosima, coupled with a portion of
self-confidence, constituted no guarantees of a successful (or
even safe) future. At this very moment, while Richard sunned
himself in contemplation of his prospects, powerful forces rallied against him behind the scenes. In the same anteroom of
the Munich Palace where they had so often gathered in vain,
the King's ministers waited again for an audience. Pfordten
was among them, as were Lipowsky and Dollmann.

"Mark my word," commented the Minister of Finance, "we
might have saved ourselves the trouble. His Majesty will not
receive us."

Pfordten's lips barely moved. "If so, there are other steps
that can be taken." He tapped his brief case. "I have here a

petition, ready to submit to the Council of State, demanding
that the King be called before a medical commission."

"But that's dreadful!" gasped Lipowsky.

"A board of alienists, to be exact. It is my considered opinion, gentlemen, that His Majesty is insane."

There were outcries from every side. "Impossible!" "We can
be accused of treason!" "Who would dare back up such a
claim?"

Pfordten remained calm. "All we need for proof is to open
the books and expose the King's financial record."

The Minister of Finance held up a protesting hand. "I would
like to concur with Your Excellency. But even though the State
Treasury is my special charge, I cannot agree that a monarch's
extravagance can be safely diagnosed as madness."

"No?" Pfordten's voice had acquired an edge. "Then let me
point out that we are here faced with an exceptionally flagrant
case. You will not deny that Bavaria is threatened with bankruptcy. Why? Because of crop failure? Industrial troubles?"

There were more outcries. "Certainly not. Our farmlands
are the best, our factories run day and night."

"Correct. Then the deficit can be caused only by a king with
a mania for impersonating characters in operas. That in itself
could be condoned as harmless if his hallucinations didn't call
for the building of fantastic castles and mountain lodges, with
furnishings, servant staffs, carriages and other appointments to
match. All this at a cost of millions, mind you!"

A murmur of disbelief and awe went through the listeners.
Pfordten pressed his advantage. "You call it sanity when a
sovereign is hit by some wild notion and up goes an incredible
pile of masonry, of no possible use to anyone, yet one more
load to be dropped needlessly on the backs of the common
people?" He paused, then stressed each word. "I say to you,
gentlemen, we are dealing with a lunatic."

The others debated among themselves. Someone quoted a
palace servant who claimed that His Majesty was often confused and irrational, unable to recognize even constant attendants, such as personal secretaries and valets. Another reported
that the royal bedroom had recently been remodeled to dupli-

cate the Venus Grotto in *Tannhäuser,* while yet a third could state positively that Ludwig's coronation chamber leaked because he had ordered an artificial lake constructed above it, for *Lohengrin's* swan. A number of ministers shook their heads and muttered "Terrible! Terrible!"

Pfordten was gaining ground. "That's not all," he continued. "Have you heard the latest nonsense being planned by the royal bosom friend, Richard Wagner? He wants to put the whole Nibelungen Saga to music. Financed, of course, by the King's purse."

The Nibelungen Saga! That ancient collection of fairy tales? The listeners welcomed a chance to laugh. That Wagner fellow would next be sending out a call for some singing dwarfs and dragons. The swan would have to go. As for the King, would he end up by remodeling his town palace into Valhalla and then setting fire to it?

Now Pfordten aimed a final shot. "Brace yourselves, my friends. There's one more item to be charged to the State Treasury."

An angry chorus arose. "What! Still more to come?"

"His Majesty has just conferred on Richard Wagner a life pension."

A life pension, paid out of the people's money? This was outrageous! That vagabond composer wasn't even a Bavarian. "He ought to be run out of town!" cried the listeners.

"Precisely," Pfordten agreed. "I move that we formulate an edict to send that Wagner scamp back where he came from. Do I hear a dissenting voice?" He looked toward the diffident and timid Dollmann.

But Dollmann appeared convinced at last. "I suppose there's no doubt about it," he mumbled. "Our king is being corrupted. Richard Wagner must be banished."

At this moment a door to an adjoining chamber opened and Pfistermeister appeared. He was in a beaming mood. "I have good news, Your Excellencies," he announced. "His Majesty is disposed to receive you!"

"Thank you" was Pfordten's chilly answer. "The audience is . . . no longer necessary."

"What do you mean?" The royal secretary looked bewildered.

"You may convey our regrets, Baron. A special Cabinet meeting is being called, to which the King will receive a written summons. Good day."

Leaving the shocked Pfistermeister openmouthed, the ministers picked up their portfolios and filed solemnly from the room.

CHAPTER 5

THE interior decoration of the Wagner villa on Brienner Strasse 21 had taken many months. Its furnishings were largely fetched from the King's huge stores of treasure, including several masterpieces from the royal picture galleries. When all was ready Ludwig himself ushered Richard across the threshold.

Together king and composer wandered from room to room, inspecting woodcarvings, tapestries, porcelains and statuary. One particularly striking oil canvas of an artist's head, with wide black beret, arrested Wagner's attention. He stooped to read the metal plaque: REMBRANDT—"SELF-PORTRAIT." An expression of approval marked his features. He turned to the King.

"I can never really express, Sire, what your generosity has meant to me. This splendid new home, these beautiful treasures—how shall I ever show my thanks?"

"Through your music, of course." Ludwig grew pensive. "I have always believed that creative artists should not waste their time earning a living. They should be subsidized by men of less talent but more wealth."

This was sweet balm to Wagner's ears. "You think so too? Most artists naturally hold that opinion, but the . . . er . . . lay mind certainly does not agree with them."

The King appeared to be musing aloud. "Some of us, though quite unable to produce a tune, love music as intensely as those who can. Therefore, my friend, you are to be made comfortable so that you may concentrate on nothing but your great work."

"Your Majesty is much too kind."

"Perhaps not. Perhaps I am selfish, nurturing a secret urge

to go down in history as another Medici—a vainglorious patron of the arts." With a twisted smile Ludwig walked on.

A few days later Richard arrived from a quick trip to Lake Starnberg, where he had gathered up his most essential belongings. In no time he was established under the new roof, enjoying the splendor and spaciousness about him as one to the manner born.

Befitting such improved outer circumstances, Richard now looked to his personal appearance. A tailor was summoned to the Brienner Strasse for a series of painstaking fittings. Standing before a tall mirror, Wagner directed the designing of all manner of highly individualistic garments, from an array of fine silk underwear to velvet jackets and trousers with rich frogging, and a Rembrandt beret.

While the tailor and his assistant busied themselves with pins and shears, Richard observed his reflection in the glass. There was a moment when the mirror became blurred and a vision emerged of the long-ago scene at Meyerbeer's Paris apartment, with its luxury and glitter. The great Giacomo himself materialized, there in his stately bed, but with a difference—for his face appeared to have changed quite unsubtly into that of Wagner.

The vision vanished, and Richard pondered its meaning. He stroked the lush materials, the velvets, satins and brocades, then turned to feast his eyes on his surroundings. This was what he had promised himself, and poor Minna, in those miserable Paris days. His face clouded momentarily. Poor Minna indeed! She had withered at his side and was now invalided with heart disease, without ever tasting the prosperity he had at last attained.

Such reflections brought him back to his plans. Ah, how his muse would spread her wings and soar in such aesthetically satisfying settings! Each floor of the new mansion, from cellar to balustraded roof, was designed with one end in view: to offer escape from ugliness, from physical discomfort and from the prosaic shoddiness of ordinary life.

He had resumed work on the *Nibelungen Ring*, laboring at top speed, alternating between music scores and the missing

portions of his librettos. In sure and mighty strokes the tetralogy was taking final shape, interrupted periodically by trial
performances, in concert form, of such salient portions as the
"Ride of the Valkyries," "Wotan's Farewell," the "Magic Fire"
scene and the new themes from *Siegfried* and *Götterdämmerung*. To please the King, such programs were invariably filled
out with favorite portions of the earlier operas, of which Ludwig could not hear enough. There were times when the Court
Theater was empty, save for the royal listener alone in his box,
while a four-hour performance was in full swing.

After one of these occasions Ludwig experienced such a
transport of ecstasy that he penned a dithyrambic and incoherent note to Wagner, dated February 1, 1865:

> Beloved! Unique one! Oh, how filled with joy I am! . . .
> Where am I? In Valhalla's blissful haunts, with Siegfried,
> with Brünnhilde. . . . What radiance about Tristan's body,
> what life eternal! To share it would be sheer enchantment.
> . . . And yonder, the heaven-sent Lohengrin "A Dove Each
> Year Descending." . . . Now Tannhäuser, the sinner cleansed
> through love, all-potent love! Would that I could join all of
> you. . . .
> My thanks, Beloved One, all my thanks! Soon to meet
> again. Until my death,
>
> LUDWIG
>
> Words are poor; they tell nothing. Only this can I write: in
> *you* lies everything; outside *you* nothing but dreariness and
> desolation.

Letters like these should have alerted Wagner to the strange
deviations in the King's chemistry. For some time now there
had been open discussion in government circles of Ludwig's
seeming reluctance to marry. Not only this. There was an
alarming absence of femininity about the Munich court since,
unlike most sovereigns of history, the youthful Wittelsbach
kept no mistress or even a favorite ballerina from the state
theaters. Nymphenburg Castle and all the other royal resi-
dences, furthermore, were staffed with none but masculine

help. Logically the suspicion took hold that Ludwig was a homosexual.

Monarchist elements recognized herein a formidable threat to the dynasty, which, without assurance of future descendants, was doomed to disappear. Negotiations were therefore opened in secret with various European nations who had marriageable princesses hanging heavily on the vine. Perhaps Ludwig could be maneuvered into a proxy courtship from which, under the compulsions of *noblesse oblige,* there was no retreat. Just how the King could then be pushed as far as the bridal chamber, no one knew. But widespread hope persisted that, once exposed to hymeneal intimacies, the most skittish bridegroom might be startled into normal channels. At any rate, from the point of view of the monarchist party, such an undercover game was worth the gamble.

Unfortunately all efforts to find a foreign bride ended in failure. Due to the idleness in which their denizens dwelled, the palaces of Europe were hotbeds of gossip. Thus Ludwig's "peculiarities" had long been grist for conversational mills, from Britain to the Bosporus. There was no shortage of high-born ladies hard pressed for husbands. But the pathological King of Bavaria did not appeal to them as a solution.

Undaunted, royalist circles narrowed the search to areas nearer home. They combed the provinces of Prussia, Holstein, Baden, Mecklenburg, and every tiny principality of the German realm. But here too the end result was failure.

At this point Ludwig's cousin, the Empress of Austria, came to the rescue. Among her sisters at the family home of Possenhofen, near Starnberg Lake, was the youngest, Sophie, a girl just blossoming to womanhood. Elisabeth, who had shared Ludwig's childhood and claimed to know him better than anybody else, banked on his mental and physical soundness so implicitly that she was willing to steer the innocent Sophie into his arms.

Actually the King offered no resistance. Perhaps because of his high regard for the fascinating Empress, he consented to a meeting with her younger, though less beauteous, relative. He behaved graciously toward Sophie and squired her about to the delight of officialdom and populace alike. He even allowed himself to be photographed at the young lady's side, gallantly offering her one arm while supporting his silk topper on the other. Finally, to confound all slanderers at home and abroad, he pronounced the blissful Sophie his fiancée and set a date for his wedding.

The date came and went, but there was no wedding. Long before her trousseau preparations were complete the prospective bride fell prey to undefinable fears. There was something eerie about her royal fiancé's quick-changing moods, his long silences and strangely erratic speech. He took to calling her Elsa and signing his notes and *billets-doux* to her Heinrich von Brabant. Also, he terrified the household at Possenhofen by coming to call at three or four in the morning and expecting everyone to rise and light up for his reception. What was worse, he addressed his future father-in-law, Duke Maximilian of Wittelsbach, as Wotan, and thoroughly alienated the Duchess by confusing her with a Valkyrie. This latter misdeed (for the Duchess Maximilian regarded it as such) proved the last straw. No man, not even a king, could get away with likening her to one of those blond Wagnerian hussies that galloped about between Heaven and Earth, up to no good, that was sure. In short, she refused to become Ludwig's mother-in-law. The engagement was off.

Young Sophie escaped one dire fate to leap headlong into another. She married a romantic Frenchman, Duke Ferdinand d'Alençon, and went with him to Paris, where, years later, she burned to death at a charity bazaar. A new invention called a cinematograph was being demonstrated. Through some error in manipulation the apparatus exploded, setting near-by booths aflame. In the stampede that followed, Ludwig's erstwhile Elsa was trapped and doomed to a harrowingly Wagnerian end.

This tragedy was bound to cast yet one more shadow on the King's clouding mind. But even before this epilogue to the royal engagement Ludwig had fallen victim to periods of intense melancholia. Neither the friendship of men nor the love of women (or vice versa!) could pull him out of these. As early as March 24, 1865, Richard Wagner endeavored to lift the monarch's somber spirit by writing:

I am saddened to see how isolated and lonely you feel. Isolated and lonely am I too, but in how different a manner! With you it is an overendowed, rich, ideal nature that longs for the utmost development of all that is benevolent. You want to understand, in order to be understood. But only they who understand *you* are deemed by you worth studying. Thus you are really condemning yourself to solitude, since nature and chance alone do not readily bring harmonious spirits together.

On the other hand my own loneliness stems from the fact that I do understand the world, yet cannot cut myself off from it, although I know that what I must seek is harmony *in isolation* and away from worldly things. In short, you are too much an introvert, and I, an extrovert.

Of course I can come close to you and share your confidence. . . . But I cannot replace your true needs, the world you should explore, the high office you must fulfill, the family you should found, and the wife you have yet to choose— all this is not to be cast aside for a mere friend. What I can be to you has value only after those other needs have been satisfied. Where their function ends let mine begin. All this will develop effortlessly, quietly. Of that I have no doubt.

It is this realization that causes me to urge you to restrain your restless yearning for perfection. What disturbs you is only the excessive wealth and sensitivity of your own mind, and it is clarity within one's own mind that is important. . . . Maturity and experience alone can bring such clarity. Experience can be likened to the sun, which throws its light on the secrets of night. But the sun cannot expose anything that has not been there all the time under cover of night. Therefore, he who by the bright lamp of living experience sees only a shabby picture gives testimony to the poverty of spirit concealed within him.

Thus Wagner tried to banish the increasingly morose moods of the King, which lay upon the royal household like a threatening pall. Medical science had no palliative as yet against the inroads of dementia. In reasoning and discoursing with his highborn patron, Richard was therefore, unconsciously, employing the techniques of a much later therapy, the psychoanalyst's persuasion.

He was not thinking of Ludwig alone. Scurrilous comment regarding the King's homosexual leanings was being bruited about Munich, with ever-bolder reflections cast on Wagner's role at court. For his own sake Richard must stem the tide of slander. With subtleness and tact he tried to escape the noose of Ludwig's devotion, yet holding on to the opulent sinecure that flowed therefrom.

Soon it would become clear that this could not be done. The easy life just opening before him was to be had only at a damning price: the pillory.

CHAPTER 6

BARON von der Pfordten had not been idle.

He was a man of manifold experience in high places. Political office holders in the Germany of that day were transferable from one province to another without regard to their place of birth. Thus Pfordten, unhappy in the socialistic strife that had clouded his term of service in Saxony, had years ago applied successfully for allocation to the Munich court. It irked him now to see another Saxon, Richard Wagner, drawing obloquy on himself which—by imputation—might ultimately reflect on a former associate, sponsor, and fellow Dresdener, namely Pfordten. To prevent this the Baron set in motion the proper machinery that would, as he put it, "rid Bavaria of the corrupting and shameless influence of a renegade adventurer, the composer Wagner."

In bolstering the legal forces at his command, Pfordten availed himself also of the press. A campaign of anti-Wagner publicity was let loose on Munich readers who until then had had little knowledge of their King's intimate life. The general tenor of these journalistic reports could not, however, miss their mark. In dark headlines it was pointed out to Bavarian burghers that a greedy intruder shared their fleshpots and daily bilked them of that which was their own. As yet the King's threatening malady was not brought into the open, for Pfordten held this in reserve as his climaxing shot. For a start he was content to alarm the taxpayers with disclosures that Richard Wagner was too expensive to have around.

In this Pfordten soon found support from Munich's ranking aristocracy, who had observed with chagrin that Ludwig II, unlike his father and grandfather before him, surrounded himself with no court life whatsoever. Of what good, then, were all those castles and palaces, erected at such outrageous costs?

"To entertain the royal favorite, Richard Wagner!" was the blanket reply held in readiness by Pfordten.

Before long Richard found himself pointed out and insulted in the streets. Cynical Munich citizens recalled the dancer Lola Montez, who, a generation earlier, had brought scandal and disgrace on the Wittelsbach dynasty. Born Marie Dolores Eliza Rosanna (and no paternal surname) at Limerick, Ireland, in 1818, this venturesome colleen had married one Captain James, who took her to India. There she wearied of him and returned to Europe, where she launched on a dancing career under the assumed name of Lola Montez. Her beauty and wild escapades attracted notoriety in every Continental capital. In 1847 she became the paramour of King Ludwig I of Bavaria, who bestowed on her the title of Countess von Landsfeld. But the revolutionary year 1848 saw the King tumbling from his throne and Lola chased out of Munich. She went to London, married George Heald, a trusting guardsman who presently came to his senses and divorced her. After that America was her chosen hunting ground. In 1851 she traveled over the United States, acting in a play entitled *Lola Montez in Bavaria*. Several additional marriages were added to the record before the lady settled, first near Lake Tahoe in California and finally in New York, where she devoted her energies to writing and lecturing as well as rescue work. She died in 1861, leaving behind some elevating reading matter, *The Arts of Beauty* and the collected texts of her lectures.

A diabolical paraphrase of that international coquette's name now was applied by Pfordten to Wagner. Not Lola but "Lolo" was the new menace threatening Bavaria's current sovereign, his morals and his pocketbook. By grapevine the epithet was picked up and sent on its rounds.

Calumny and invective were bad enough, but ridicule was fatal. Richard knew he must face the issue before the campaign of mockery gained such headway that any defense would be drowned in devastating guffaws. He addressed a quick appeal to Ludwig II, accusing no one but letting it be known than an organized plan of persecution was at work:

My King! I bring you unrest. Let me depart to some distant land where envy and misunderstanding cannot torment me further.

I don't know how to hate. The strongest negative feeling of which I am capable is revulsion. As a boy I was revolted by spiders, though even this I have learned to overcome. Today I recognize the spider as a poor creature struggling to survive, like all things that live. I might act against it to the extent of rescuing the miserable insect caught in its net, but I can no longer, as in childhood, tread on the spider itself simply because it is guilty of appeasing its own hunger. . . . Here you have my point of view, kindest of friends! I can and shall forgive everyone who chooses to spin a vengeful web for me, because I recognize and comprehend the suspicions behind it. They who think little of art must have even less use for artists.

The placating tone of this missive had only one purpose. If Ludwig consulted his ministers regarding the malevolent crusade that seemed to be afoot, he, Richard, wished to conciliate and meet his enemies with open mind.

Alas, the storm did not abate. The voice of slander grew louder and more ominous. Was Ludwig deaf to outside warnings? Had he not read the papers? It did not occur to Richard that someone might be intercepting the royal mail. He waited two days, then wrote a second letter:

I beg for a word, my sublime friend, that will tell me what to do. Shall I leave town? Am I to remain? Whatever you wish, that I wish too.

If I go, I shall move to foreign parts and never again return to Germany. . . . As to my work, its fate rests in your hands, and in the stars, for it was destiny that brought me to you, the noblest of German princes. Far greater than the blessings accrued to Prussia by Frederick II and his friendship with Voltaire is the miracle wrought by Ludwig of Bavaria. This, my lord, pray remember! Your service to art, with or without me, is the goal. None but you can decide. . . . I await your word, whatever it be, as my command. Until death, truly,

RICHARD WAGNER

Beyond a doubt the King received this new dispatch, for on the same day and by special messenger an answer was delivered at the Brienner Strasse villa. It contained a short, emphatic exhortation:

> Remain! You must remain here. . . . All will be perfect, as before. I am busy. Until death.
>
> LUDWIG

Just what was the nature of the King's "busy-ness" Richard had no way of knowing. Contact with the Palace became more and more difficult due to the barrier raised by Pfordten around the sovereign. A canny pattern of duplicity was followed to this end. For public consumption the friendship between Ludwig and Wagner was stigmatized as an unnatural and onerous relationship, while undercover reports to the King stressed a blossoming romance between Bülow's wife Cosima and the composer. In this manner Pfordten counted on arousing one or the other side to action, either Munich's respectable citizenry or the jealous monarch.

While waiting for the blow that was certain to fall, Richard jotted a line on the margin of his *Nibelungen* notes. "The dragon Fafner, breathing fire, and symbolic of evil," he wrote, "is none other than my relentless enemy, Von der Pfordten."

He needed no mystic conjuring, no Waldweben warnings, no magic bird to caution, "Hei, Siegfried!"

He was conditioned to danger.

PART IV

Cosima

CHAPTER I

A T AN early age Franziska Cosima Liszt had learned that she was an ugly child.

Her handsome mother, the Comtesse d'Agoult, and her brother and sister had pre-empted all that there was of family looks and charm. From the moment she took her first appraising glance in a mirror Cosima recognized herself to be fortune's stepchild.

She grew up with a firmly lodged chip on her shoulder. In the manner of slighted daughters, she adored her famous father with a possessive intensity, resentful of the devotion which he spread equally over his three offspring. She was particularly jealous of her beautiful sister Blandine, a flowerlike creature toward whom all hearts seemed naturally attracted. At times Cosima hated Blandine.

The ambiguous situation in the d'Agoult home was, of course, no mystery to the children. Servant talk and parlor gossip alike had clarified, before Cosima was six years old, that the Comte d'Agoult, *"Papa le Comte,"* was only a casual caller in his wife's drawing room, while the celebrated Hungarian pianist, Franz Liszt, enjoyed husbandly privileges. Nineteenth-century upper-class mores deplored but tolerated domestic triangles while frowning inexorably on divorce. The d'Agoults were respectable nobility who had married to keep pedigree and family fortune intact. The Count and Countess did not love each other, but Church and tradition demanded that they keep up appearances and bear the yoke of wedlock to the bitter end. This they did with grace, and much pleasure on the side.

Things were a bit less gay for the children, who played secondary roles in a strictly adult world. The adage that offspring were to be seen but not heard was hardly accurate. Whenever possible, they remained altogether invisible. This was especially true of the hawk-nosed and spindly Cosima, whom even the most doting mother would avoid showing off.

Actually all three children of the Comtesse d'Agoult were strangers to their fashionable *Maman*, for ladies of that era seldom entered the nursery. Contact between moppets and their elders was limited to a hasty good-night kiss administered under a paternal silk topper or to the accompanying rustle of ballroom taffeta and a warning not to wreck *Maman's* festive coiffure.

Apart from her plainness, Cosima's added grief was that she had no talent. The fire of her father's Magyar blood pulsed through her veins, yet she had inherited no trace of his magical gifts. This fact, slowly dawning in adolescence, ate into her soul, for she was consumed with *Geltungsbedürfnis*—the need to count for something, to rate, to be something or somebody. This was the era of Clara Wieck, pianist wife of Robert Schumann, a brilliant woman who was concertizing all over Europe and making a name for herself while enjoying a husband's love and rearing a houseful of children. The pubescent Cosima had attended one of Clara's recitals without being able to relish a single note for envy of the artist's phenomenal endowments. How poor, how insignificant that Schumann woman made her feel!

Franz Liszt was not unaware of his homely daughter's inner conflict. He saw Cosima's resentment when her sister Blandine was wooed and won by a dashing Paris attorney, Daniel Ollivier, while belles in quantity flocked about their dashing brother. It was obvious that, paired with good looks, illegitimacy proved no handicap. But to be unlovely and a bastard to boot, even with the divine Liszt for a progenitor, was calamitous indeed.

A sense of guilt weighed on the paternal heart. As Cosima entered her 'teens, Liszt made a point of taking her with him on tour. This enabled her to meet people of many lands and varied backgrounds. Nobody fell in love with her, but her judgment sharpened and her mind attained an early maturity that verged on the precocious. Presently she was able to hold the interest of Hans von Bülow, one of her father's music pupils. Bülow, an impecunious youth of distinguished family background, worshiped the ground Liszt trod. His devotion to the master caused him, for a long time, to waste barely a glance on the daughters of the house. But when Cosima set her cap for him a ravishing prospect opened up: the talented disciple saw himself as a potential son-in-law of Franz Liszt! This could be for Bülow nothing less than a design of fate.

There was hardly any courtship. And the marriage that followed could by no stretch of the imagination be called a love match. In Cosima's eyes the gentle, sensitive, ethereal Hans was not the ideal she had cherished for years in the secret recesses of her heart. At thirteen she had met Richard Wagner, in transit through Weimar on his flight from Saxony. Later, at sixteen, she had seen him again in Paris. The impact of twice encountering this man whom Liszt pointed to as the greatest creative genius of the century had left an ineradicable impression. On either occasion Wagner scarcely noticed the ungainly girl, but Cosima had taken him in, head to toe. She thought him inordinately handsome, which he was not. But there radiated from him a virile charm, a magnetism compounded of intellectual power and sheer erotic exuberance, too mystifying as yet for her young grasp. Only this much was clear: Bülow would never measure up to such a one. However, neither could an ill-favored mite like herself ask for the sun and moon. She told herself also that Wagner had been long married at the time of those early encounters and could therefore have offered no hopeful outlook to a girl on the threshold of growing up. With the disparity in their ages, furthermore, she had—reluctantly but wisely—put him out of her mind.

It happened that their paths crossed anew practically at the start of Cosima's honeymoon. The reason for this was a paradoxical one. Over the years Franz Liszt's esteem of Wagner had grown and deepened to the point where the older artist made it his mission to promote the struggling opera composer's works. He proselytized and won adherents by storm, simply through personal praise of Wagner's gifts and by including the latter's compositions in his own repertoire. In this manner Liszt

won over his own son-in-law, who became so fervent a Wagnerian that he lived for the day when he might make a pilgrimage to his idol's exile home. It took little persuasion to
win Cosima to this plan. As the young couple's marriage coincided with Liszt's contemplated trip to Switzerland, the honey-
mooners chose the same itinerary for their nuptial voyage.

The Zürich visit was to leave an everlasting imprint on Cosima's heart. Her inflammable nature caught fire all over again
when, with husband and father, she faced Richard. Nothing
had changed, for to her eyes he was ageless. Only the circumstances surrounding him, there on the Wesendonk estate, were
different. This was the first time she had seen Richard against
a domestic background, and, of course, it was her first meeting
with Minna.

A rift had come between the Wagners at this period, visible
even to strangers at a glance. A new love had crowded out
the old, charging the very air with sparks. Mathilde Wesendonk was the temptress who had won the titan's soul. Cosima
saw all this and more. She saw that, again, she herself made
not the slightest impression on Richard. He was like one struck
blind, impervious to the presence of all others as long as the
luscious Mathilde was around.

It was a bittersweet experience, to be in the beloved's vicin-
ity, yet at the same time almost nonexistent. But Cosima's ardor
was equal to the test. The thin, aquiline-featured bride sat in
unconnubial meditation, her enormous dark eyes fixed on Wagner's every move. How utterly she concurred in her father's
estimate of him! Here was a unique phenomenon: a musician
who was poet, philosopher, dramatist, composer and patriot,
all in one. With her own sharp intelligence and emotional
depth she encompassed and appreciated him. She wondered
in secret whether either of those two women, Minna or Mathilde, could really recognize his worth.

Yes, though she saw herself reduced to crushing insignificance during that Zürich visit, Cosima made every minute
count by drinking in each word that Wagner spoke. Fervently
she listened to his music and basked in the warm glow of his
personality. He was evolving in those days the great second

act of *Tristan und Isolde,* with its prodigal wealth of tunes. Sitting at the piano, he tested each thematic line, waiting for approval and praise from one person alone—Mathilde.

If only he could have looked to Cosima for understanding! Young as she was, she knew the vastness of his mastery. Better perhaps than all the others who seemed so close to him, she was capable of fullest dedication, such as he needed and deserved.

In the turbulent Zürich days none of this registered on Wagner's mind. Cosima had devoured him with her grave and fervent gaze while he looked elsewhere, mostly at Frau Wesendonk. Once or twice his eyes had rested on the fragile bride of Hans von Bülow, just as her luminous pupils fixed on his. But he could not decipher, any more than Cosima could have guessed, the destiny that had begun to spin its threads between them.

It was some years before she saw Richard Wagner again, and then only for brief and superficial contact. Actually Hans von Bülow kept the friendship alive, for in his fast progress to a top-ranking conductor's position he exerted himself in familiarizing the public, as Liszt had done, with Wagner's work. In return the composer pushed Bülow's interests by summoning him to direct the Munich *première* of *Tristan und Isolde.* Richard also obtained for the young couple an invitation from King Ludwig to take up permanent residence in Bavaria, with Bülow in the job of royal music director.

By the time this move was undertaken Cosima had already become twice a mother. Her two small daughters Daniela and Blandine arrived in Munich with servant staff and family baggage, to be established in a town house chosen by the King. Here, in the immediate proximity of court ceremonial, Cosima blossomed from erstwhile subdued shyness to the poised assurance of a great lady. She remembered her maternal Flavigny ancestry and her heritage, if not through the d'Agoult line, of the blood strain of a vicomtesse. Almost, though never quite, she forgot that she was illegitimate.

If anyone or anything could make her forget that gnawing fact, even for moments, it was Wagner and his art. Only his presence gave her faith and conviction that human statutes shriveled to chaff where intellectual values were concerned. In Richard there was greatness that, no less than Liszt's, could mock convention. Small wonder then that with the beginning of their Munich association Cosima sought to tie ever-closer bonds between Wagner's bachelor household and her own. There were receptions and small intimate soirees, launched inevitably under the aegis of music, which appeared to enhance the rapport existing between Hans and Richard but actually filled a need in Cosima's own heart. She no longer deceived herself. She knew that there was in her life only one love: Wagner.

The object of her adoration remained for a long time strangely obtuse. However, the Munich years were far enough removed from the storm and strife of Switzerland and the *Tristan* period. Memories of Mathilde had—incredibly—at last grown dim. Also, Richard's mounting success, under royal patronage, brought the discovery that feminine hearts fluttered readily in his direction. Whether they were opera divas, society beauties or servant girls, women vied nowadays with one another for his favor. While in his years of hunger and bitter struggle Richard had displayed no pronounced Don Juan proclivities, now he found the time, leisure and inclination to look around. Even so, promiscuity was not his dish. All his life he seemed to have remained, except for the first blissful months of his marriage to Minna, a lost and lonely man. Never had cheap, temporary amours provided a real solution. It would take a deep and overpowering emotion to fill his need.

He became aware of Cosima's growing devotion at the time that the first murmurings began to be heard against King Ludwig. At a Bülow dinner reception Cosima leaned toward Richard and whispered, "There were demonstrations in town this afternoon, directed against His Majesty, but—" her hand pressed his—"they, the King's enemies, also mean *you!*"

"Nonsense!"

Her voice grew more intense. "Please, Richard, be careful! If something happened to you, I . . . I wouldn't want to live."

He listened, not to her words of warning nor to the greater

threat of which they were an echo but to the message of love that his danger had permitted her to reveal. Could this be at last what he had waited for and had missed all through life? Swiftly his memory went back to a Berlin afternoon and a carriage ride during which he and Cosima had recognized, and then forced back, the promptings of undeclared passion. Conscience had come to his aid at that time, warning against another Wesendonk triangle in the making. The weak moment had passed, giving way to the well-guarded masquerade of friendship. Years went by without repetition of that dangerous scene.

Yet here it was again, the same turbulence unleashed with all the accumulated vigor of a disease germ that has lain dormant, but is not annihilated by controlling antibodies.

Richard did not close his mind to the enormity of this crisis. His friendship for Hans von Bülow was genuine and tested by long professional association. The last thing he could have wished for himself was to become involved again with another man's wife. But the spark had ignited with uncalculated fury and there was no stopping the ensuing blaze. He looked into Cosima's eyes and pressed her fingers in return.

Let Munich streets explode with howling agitators. What Richard wanted to know was when, where and how he could see Cosima alone.

THE anti-Wagner movement in Bavaria did not remain for long confined to officialdom. Von der Pfordten's well-organized aides managed to bring the issue before the public, both through a whispering campaign and by polemic broadsides in the press. Soon Munich citizens and the populace of surrounding towns knew about the Saxon composer who had insinuated himself into the good graces of the King. People openly spoke of Richard Wagner as an expensive intruder whose pretentious "music dramas" drained the national treasury.

Matters did not improve when Ludwig facilitated a first experimental tryout of the *Nibelungen Ring*. Newspapers leaped on the chance to caricature and lampoon the technical difficulties involved: the Rhine Maidens being pushed about on absurd wheeled platforms to simulate their swimming motions behind a river of gauze, singing the while at the top of their lungs; the dragon Fafner opening his papier-mâché jaws and coming apart at the seams of his ferocious tail; or that marvel of a Rainbow Bridge to Valhalla, looking for all the world like a vast cataract of lemonade.

Added to the above bones of contention was another matter, lately rumored. Following the ministerial veto of the Wagner Theater project, a new scheme appeared to be taking form in the bold composer's brain. The city fathers of the small north-Bavarian town of Bayreuth were being approached with a staggering plan—the erection of a national shrine, to be dedicated strictly to "German opera in its purest form."

"He means his own operas and no other kind!" cried undeceived anti-Wagnerites.

They were right. During his hiking tour, only a few years ago, Richard had lingered fondly in the environs of Bayreuth.

He particularly remembered the pretty little hamlet at dusk, glowing like a baroque jewel in the sun's slanting rays. Since the Semper project in Munich had fallen through, a vision took form in his mind regarding some rustic retreat that might serve as a haven and sanctuary for his art. To this end Richard hoped to find a patron or a whole society of patrons to finance the construction of a *Festspiel Haus* (Festival Theater) which, on a nonprofit basis, might present and cultivate the kind of opera he intended to bequeath: Wagnerian Opera.

With the exception of King Ludwig and the Bülows, recruits for this idea were difficult to find. Germany was dotted with state-subsidized theaters, opera houses and concert halls, which —even under commercial operation—showed permanent deficits. Munich citizens looked on the projected Bayreuth extravaganza with smoldering resentment.

To top these accumulating grievances there now arose avid speculation regarding the Richard-Cosima friendship. Gossiping servants spread the rumor that Frau von Bülow appeared to have lost her head over the Saxon composer. A coachman revealed that he frequently drove Cosima to Wagner's Munich home and also to his villa on Lake Starnberg. At first the lady had been "chaperoned" by her two little daughters, Daniela and Blandine. But soon this precaution was abandoned. The Bülow children were left behind as their infatuated mother grew ever more brazen.

Catholic Bavaria was expecially outraged because of Wagner's Lutheran affiliation, though to be sure his fondness for Norse mythology colored even his Protestantism with pagan overtones. Church authorities in any case took offense at the immoral goings-on right under the eyes of the unsuspecting Herr von Bülow, who, it was angrily pointed out, counted among Wagner's few faithful supporters.

On April 10, 1865, scandalmongers were confounded by the announcement that a new infant had been born to the Bülows. Since crinoline fashions of the epoch lent themselves to perfect concealment of feminine anatomy, and pregnancy belonged among the conversational taboos, Cosima had managed to keep her secret well guarded. Only the joyful Hans, and the more knowing Wagner, had been aware of her blessed state. When the infant was safely delivered, Herr von Bülow presented his wife with a beautifully designed sapphire brooch. But Richard wrote a trenchant line into his diary: "Isolde born."

The choice of the baby girl's name was not necessarily condemning. But wagging tongues made much of it. Public hostility mounted until, late that same year, a deputation of government officials agreed to Minister Pfordten's carefully laid plan. The King was confronted with a demand that Wagner be taken off the state pay roll and banned from Bavaria.

Ludwig rejected such an exaction point-blank, whereupon he was pressed with threat of forced abdication. The grounds: disregard of his country's welfare and irresponsible waste of public funds. The palace buzzed with excitement and alarm at the royal dilemma. Only Richard, characteristically, knew nothing of what was going on.

It was Cosima who brought him news of the crisis. She appeared hatless at the Brienner Strasse house and pushed her way past the doorman, into Richard's study. The heavy carpets silenced her footsteps until she stood beside the desk.

Wagner looked up with a quick frown. "Cosima! It's evening. You shouldn't be coming here at such an hour. There's bound to be talk!"

"Talk? What do I care about talk?" She held up a newspaper. "Something terrible has happened!"

He read the headline proclaiming that the Bavarian State Council had demanded the dismissal of the court favorite.

"Court favorite?" A laugh burst from him. "Who is she? I've seen no Lola Montez around."

Cosima's anxiety was mingled with impatience. "Read on! They mean *you*, Richard. There's an order of banishment being submitted to the King right now, forbidding your further stay in Munich."

"Banishment? Why?"

"The King's finances, his generosity toward you. I don't know. But you must flee before—before . . ."

"Before what? I've done nothing. I have no say in how the King spends his money."

"You're having to answer for it anyway. There's a conspiracy against you, and His Majesty is faced with an ultimatum."

"What sort of ultimatum?"

"Either you leave Munich or the King must abdicate." She gripped his arms urgently. "Please, Richard, listen to me. I've told you before and you must believe me. If something happened to you, I couldn't go on living."

She threw herself into his arms, turning her face up to his, but he shook her gently by the shoulders. "Not go on living? What sentimental nonsense from an intelligent and responsible person like you!" The fanatical earnestness of her expression gave him pause. "Look here. Just what is it you want me to do?"

Her words came breathlessly. "I have a closed carriage outside. We can drive all the way to Augsburg and catch the Paris Express from there."

"*We!* What wild ideas are sprouting in that young head of yours?" His voice grew stern. "No matter how you and I might feel, have you thought of the consequences? There's your husband, whom I can't bear to face because he believes me still his friend. His name shields our own child from scandal. If Hans means nothing to you, what about the little girl?"

"I love you!" she cried out fiercely. As he remained stern she broke from his grasp and took several steps, then paused in her tracks. With her back to him she spoke in a low, tortured voice. "I've *always* loved you. From the first moment we met—no, even before that, when my father told me about you and taught me to love your music." She turned her head. "Of course, if you don't want me ..."

"My dear, it's not a question of wanting you but of stopping an untenable, a degrading situation right now." Despairingly he pressed a hand to his forehead. "I've sunk low enough, Cosima. Don't ask me to despise myself even more. Please. We must be sensible."

Her eyes filled with tears. "Sensible! Sensible! All my life I've been sensible, and what has it got me? A husband I don't love and never *have* loved." Her voice broke.

"Just the same, he *is* your husband. He and your father are as brothers to me. On top of that I'm old enough myself to call you my daughter!" He laughed harshly. "That's capping scandal with ridicule."

"You talk like a pious shopkeeper, not an artist. I never expected Richard Wagner to be so subservient to convention. Not after all that's happened between us." Her thoughts suddenly reverted to the danger threatening him. "Oh, let's stop arguing! You've no time to lose. We've got to leave here while we can."

He now took her firmly by the elbows. "You are *not* going with me! Is that clear?"

Her defiance wilted under this command. "Yes." Then, pleading, she added, "I'll drop you at the edge of town, where you can pick up another carriage."

In silence she helped him gather up his manuscripts, a few books, a jumbled pack of clothes. A short time later they stepped from the villa into a closed vehicle waiting at the gate. Hastily Cosima signaled the coachman before drawing the carriage curtains. As the wheels were set in motion her stormy nature burst forth in a last rebellious impulse. Reaching for Wagner's hand, she whispered passionately, "You can't stop me! I'll run away and follow you to Paris. I will, I *will!*"

He remained hard. "I forbid it, do you hear?" Then, aware of her obstinacy, he tried a different tack. "Besides, I am not going to Paris."

"Oh!" She was shattered, then plagued by quick suspicion. "Where are you going? Please, Richard, *please!*"

He looked straight ahead, determined not to speak. She studied his rigid face, then listened to her own heart. Now she guessed the answer.

"No, don't tell me. I know." Her throat tightened. "Switzerland. You are going where *she* is. Nobody else exists for you. You've never thought of anyone but *her*—Mathilde!"

Now Cosima had done with weeping. She sat bolt upright, bearing her defeat. Richard, visibly touched, started to contradict her. But he checked himself, letting Cosima suffer this hurt so that she might come to her senses.

"It's true," she was whispering in the darkness, "isn't it?" And, as he still did not answer, she repeated, "It's true."

The carriage sped through dimly lighted streets. Now Cosima drew back the tasseled curtain and looked out. She tapped the glass partition to the driver's seat, signaling a stop. She turned to Richard with a sad little smile. "We're at the Isar Bridge. This is where I leave you."

Before Wagner could assist her she had jumped from the carriage and hurried out of sight. He peered into the darkness that closed behind her. Then, with taut features, he nodded to the coachman to proceed.

The rest of that night was filled with mental torture. If Cosima and the newspapers were right, the King had bowed to necessity. He, Richard, was on the move again, discharged, jobless and—for the second time—a political outcast. The full realization smote him now with all its import. Too long had he dwelled in an imaginary world of gods and goddesses (he was still in the midst of ironing out technical flaws in *The Ring* and making score revisions) beyond the pale of ordinary mortals. Just as the moral concerns of earthly men did not touch the creatures of his fancy, so Wagner himself subconsciously had stepped, in his own sight, on some higher plane of special immunity. Here neither censure nor gossip could reach him. But there was still the voice of conscience. He could not quite close his ears to the jingle of coins that had indeed flowed lavishly from state coffers into the King's operatic fund, in addition to incalculable sums earmarked for the personal comfort of Richard Wagner. Similarly he was not fully at ease in his relationship to Cosima. No matter what sophistry might be applied to explain away the forbidden indulgence of physical passion, she was still another man's wife and, like Frau Wesendonk before her, a mother.

Ah, but there was a difference. Mathilde had remained forever unattainable, whereas Cosima was made of less ethereal stuff. All was fire, ferment, willfulness in the daughter of Franz Liszt, whose dominant emotions were not to be denied. In truth, Richard had not seduced Cosima. She had demanded her own seduction.

On both counts, then, Richard debated with his conscience. Wasteful expenditure of the King's funds? How could the value of art be mathematically computed? Adultery? What had so vulgar a term to do with the love transport of a Siegfried and a Brünnhilde?

The fact that, at fifty-two, Richard resembled the aging Wotan far more than the boy hero of his Nibelungen drama did not give him pause. The twenty-seven-year-old Cosima had imbued him with a sense of recovered youth. He had accepted her adoration as destiny's gift and tribute. What was more, the poor duped Hans von Bülow ought to see it that way too.

Such casuistries did not alter the simple fact that, despite his exaggerated self-esteem, Richard Wagner had been given the sack. He realized painfully that he was not leaving Munich in a blaze of glory but under the stigma of dishonor. A penniless fugitive once again, he was on his way to Switzerland, the scene of his former exile. There was a difference, however: the former champion of democracy and of the underdog had meanwhile acquired expensive habits. He had been bosom friend to a king, from whom he had received a handsome allowance and a taste for royal trimmings. He had learned to dress in silks and velvets. In a way, his accusers were absolutely right: before the bankrupt Wagner's appearance on the Munich scene Ludwig II had been solvent, while today both king and composer were over their ears in debt. Plainly these two egregiously idealistic knights errant had one failing in common—a fatal ignorance regarding the value of money.

CHAPTER 3

A MAN headed for exile has, generally, no travel plan. He
journeys not from choice but under pressure and in
haste.

Richard Wagner, after the quick parting with Cosima, was
left in a quandary as to an immediate destination. At length,
after ordering the hack driver back to the blustery square of
Munich's railway station, he consulted the schedule board. A
train was about to depart for Geneva. He had just time to buy
a ticket and climb into a third-class compartment.

Sitting up the rest of that night, he turned his thoughts mo-
rosely on fate's cruelties. Toward morning he took out paper
and pencil and wrote a letter to King Ludwig, which he posted
during a short stop at Vevey. It was dated December 20, 1865,
and ran:

> No! Things cannot end this way! After half a century dur-
> ing which the creative urge within me awakened and ma-
> tured, the sun of your friendship cast its rays upon it. Yet now
> the brutal gambit of some demon makes me the victim of
> misunderstandings and confusion. No! Surely after quiet re-
> flection all this will prove a meaningless fog, and vanish.

The King, it happened, was equally distressed. In repeated
missives he assured Wagner that no decree of permanent exile
was contemplated by the Cabinet. At most, Ludwig himself
hoped to counter the Pfordten maneuvers by agreeing to the
composer's temporary banishment (six months, perhaps) pending judicial examination of the case. In the meantime, out of
the King's own pocket, Wagner was to receive a continuing
subsidy, to mitigate the hardships of life abroad.

Well, this was something else again. Relieved of any immediate threat of depressing pauperism, Richard perked up and looked about for a place to settle. He found agreeable lodgings in Geneva, but his roving eye also gave consideration to southern France. On intermittent excursions, no longer by third class, he got as far as Marseille before deciding after all on Switzerland for his most suitable milieu.

At Marseille a telegram reached him from Dr. Pusinelli in Dresden. It concerned Minna, and had been sent to the Bülows in Munich for forwarding. Obviously Pusinelli knew from press dispatches that Wagner was no longer on Bavarian soil. The telegram, dated January 25, 1866, read:

> FRAU WAGNER DIED SUDDENLY TODAY. BEG YOU TO NOTIFY RICHARD. PLEASE SEND ME HIS ADDRESS.
>
> PUSINELLI

An exchange of somewhat hypocritical verbiage followed between Cosima and Richard. Surely aware of the long estrangement and apathy that had doomed her beloved's marriage, the enamored Cosima wired "My soul hovers about you in this heavy hour. Please give me news as soon as possible."

The hour was not particularly heavy. But Wagner took his cue and followed through with equal bathos. "Be calm," he answered, gazing from the telegraph office toward the sunswept Mediterranean. "I am composed, though in need of rest. See you soon. All will clear. Am stunned, but strong."

Stunned but strong he hurried back to Geneva, where, four weeks later, Cosima joined him. It was no more than fitting, she had told her husband, that someone stand by the lonely Richard in his hour of need. Furthermore, Geneva was not the right place after all for the Wagnerian muse. Richard wanted advice and aid while househunting in the Germanic portion of Switzerland, around Lake Lucerne. Since Hans von Bülow could not leave his job, and in any case would have proved thoroughly unversed in such matters, Cosima hastened to shoulder the burdens of friendship. She would see the composer suitably established, and return promptly thereafter.

On March 31, while exploring the environs of Lucerne, Richard and Cosima came upon a sheltered little villa on an estate called Triebschen. The property, stretched out along a narrow neck of land and skirted by water, entranced the composer on sight. To cap his joy, it was for rent. He signed a year's contract forthwith, and Frau von Bülow set out for home.

In taking on so long a lease Richard admitted to himself that he had little faith in King Ludwig's power to reduce the exile term to a mere six months. But other considerations had meanwhile evolved. He was not at all certain that he wanted to return to Bavaria. A widower now, he would be free to marry again. He was not desperately in love, but he knew himself worshiped beyond all reason—a gratifying state to find oneself in. The next logical step was for Cosima to seek a divorce. Naturally this would eliminate all chances of settling again in Munich. If the Bavarian capital had been scandalized before, it would fairly explode with shock at that which lay ahead.

As things turned out, Cosima did not obtain a divorce. Hans became difficult. In a confrontation between husband and wife the latter's romance with Wagner was brought into the open. With stunning matter-of-factness Cosima confessed her illicit love and her determination to end a marriage that was now only a mockery. Von Bülow took a heavy tumble from the cloud of serenity and contentment on which he had so long and so innocently dwelled. He was shattered by these disclosures. But he had no intention of allowing his home to be broken up. Sternly he recalled to Cosima her duties as a wife and mother and, for the rest, demanded that she take herself in hand and put Wagner out of her mind.

In this he did not reckon with the indomitable will of Liszt's daughter. Denied her legal freedom, Cosima packed up and left for Lucerne. She took with her the Bülow children and the one-year-old infant of dubious paternity, Isolde.

At Triebschen, in seclusion, Richard awaited her. He had spent his time refurbishing the villa, with the aid of a decorator summoned especially from Vienna. The cost, had Minister Pfordten but known, was still borne by the purse of Bavaria's king.

Cosima made a triumphant entrance into this lavishly prepared love nest. It was her purpose, let happen what would,
to dwell thenceforth and forever at the Master's side. Here was
a new note: she spoke of Richard nowadays only as the Master. Deliberately and with shrewd awareness of theatrical effects, she was launching a Wagner cult which in some of
its ramifications would verge occasionally on the ludicrous. Herself the daughter of a supreme showman, she soon reveled in
a well-calculated aura, conjured up expertly around her illustrious lover.

The Triebschen ménage inevitably stirred up buzzing com-
mentary, both in local society circles and on the part of an
international press. But Richard remained unruffled by either
public favor or reproof. He was now composing some of his
finest music, the revised *Siegfried Idyl* and portions of *Götterdämmerung*. Earlier parts of the *The Ring* (*Rheingold* and
Walküre) were in their final form, ready for printing.

Cosima thrilled to her self-chosen role as high priestess to
genius. She made of Richard's schedule a ritual that did not
lack elements of absurdity. While he sat at the piano scribbling notes, she solemnly drew shut the brocade-and-plush
curtains that draped the tall windows. Next, she lighted an
array of silver and crystal candelabra as well as an enormous
Greek urn that gave off perfumed vapors. Richard himself was
persuaded to don more picturesque costumes than ever, designed to intensify his inspiration. He now took to long flowing
Othello robes and embroidered satin slippers, in addition to
the by now obligatory Rembrandt cap.

In her capacity as the great man's handmaid Cosima rounded
out her functions by giving birth, on February 18, 1867, to another child. This baby, named Eva after the sweet heroine
of *Die Meistersinger*, proved too much for the long-suffering
Bülow. He could deceive himself no longer that Cosima might
repent and come back. She was lost to him forever. In his
sorrow he wrote Franz Liszt:

You will have heard by now that Cosima has left me. She
followed Richard to a hide-out called Triebschen, near Lucerne. I have no choice but to seek a divorce. . . .

Liszt received the letter in a monastery garden outside Rome, where he dwelled in peaceful seclusion since his retirement from the world. At sight of his son-in-law's handwriting he had paused in his hoeing of an orchard patch and pushed back his cleric's hat. He was quite fond of Hans, who, far more faithfully than the erratic Cosima, kept him abreast of family news.

A first reading left the gaunt Abbé Liszt wondering if he had exposed himself too long to the stinging Italian sun. Surely his eyes were playing tricks on him. This message—it couldn't, mustn't be! He pulled up the skirt of his soutane and stalked to a splashing fountain, cupping his hands for a drink. Refreshed, he scanned the page again, then crumpled it in anger. A covey of tame pigeons flocked about the garden path, pecking at fallen seeds. They shot up into the air as the tall, priestly figure stormed past them toward the near-by cloister.

In the prior's office the Abbé Liszt made an urgent request. "I beg leave to go on a short trip to Switzerland."

"You are not under full monastic orders, Brother Francesco," the prior reassured him. "You may go where you wish."

A great sadness marked Liszt's face. "It is no wish of mine, but a duty. I shall come back when I have done what must be done."

He traveled all night on the Rome-Berne Express, changing the next day to the spur line for Lucerne. By mid-afternoon he pulled the bell cord of the garden gate at Triebschen. As he did so the tinkling sound mingled with piano music from an open window. He took a step toward the ledge, listening eagerly. Then, as quickly, he checked himself. The expression of involuntary delight that had registered on his face gave way to deliberate austerity. Again he reached for the bell and gave it a brisk shake.

A door opened and Cosima appeared. She recognized her father instantly. With a gasping cry and her arms outstretched she ran toward him. But he brushed her sternly aside. Very erect, Franz Liszt strode into the house.

He followed his ear to the music room, which he entered without knocking. Wagner, seated at the piano, looked up with irritation, then jumped joyously to his feet. But the scowling face of his visitor halted further civilities. There was no shaking of hands or verbal greeting. Only a long silence, broken at last by Wagner.

"I expected you."

Liszt gave a tight-lipped answer. "Amazing. Since I regret the necessity of ever again setting eyes on *you*."

"Then why are you here?"

"Because there are things that even genius—and I was the first to call you that—*even genius must not do*."

Wagner gulped. "Franz, what happened was less of my *doing* than something I could not prevent."

"You don't say!" Liszt flared up. "Surely you aren't asking me to believe that my daughter took advantage of your . . . er . . . inexperience!"

"Of course not. But if you insist on twisting my words, you will have to do without an explanation."

"Rubbish! Spare me such weak schoolboy evasions, which only point up your intolerably pampered ego. As for your words, I'm not concerned with them, but with your behavior."

"*My* pampered ego!" Wagner's face flushed with anger. "It seems to me the pious and respected Abbé Liszt was once a preening peacock, as successful with boudoir conquests as on the concert stage." He smiled acidly. "Naturally, in later years, one's youthful indiscretions can be minimized by—" he touched the sleeve of Liszt's cassock—"taking the cloth. That's something I hadn't thought of."

The visitor flinched at this rapier thrust. For a moment he appeared ready to cut off the interview, but he mastered himself and carried out the purpose of his call.

"*Touché!* I deserved that." There was a pause, then Liszt pulled himself up to his full height. "Yes, I lived lustily and unwisely, and there is much in my past of which I am not proud. But never did I make myself an object of ridicule."

"Ridicule?" Bewilderment showed on Wagner's face. "I don't understand."

"No, I really don't think you do." Liszt pointed to the beret and costume. "That fancy dress of yours, the velvet robe, the Rembrandt cap. Who are you—one of the Three Musketeers?"

Wagner made a gesture of protest, but his old friend cut him short. With an expression of distaste Liszt's eyes swept the studio. "Take a look at this room. It's all part of the absurd masquerade. Candlelight, incense, and my foolish daughter to complete the picture, or, rather, the *caricature* of a supposed artist. Believe me, I never would have thought you capable of such humbug. Truly I expected something worthier of you."

There was pallor now on Wagner's cheeks. "Have you finished?"

"No." Liszt began pacing the floor. "I want to be fair. I haven't forgotten the hungry, struggling young man I first met in Meyerbeer's gaudy apartment. That's where your false ideas of 'luxury' and 'the good life' must have started. I saw you then as your eyes filled with envy. You grieved because your wife couldn't have some of that food. No, I can't blame you for having hankered for riches when you'd known nothing but want." He halted now, facing Wagner and raising his voice to a shout. "However, stealing the wife of a friend who worshiped you as some sort of paragon or demigod—well, it takes a real swine to do that!"

He broke off, embarrassed at his own vehemence. The fury of his accusations appeared somehow to be tempered by regret over the necessity of making them. But nothing mellowed the bitterness that burst forth now from Wagner.

"And you came all the way from Rome to call me a swine?"

"I came to stop my daughter's divorce and to take her back where she belongs."

"I'm afraid it is a little late for that." Wagner turned toward the far end of the room where Cosima stood silently, leaning against the door. Now she stepped forward.

"Yes, Father. Richard is right."

Liszt was beside himself. "How dare you say that? You, the mother of four children!"

Cosima remained calm. Here was her chance to strike back for the wound that had festered throughout her life. She aimed her thrust without haste. "You had three yourself, Papa, all born out of wedlock."

Conventions were not at stake so much as human values. Liszt brushed her words aside. "I stayed with them and with their mother, although the Church forbade our marriage. But you are making orphans of your children by taking them from their father, to share your life of sin."

She cut him off with a wave of her hand. "It can be told now," she said with defiance, "since Richard and I shall never be parted. Though it would come hard for me, Hans has a claim on the older girls. But the two younger ones do not belong to him."

A pall of silence fell on the room. Cosima leaned her head against Wagner's shoulder, while he put an arm around her and nodded in confirmation.

Liszt's lips tightened as he passed a shaky hand across his face. Then, without another word, he walked out.

CHAPTER 4

A S MENTIONED in his letter to Rome, Hans von Bülow started divorce proceedings. He did not name Richard Wagner as corespondent, nor was Cosima stigmatized by use of such terms as "adultery" or "willful desertion." The whole sorry business was veiled under a cloak of respectability, thanks to Bülow's innate chivalry. He charged estrangement by reason of incompatibility.

In return for his trouble he received news from Switzerland that, on June 6, 1869, Cosima had given birth to yet another child, Wagner's only son, Helferich Siegfried Richard. The divorce did not become final until more than a year later, July 18, 1870. With the decree Bülow was given legal custody of his daughters, Daniela and Blandine. But contact with the children served only to intensify his sorrow and to cast needless gloom over their innocent lives. Without further friction the little ones were restored to their mother's care.

Some time before the above events King Ludwig had managed to ease the restrictions against Wagner. That is, although the decree of exile was not revoked, the Cabinet relented to the extent of lifting the ban on the composer's works. Accordingly a full scale *première* of *Die Meistersinger*, seen heretofore only on the King's private stage, was planned for June 21, 1868, at the National Theater. The cast of vocal artists was of the best, including such luminaries as Mathilde Mallinger in the role of Eva, Franz Nachbaur as Walther, Karl Schlosser as David, Gustav Hölzel as Beckmesser and an obscure Herr Betz for the cobbler Hans Sachs.

The performance proved a musical triumph, though it was followed by a lamentable incident. On a reckless impulse, and with the King's connivance, Wagner had slipped into Mu-

393

nich and attended the theater. He was safely lodged in the back of the royal box, hidden by Ludwig's gigantic frame (the King had taken on much weight in recent years), when the first intermission brought forth a tumult of applause. So delicious was this sound to Richard's ears that he forgot his need for incognito. Leaping from his chair, he rushed to the balustrade and bowed grandiosely to his public.

The consequences were appalling. The hand clapping, it became quickly evident, had not been for Wagner's person but for the opera, the orchestra members, the artists on stage who had acquitted themselves so admirably, and, not least, the brilliant conductor, Hans von Bülow. At sight of Richard, the applause ceased. There were boos and catcalls to inform him unequivocally of his low rating. He left Bavaria in haste and with a bitter taste.

Up to now Ludwig had cherished an untainted picture of his beloved friend. Despite the rampant gossip that circulated not only in Munich but throughout Europe's capitals, he saw in Wagner a superhuman being who could do no wrong. Even Frau von Bülow's departure from her husband's side induced no qualms in the trusting king. But the shouts and insults hurled now at Wagner's head, as well as a battery of anonymous letters and broadsides with which His Majesty was presently bombarded, put illusion to rout. It was all there, in newsprint clipped from foreign papers: the Triebschen "love nest," the expanding nursery, Liszt's alienation from his wayward daughter, and the visible martyrdom of Von Bülow.

Ludwig took it hard. A storybook prince in the worst sense of the word, he was himself a fugitive from reality, deliberately imprisoned in an adolescent dream. The idealistic figure of Richard Wagner, which he had fashioned to fit that dream, was both implausible and grotesque, the product of an immature fancy. Measured by such standards an adult man of normal virtue would have proved disappointing. Wagner, whose virtues and faults were as glaring as his excess of genius, could not for long live up to a fey king's fiction. He broke the mold that was not built to hold him and stepped forth on feet of commonest clay. The golden idol was still golden. No question of that. But henceforth Ludwig saw only the clay.

Quite rapidly the King now went into a decline. The melancholy moods that had plagued him since early youth deepened and darkened. Morose, solitary, the royal hermit cut himself off still farther from all human contact outside the closed circle of palace servants. The stage of his beloved private theater was boarded shut and the orchestra dismissed, for Ludwig wanted no more music. What was left to him who thus barred himself from love, art, philosophy and even plain physical exercise? Eating. Numbed with emotional shock, stultified, apathetic, the King took to his table. He ate—voraciously, prodigiously. He neither tasted nor enjoyed; he just devoured. And all the while his once splendid body grew to hideous proportions, bloated, deformed by gluttony.

No news concerning these developments reached the outside world, for Bavaria was doggedly loyal to its dynasty and loath to change government patterns. Until a solution to the political dilemma was found, the King must be protected from exposure or ridicule, especially abroad. Ludwig II was still ruler, by the grace of God, over his loving subjects.

Triebschen was far removed from all this. Richard and Cosima, who had deemed security, position, respectability—the world, in short, and its canons—well lost for a prize they alone could evaluate, knew nothing of their patron's extremity. They were engrossed, like the most youthful of affianced couples, in preparations for their wedding. For Richard this third major involvement with a woman differed from each of the other two. In the case of Minna, he had loved and she had not. Today Cosima was the adoring party, and he the passive one who let himself be adored. Only between him and Mathilde had the flames burned equally in a fusing, all-consuming fire. Clearly Cosima sensed this. But she was a "bird in hand" philosopher, proud of her triumph and eager to broadcast it. She wanted a wedding reception with guests, music, fanfare. Newly acquired friends, among them a neighbor, Friedrich Nietzsche, were bidden to the feast, which was set for early August, barely a fortnight after the Bülow divorce.

History altered these arrangements, however, as on August 2, 1870, the Franco-Prussian War broke out. Citizens of the belligerent countries currently in Switzerland were notified by their consulates that if they wished to return to their respective homelands they must do so by a given date before the borders were closed. The bride and groom at Triebschen thus underwent a perfunctory marriage ceremony and, forgoing further celebration, packed their trunks. Beating the deadline, Richard, Cosima and the children left Switzerland behind.

They had no immediate destination, nor indeed any great longing to re-enter Germany. They could think of nobody in their homeland who might await them with pride or open arms. But the upkeep of Triebschen would have become too expensive if the war lasted a long time and if Richard's present cash supply ran down. The allowance from King Ludwig had suddenly stopped, an impasse which Wagner credited to the international crisis rather than to a breach between himself and his royal benefactor. In short, Switzerland had been fine as long as one had a dependable income; but the hospitable Helvetians minced no words in making known that foreigners running out of funds would face internment. The newly-wedded Wagners had no choice but to be on their way.

A crowded refugee train rattled toward Basel and the Rhine. The narrow compartments, jammed with excited passengers and their ill-assorted luggage, echoed laments and grumblings. People elbowed one another or shrank into unlikely corners, trying to sleep. They argued, ate, changed infants' diapers and ceaselessly checked off their belongings. All were uprooted and without destination.

Through the long night Cosima sat, eyes closed, leaning against her husband's shoulder. On her lap she held the baby Siegfried, while the older children lay curled up in overhead baggage nets. At each jolting stop of the train Richard looked up in terror, but the cord weaving was stout and none of the girls toppled out.

Morning came and with daylight there was clarity at last in Wagner's mind. All night he had racked his brain for a solution, and now he knew the way that he would take. There was a spot of earth that long ago had left an imprint on his fancy, during that happy hiking tour he had made in younger years: Bayreuth. He had never forgotten its idyllic woodland setting and serene bucolic mood. Why not seek sanctuary in this calm retreat where Cosima and the little ones could thrive in health-ful surroundings while he undertook the rebuilding of his in-terrupted career?

A minor deterrent presented itself. Bayreuth was in Bavaria, the very state Richard had managed so completely to alienate. But thanks to King Ludwig's intercession the ban against Wag-ner, originally encompassing the entire province, had shrunk to the limits of Munich alone. Bayreuth might not delight in receiving the composer and his family, but there was no legal restriction to bar the way.

After a short wait in Stuttgart the travelers changed to an-other train. Again a stretch of sleepless riding, and then, through smoke-darkened windowpanes, a station sign reading: BAYREUTH.

Richard shook Cosima out of a listless stupor. "We're here! We're here!"

The little girls pressed their faces against the glass. "Is this where you came on your walking tour, Papa?"

"Yes, and you will see how beautiful it is!"

Gathering up wraps, bundles and the baby, the family started —with apologies to snoring travelers on right and left—for the compartment exit. As the train puffed on, leaving them stand-ing on the red-brick platform, they looked up at the green hills and the blazing late-summer sky. They knew no one in town and had not the faintest idea of where they would betake them-selves next. But a profound conviction took root in Richard's heart. He had come home.

The life that now followed was a far cry from the splendor once enjoyed at Brienner Strasse 21 or even the gracious ameni-ties of Triesbschen. Temporary lodgings were found in a room-ing house, where Cosima and the children would have to manage in close quarters until Richard surveyed the town's professional prospects. He had in mind returning to creative work as soon as possible, but for a start he must look to some regular income. In short, he needed a job.

After a night of much-missed slumber he set out on his search. His first goal was the Bayreuth Opera House, an ornate baroque structure in the provincial hamlet's center. He carried a music roll under his arm, containing the finished orchestral arrangement of *The Ring*. While seeking employment he might as well negotiate a trial performance of his latest work.

As it happened the Bayreuth Opera Association was curtailing its season, due to the war. The small resort town depended on summer visitors for its main revenue, a factor greatly undermined by the national emergency. Not many visitors were expected during the coming year.

"It's most regrettable," Richard was told by a polite Herr Direktor, "but our reduced schedule means we must also cut down our staff." A noticeable coolness was in his voice.

Wagner's next stop was at the cramped headquarters of Bayreuth's small Philharmonic Society. This time Cosima went with him, a tactical mistake. Obviously scandal had preceded them, even into so remote and Arcadian a community as this, for the name of Wagner again called forth no warmth. Indeed, the secretary in the Philharmonic's office appeared deliberately to snub Cosima, speaking to Richard exclusively.

"I am sorry, Herr Kapellmeister, but we have all the personnel we need."

Richard unrolled his manuscripts. "Perhaps your program director would consider running through these?"

The secretary waved a protesting hand. "Our repertoire is set up. Besides, we hold here with the classical tradition of Mozart and Gluck—" he cleared his throat, then went on pointedly—"as, I imagine, do most German music centers."

He helped Richard gather up the pages, then led the way to the door, again letting Cosima feel the full weight of his disapproval. A sinning woman, it was evident, drew greater censure than a guilty man. Also, public opinion held Cosima's conduct to be the more reprehensible, since she had outraged the most sacred tenets of wedlock and motherhood, while Richard—though branded a rake—had been unencumbered by family ties. In any case, it was plain that this second rejection could not be ascribed solely to musical considerations.

A third organization, the Symphonic Choir, had its practice

hall half a block down the same street. This time Cosima urged Richard to go in alone while she waited on the footpath. He agreed reluctantly, only to hear another negative answer delivered with a thin smile. "Too bad, Herr Wagner. There's no demand, believe me, for your kind of . . . er . . . newfangled experimentation."

He emerged in dejection.

Cosima rushed forward to take his arm. She murmured words of comfort. "Don't worry, dear. This is just a backwoods town, with few musical outlets."

"I can't help worrying!" he protested. "What are we going to live on?"

"We'll try Nürnberg or Berlin, where an artist of your reputation——"

He interrupted with a harsh laugh. "That's just what's wrong —my reputation."

She winced. "You mean *my divorce,* and the fact that you married me." Her voice grew bitter. "The gossips have been busy, and I'm to blame."

He flared up. "Stop that! It isn't true."

"Isn't it?" She opened her reticule and pulled out a sheaf of papers. "Look at these. They're anonymous letters and threats. Each one assures me I shall never be forgiven."

There was a long silence during which Richard helplessly stroked her hand. "The cowards!" he muttered under his breath. "I swear I'll——"

"You'll what? There's nothing to do but to let wagging tongues wear themselves down, as they will eventually."

She was right, of course. But the prospect held little cheer. Despair gained the upper hand as Richard nodded toward the building he had just left. "You know what they told me in there? They wouldn't have me for a piano tuner or even a washroom attendant!"

"I wonder how many of these so-called respectable citizens condemning us are themselves enmeshed in a lifetime of cheating, simply because they lack the courage to be honest." She raised her chin defiantly. "It takes nerve to admit what is in your heart!"

He kissed her, there, within sight of astonished passers-by. Almost reverently he said, "Yes. And I know no one more brave than you."

They walked on arm in arm. Almost immediately, however, Richard plagued himself with recriminations. "This is what poor Minna had to put up with: cheap boarding houses, no money coming in, and my walking the streets day after day in search of work." An agonized expression crossed his face. "And now I've brought the same kind of misery on you."

Cosima stood still and took his head between her hands. She fixed his eyes with her own steady gaze. "Listen to me. I would rather starve with you than share a world of luxury with any-one else."

"Luxury!" He sneered ironically at the figure of failure he saw himself to be. "You'll do without it all right if you stay with me!" Then, suddenly, he was ashamed of his quick answer. The full import of her words flowed like balm through his consciousness. "Thank you, my dear," he whispered softly. "Thank you with all my heart."

CHAPTER 5

LOVE and devotion were treasures of surpassing worth. But they did not put food on the table.

After two weeks of stretching the family savings to the utmost, Richard came to a desperate conclusion. King Ludwig! Why hadn't he thought of this before? He would write an appeal to the King!

Cosima shook her head. "That's impossible. Have you forgotten your last Munich visit? His Majesty, too, has dropped us like outcasts."

"Then I'll write the President of the United States, the Tsar, Bismarck, the Empress of China. I'll ask each one for a loan, to be paid off after I have built my own theater."

He must be running a fever. Cosima stared at him, completely baffled. "Your *own* theater?"

"Why not? If no one else employs me, I'll have to employ myself. King Ludwig planned a theater for me once, in his own capital, didn't he? Well, the place to build it is here, in Bayreuth."

She stroked his brow. "Dear, you are tired. Your nerves are unstrung."

There was no holding him. "In all of Germany there are no jobs for me. Nobody wants the risk of producing my works. Yet I know—" he warded off her gestures of protest—"don't stop me, I must say this—I know that my music speaks for this piece of earth, for this race of people, as no voice has spoken before."

His face had become transfigured, and now Cosima herself was carried away. Intoxicated by his words, she cried, "Yes, yes, that is true!" Then her cool judgment caused her to grow sober again. "But what chance have you in Bayreuth, Richard? It's small, provincial."

"Hopelessly provincial, that's just it! Here in this artistic backwater is where I can best prove my point, by building a shrine for the rebirth of opera into its consummate form, the music-drama." He whipped himself into ever-higher excitement. "It won't even be called an Opera House, but a Festival Theater. And pilgrimages will be made from the four points of the compass when I have finished putting this Bayreuth on the map!"

Under the spell of such visions he sat down at his worktable and began to write. He addressed a string of letters, all flamboyant in their eloquence, to half a dozen heads of state. Among these, despite Cosima's warning, was King Ludwig.

After the letters were posted, there followed a difficult time of waiting. Impatiently Richard paced from one window to another, watching for the postman who passed each day, leaving nothing. He could not expect a quick answer from Washington or Peking, to be sure. But Ludwig, Ludwig!

"Ha!" he cried savagely after a week of disappointment. "The courtesy of kings!"

Then suddenly the incredible happened. Outside the nondescript rooming house the trot of horses was heard and a stately carriage drew up. From it stepped an equerry in the uniform of a royal Bavarian huntsman, or *Jäger*. Before the strange caller could knock, Richard was at the door.

"You are looking for someone?"

"Yes. Is this the residence of . . ." The equerry gave a relieved sign of recognition. "I beg your pardon, Herr Wagner. It's you I've come to see!"

Richard leaped down the steps. "You have a message for me, of course—a letter from King Ludwig?"

"Unfortunately not, sir. Had you not heard?" There was a tense pause. "My master is very ill."

"Ill? Surely it's nothing serious. His Majesty is still young."

"The King is young, sir, but of an ancient line. The illness *is* serious." The equerry stepped closer. "I beg you to come with me at once. My master is in gravest danger!"

Wagner paled, then turned to Cosima, who stood beside him. She nodded and hurried inside to fetch his hat and cloak. A moment later the carriage swept him along at galloping speed on the road to Munich.

Not until late the following afternoon did Richard enter an anteroom of the Royal Palace. Here a medical commission appeared to be in conference. A stocky, middle-aged man, with glasses and a nervous squint, stepped forward.

"I am Dr. Gudden," he introduced himself, "His Majesty's personal physician, and these are my assistants." He presented the others in turn, then put his hand on Richard's shoulder. "Thank you for coming, Herr Wagner. I realize that in bringing you here we are circumventing the law."

Richard bowed. "The King is my friend. No law can stop me if he is in trouble. Will you take me to him?"

"Just a moment." Gudden paused to rub his glasses. "It is not so much the King who needs you as His Majesty's Cabinet, and we, the Medical Commission."

"Yes?"

"His Majesty has suffered a breakdown, and . . . er . . . ought to be taken into special custody."

An uncomfortable feeling came over Richard. "What kind of breakdown?" he wanted to know.

"We have not determined its exact nature as yet." Gudden chose his words with great precision. "A nerve seizure, no doubt, brought on by political pressures to enter the Franco-Prussian War, to which His Majesty is bitterly opposed. To sustain his position on this issue the King has chosen to take refuge in flight."

"Where has he gone?"

"Flight from reality, my friend," Gudden stressed gently. "I was referring to a purely imaginary escape."

Richard's patience began to wear a little thin. "I am a layman, *Herr Doktor*, to whom you are talking in riddles."

"Riddles! Ah, that is what has happened to the King. His illness has taken a mental turn."

"Oh?"

The physician tapped his temple, nodding significantly. "That is why we have sent for you."

"And what am I to do?"

"His Majesty believes himself surrounded by enemies, which means that even we, my assistants and I, are looked upon with suspicion. Yet some form of therapy is urgent, believe me."

"Go on."

Gudden drew closer. "We are counting on the helpful influence of someone whom His Majesty loves and trusts. That someone is *you*."

As Wagner weighed these words, Gudden nodded at his colleagues and pointed the way through an adjoining chamber to the King's private apartments. In silence they approached the royal bedroom and were admitted by two stalwart guards.

Heavy curtains hung over all but a single window, where Ludwig sat in an armchair, his gaze fixed on the fading dusk outside. He seemed unconscious of any other presence.

For several seconds the visitors stood quietly, and Wagner was able to study his former patron and friend. Ludwig's boyish beauty had given way to corpulent middle age, though the features were still handsome. He wore a voluminous and shapeless dressing gown; his hair was bushy and unkempt.

A valet stepped forward to face the King. "Dr. Gudden is here to see you, Your Majesty."

A wild look came into Ludwig's eyes as he flared up violently. "The Devil take him, and all the others! I told you I won't see him. I will see no one!"

Gudden brushed the valet aside and rounded the King's chair. "I have brought someone, Sire, whom you will not send away."

Ludwig swung about menacingly, then halted as his eyes fixed on Wagner. With a cry of recognition he rose and came forward, hands outstretched. "My friend! My friend!" He waved the others aside. "Leave us alone."

He led Wagner to the window and offered him a chair. They sat in awkward silence, estranged by time. Wagner at length was the first to speak. "It's been many years, Your Majesty. We have both aged." He paused. "I am told, Sire, that you are not well."

Ludwig's eyes narrowed with suspicion. "Who told you that?

I am fit as a fiddle!" But he crumpled suddenly. "No, I am not. There's something wrong, very wrong. But it's not what those quacks out there want you to believe." He laid a hand on his heart. "Here, here is my trouble."

"Your Majesty is too much alone."

Ludwig nodded. "I am not a monarch after the pattern of my ministers. They wished me to marry, but only if *they* could choose my queen. They care not how large a budget is required to join a useless war, but I am declared incompetent because I have financed the works of peace, of art, of beauty."

"History will not fail to record this, Sire."

"History? It's full of bloodshed and horror. Men would have no need of making history if they loved loveliness. They would be happy, and that is something not to be catalogued in books."

"That is true."

Ludwig looked about him to make certain that they were alone. Then he rose and went to a near-by desk. From a hidden drawer he pulled forth an ornate coffer. He turned back to Wagner with a sly expression.

"They have cut me off from outside contacts. Even the royal treasury is barred to me, so that I cannot purchase so small a thing as a box of snuff." He opened the coffer. "But here's something no one suspects: my mother's jewel collection, and a small hoard of gold."

He emptied the glittering baubles and coins on a velvet table cover while Wagner stared in awe.

The King spoke again. "Here, my friend. They are yours!"

"Your Majesty is joking!"

Ludwig frowned ominously. "What's the matter? Aha, you too think I'm insane!" He tried to control himself, speaking now with forced calm. "Long ago I promised you a theater in which your work, and that of future artists, would be fittingly honored and given sanctuary. I did not keep that promise. That is, not until today." With both hands he refilled the coffer, then held it up to Wagner.

"Thank you, Sire, but I cannot accept."

"Why not?"

"It is known, outside, that Your Majesty has been ill. Even abroad, the newspapers no doubt have printed it. People would scream from the housetops that I am exploiting a . . . a . . ."

He broke off, but Ludwig finished for him. "A madman! Is that what you were going to say?"

"Your Majesty must not use that word—no, not even think it!"

Ludwig stared into space. "What is madness? Are you not mad, my friend, beating your brains out to give the world a new concept of music, which mankind is too dull-witted and brutalized to grasp? Or are they mad, the fools who map out battlefields, and glory in the slaughter of their fellow men?" He placed the coffer under Wagner's arm and urged him to go. "Take this, I beg you, before it is snatched from me and stuffed into the pockets of rogues and politicians." A faint smile crossed his face. "It won't cover the building cost of that promised theater, but at least you'll be able to make a start."

Richard hesitated, deeply moved. Then he set down the coffer. "A gift of money, Sire, I can accept in the name of all who one day will enjoy the realization of your dream and mine. But jewels—they are property of the Crown. I cannot take the jewels."

The King did not answer. Slowly, however, he separated the gold coins from the precious gems. In silence Wagner slipped the money into an inner coat pocket. Then the men clasped hands. Ludwig rang for the valet, who ushered the visitor from the room.

At the end of a long corridor Gudden was waiting. He buttonholed Wagner instantly. "What happened? Were you successful in persuading His Majesty to undergo treatment?"

Richard temporized. "Do not worry, *Herr Doktor*. The King seems very tractable. My impression is that his illness has been grossly exaggerated."

Gudden took this as an affront. "I beg your pardon. The best medical opinion——"

Undaunted, Richard went on. "If I may offer a nonprofessional opinion, your patient's condition calls for gentleness and forbearance rather than . . . er . . . violent techniques."

A scarcely veiled sneer met this remark. "Very enlightening, *Herr Kapellmeister,* I'm sure." Without further greeting, Gudden turned on his heels and stalked away.

Richard was left standing purposeless and certainly unwelcome. He decided to catch the next train back to Bayreuth, where the worried Cosima was waiting. How pleased and startled she would be when he spread out before her the evidence of the King's bounty! Yes, he must hurry and lay the cornerstone of his Festival Theater.

The corridors and stairways of the Munich Royal Palace formed an intricate labyrinth. Richard had long been familiar with the ground floor of the *Residenz,* but the King's private chambers and the approach thereto were unknown to him. He became confused, following various passages that seemed to lead invariably to his starting point. It was after some ten minutes of aimless wandering that he was startled by a great commotion. Amid banging of doors and the mingled outcries of many voices Ludwig came storming from his room. He was in full riding dress, with crop brandished aloft in his right hand. Followed by servants and the small body of palace physicians, the King raced about an upper rotunda that led, in some characteristically unfathomable fashion, to the main stairs.

Richard attached himself to the hurried procession, plucking a valet's sleeve. "What's this? Where is everybody heading?"

The servant answered on the run. "His Majesty is starting for Innsbruck, across the Austrian border."

"Tonight? On horseback?"

Dr. Gudden was suddenly at Wagner's side. He appeared no longer angry but rather eager to prove a point. "Here is the evidence, *Herr Kapellmeister,* of what I have been talking about. The King is engaged in another imaginary escape. He thinks he is going to ride to Innsbruck, but actually he will not move beyond the limits of the royal paddock." He took Richard's arm. "Come with me."

The strange group gained the lower palace level and hurried across a courtyard and mews to the portal of a large indoor arena with an artificially lighted tanbark oval. Here a number of stableboys and grooms had already been alerted. They stood at the barrier, coming to attention as His Majesty approached.

Gudden nudged Wagner. "The white horse is the King's. The other two are for his escorts, who must 'travel' with him."

Richard looked on aghast at the farcical events that now followed. Gravely the King mounted his steed and waved farewell to the assembled royal household, while two riders moved up close behind him. There followed a dull clatter of hoofs. The odd journey had begun.

"There you have it," Gudden remarked. "This sort of thing goes on about once a week, sometimes for days on end. It's all very methodical too. There will be a change of horses every three hours."

Appalled, Richard could not believe his ears. "I don't understand. You mentioned Innsbruck. But how do you learn what is in the King's mind?"

"That is simple. His Majesty picks a place on a map, then calculates the exact distance in terms of laps around the paddock, allowing, of course, for stopovers en route for meals."

"He eats?"

"Oh, yes." Gudden indicated a near-by table set with dishes. "The King halts at different imaginary villages along the way. These places are marked on the map. He dismounts, greets the natives—his own stableboys, you understand—and then asks for some special dish of the region, which has been carefully prepared in advance."

Richard shook his head. "No. No, this can't be!"

"Nevertheless, it is."

"But—but when does this dreadful comedy end?"

"Remember, the King's hallucination demands that the equivalent of the distance between Munich and Innsbruck be covered."

"That would mean galloping through the night and most of tomorrow!"

"It will. Unless you help us."

Wagner's eyes widened, incredulous. "What could *I* do to help?"

"Possibly a great deal." Gudden drew nearer, lowering his voice. "His Majesty, at this moment, recognizes nothing of his

daily environment. He sees only what he wishes to see. If I or
one of my colleagues, for example, were to stop him forcibly
right now, we might have an outbreak of raving violence."

"I see." Wagner paused. "Is that why you sent for me?"

"Exactly. We are counting on the King's tractability in the
presence of someone whom he trusts and cherishes."

While Gudden talked, Richard for the first time noticed two
husky attendants standing by, holding a straitjacket with heavy
buckles and straps between them. He recoiled in horror.

"Is *that* how you mean to 'help' your royal master?"

"In cases of this kind, Herr Wagner, restraining measures are
necessary. Unfortunately we cannot apply them except by
means of a snare."

"And so you lifted the Munich ban against me because I am
to spring your trap."

"I wouldn't put it quite so crudely."

"No, you wouldn't, Doctor. But I am a crude man with a
plain answer. This is no task for one who loves the King. I
want no part of it."

Gudden grew insistent. "Please, sir, the matter must be
looked at reasonably. If I used force, and word got out that
His Majesty was beaten into submission or otherwise harmed,
there would be demonstrations in the streets. My own life
would not be safe. You, on the other hand, could bring about
the ... er ... patient's voluntary surrender without unpleasant
repercussions outside these walls."

"Sorry." Wagner seemed far away. "The King made me his
friend. He was the noblest and most selfless benefactor ever to
touch my life." Now he faced Gudden squarely, crying out
with passion, "No! I will not deliver him into your hands!"

He turned for a last agonized look at the tragic Ludwig, and
then rushed from the arena.

At Bayreuth that same week Richard unburdened his heart
to Cosima. "Never," he said firmly, "shall I use madness for
an operatic theme." He recalled Ludwig's grotesque gallop
over the tanbark, with the palace servants huddled near the
ramp, their eyes glazed and staring. None had spoken. None
had laughed. Insanity was not funny.

CHAPTER 6

T HE Franco-Prussian War rolled on toward a swift and
dramatic conclusion. Fortune was not on the side of
France's armies. Under the guidance of its Iron Chancellor, a new German Reich had come triumphantly into being.

On October 27, 1870, the fortress of Metz surrendered, and
a Prussian force closed in on Paris. After four months of siege
the French capital fell, and soon thereafter, on March 1, 1871,
preliminary peace terms were signed and ratified at Bordeaux.

This historic moment coincided with a less portentous event
in the Wagner family circle at Bayreuth. The baby Siegfried,
though named, had not yet been formally baptized, due to the
hasty departure from Switzerland. A proper celebration now
was planned, with special emphasis on one of the chosen ap-
pellations: Siegfried meant "Winner's Peace." Incidentally, an
important correction was now made on the records. The infant
and his sisters Isolde and Eva had thus far, in quaint deference to convention, borne the patronymic of Bülow. That fiction could at last be dropped.

With the silencing of the drums of battle, men returned once
again to the pursuits of peace. Interest in art and music reawakened, causing Wagner to push ahead with plans for his
Festival Theater. With King Ludwig's cash gift for a start,
he hoped to raise additional contributions from wealthy patrons and sponsors. This was, however, a miscalculation. The
burden of war, with its armament costs and supply needs of
troops and wounded, had drained off heavy sums from Germany's moneyed class. There was no surplus to channel into
artistic uses. Richard had no choice but to strike out for himself, singlehanded, in search of coin. He hired himself out as
guest conductor on another concert tour.

Through November of that year he led the Berlin Philharmonic, while the following weeks took him to Mannheim, Mainz, Wiesbaden, Brussels and London. At the same time he supplemented the earnings thus accrued by venturing again into journalistic fields. He became once more a hack writer of newspaper articles, musical critiques and short stories for local and foreign magazines. Some of his material went back a number of years and had to be dug up from accumulated notebooks. He managed to get into print such diverse prose efforts as:

"A Comment on Gluck's Overture to *Iphigenia in Aulis*"
"A Theater in Zürich"
"Homage to Spohr and Fischer"
"A Letter to Hector Berlioz"
"The Music of the Future"
"Account of the *Tannhäuser* Production in Paris"
"Experiences at the Vienna Court Opera House"
"Religion and the State"
"What Is German?"
"German Art and German Policy"
"Recollections of Ludwig Schnorr von Carolsfeld"
"Recollections of Rossini"
"Edward Devrient"
"On Conducting"
"Poem: To the German Army before Paris"
"Recollections of Auber"
"On the Destiny of Opera"
"Actors and Singers"
"On the Name: Music Drama"
"To Friedrich Nietzsche"
"Letter to an Actor"
"A Glance at the German Operatic Stage of Today"
"The Rendering of Beethoven's Ninth Symphony"

Along with this output he launched repeated expositions of his favorite theme, the projected building of a Bayreuth *Festspiel Haus*. To this end he allowed passages from *Der Ring des Nibelungen* to be published, while yet again he gave a final polish to the music score. Not until February of 1872 did he declare himself at last satisfied with the third-act music of

Götterdämmerung. Then, by May of that year, Wagner had assembled enough money to negotiate for a spot of land on a hilltop overlooking Bayreuth. The foundation stone was laid on the 22nd of that month.

Richard was present for the ceremony, but he returned on tour almost at once. While he concertized in St. Petersburg, Moscow, Prague, Budapest and Vienna, Cosima took charge of matters at home. She supervised workmen and, with architects' plans in hand, checked each day's progress. Stonemasons and bricklayers alike found her a hard taskmistress.

Cosima also kept careful track of the building fund. Richard's desperate letters, peddling his genius in the international market, drew a response from America, where preparations were being made to celebrate the first hundred years of independence. The Centennial Committee at Washington wanted a suitably glorious "Centennial March" from the pen of Richard Wagner.

Dollar earnings were most welcome. The pleased composer boasted to his wife, "You see—even America has, indirectly, a hand in building our Bayreuth Theater!"

The concert tours over, Richard returned to his desk. Here musical creation alternated with architectural calculations, ending in a draw. That is, the "Centennial March" and the *Festspiel Haus* reached completion by the summer of 1876, the former to be submitted to an overseas board of judges, while Bayreuth citizens made a first inspection of the new theater.

The "March" met with hearty approval. Not so the opera house. For one thing, economy had dictated avoidance of all interior and exterior ornamentation. Visitors accustomed to traditional cherubs and ormolu gilt scrollwork found the bare structure chilling and austere. It was as modern and unfamiliar as the composer's ideas on music.

Actually, in constructing his theater Wagner displayed a profound grasp of acoustical demands, even if his architectural taste was denounced as execrable. The enormously high proscenium of the *Festspiel Haus* would lend unequaled majesty to the visual effect of his tremendous tone dramas, while the device of a concealed orchestra pit served to intensify theatrical

illusion by removing all distracting elements between audience
and performers on stage. The auditorium itself followed a crude
amphitheater design, with unbroken rows (no aisles, no boxes)
of cane-bottom seats mounting at a steep angle. As for the
building's exterior, it lacked all pretense to aesthetic distinction,
resembling nothing so much as an oversized late-nineteenth-
century brick brewery. Bayreuth burghers soon named it The
Big Barn, while continuing to cherish their highly garnished
rococo opera house in the center of town.

Despite this reaction on the part of average onlookers, the
city fathers began to see this man Wagner in a different light.
Was he not drawing world-wide attention to their obscure and
insignificant community? However queer his doctrines on art
might be, his choice of Bayreuth as an experimental laboratory
lent a certain intellectual distinction to the town. It cast a flattering reflection on the citizenry. The more the city fathers
thought about this happy conclusion the better they liked it.
In a specially held convocation they proposed participating,
with borough funds, in the Wagner project. Also, taking note
of the dingy quarters in which the composer and his family
lived, the good councilmen rounded out their generous deed
by voting an additional increment for the building of a decent
home.

News stories regarding this decision spread through word of
mouth and printed page to other cities. From remote parts of
Germany small contributions began to trickle in as music lovers
loosened their purse strings. In Mannheim a Wagner Society
disclosed its existence, having been formed as early as 1871
under the leadership of one Emil Heckel. The example found
imitators elsewhere. The trickle of donations swelled into a
livelier flow.

Richard was overwhelmed by these developments. In a burst
of enthusiasm he found a name for the home yet to be built.
Villa Wahnfried ("Illusion's Rest"), it was to be called. He
had no idea of its size or shape. Cosima, the strong-willed, the
wise, the efficient, would see to that.

She was in her true element. Her organizing talent made
her an ideal partner in the vast undertaking that presently had

outgrown Richard's wildest hopes. She kept an eye on everything, from the quality of floorboards to the shades of paint
mixtures. Workmen trembled at her approach, for she fearlessly directed Brückwald, the draftsman; Hölfel, the architect; Weiss, the chief carpenter; and master mason Wölfel. Her
commanding manner was that of a field marshal. If she chose
to "out-Wagner Wagner" at times, it was in the interest of a
cause she fervently believed in and one for which posterity
would owe her unending thanks.

Bayreuth itself presently underwent an almost complete rebirth to serve the same end. From an obscure medieval principality the town had passed through the powdered-wig era as
a quaint eighteenth-century pleasance. But there its prominence had ended. Under the Wagner impact, however, and
prodded by Cosima's generalship, a new Bayreuth wakened
from idle slumber to become one of the world's great music
centers. With veneration equal to that shown by religious devotees to Lourdes and Oberammergau or by Mozart addicts to
Salzburg, future Wagner disciples would band together for annual pilgrimages to their idol's shrine.

With this in view the newly formed local Wagner Society
arrived at another pertinent decision: not only Richard's work
but his earthly remains ought one day to be identified with the
same spot. The garden of Villa Wahnfried was to hold the
master's tomb, with Cosima's right there beside him, sharing
the honors.

The consecrated high priestess regarded this as no more than
her due. She lived, thought, breathed, worked only for Wagner. When all the turmoil of building and spending had subsided she set herself one more task. She took down in nightly
dictation, after Richard was done with the day's composing,
the verbal account of her husband's stormy life, to be published
by him under the title *Mein Leben.*

In doing so she could not help but wield an understandably
editorial pen. Events were shaped by Cosima so as best to enhance the central character's portrait, generally at the expense
of secondary figures in the plot. This was particularly true
where persons of feminine gender were concerned. Cosima
saw only shallow, trivial and flirtatious women in Richard's

past, and it may well be that under her formidable scrutiny the reminiscing husband lacked courage to describe his earlier loves with adequate gusto.

Mathilde Wesendonk's picture emerged in especially jaundiced colors. Of this alluring woman who inspired the sublime music-poem of the ages, *Tristan und Isolde*, Cosima could bring herself to give only the most sketchy (and catty) delineation, topped by a gratuitous surmise that the lady dyed her hair.

Through all this, unconsciously, Cosima revealed that she knew her own triumph could never be absolute. It was she who had fallen in love with Richard, not he with her. She could not banish that realization. To enhance her own image and position she did not hesitate to minimize the worth of her forerunners. But the loveliest of these, Mathilde, never ceased, even in memory, to plague her.

This hidden weakness in Cosima's make-up was the more remarkable when the temperaments of the two rivals were juxtaposed. Stopped by no barrier of social code or conscience, Cosima had gone after what she wanted, throwing herself into Wagner's arms without concern for the husband and children she thereby disowned. Mathilde, her opposite, had done nothing. She had denied herself to the would-be lover and taught him renunciation. Yet she, whom he had not possessed, was to remain forever unforgotten.

One mark of proof, if such were needed, lay in the fact that the wooded elevation on which Wagner built his Festival Theater was called by him *Der Grüne Hügel* ("The Green Hill"), the same name by which Mathilde's home on the outskirts of Zürich was known. Cosima could never become quite reconciled to that.

As the metamorphosis of Bayreuth neared completion, news came from the outside world regarding an operatic sensation: the triumphal tour of a Verdi work called *Aïda*. A few years ago, on Christmas Eve 1871, this showpiece (commissioned by the Khedive of Egypt in honor of the Suez Canal) had been given a rousing *première* at Cairo. Since then it created a furor of enthusiasm wherever seen.

"That Verdi fellow," complained Cosima as she read a sheaf

of critiques on the breakfast terrace at Wahnfried, "he's a shameless imitator!"

She was convinced that Aïda, the Ethiopian heroine, could be nothing but a copy of Meyerbeer's *L'Africaine,* while musically the Italian composer had long been accused of "borrowing" from Wagner. The latter claim was based on Verdi's employment of thematic repetition, similar to the Wagnerian leitmotiv; but actually there was a noteworthy difference. In Verdi's works the recurring of a melody or an orchestral phrase never amounted to more than simple reprise, while Wagner's use of the same device involved modulation of tone and key to denote shadings of mood or psychological change.

Verdi himself was sensitive about the rumors. In self-defense he protested, rather too often, that his first experience of a Wagner opera had come to him in Bologna (after *Aïda* was already finished) during a performance of *Lohengrin,* at which he admitted taking copious notes on his program. However, the texts and music scores of Wagner's works had been published for years, and contemporary composers could study them at will. Hence the great Giuseppe might not have been completely ignorant of his German colleague's technique.

More significant was the fact that, as an Italian and a patriot, Verdi opposed the dominance of Germanism in music as in politics. At the outbreak of the war of 1870 his sympathies had been unequivocally with the French.

"I am desolated by the news," he had written to his librettist Antonio Ghislanzoni. "Poor France and poor we!"

A victory for German arms, he felt, could leave only the prospect of future vengeance and ever-bloodier conflicts to follow, in addition to the Nordic threat to Mediterranean culture.

Even the launching of *Aïda* had suffered under the Franco-Prussian campaign. Originally the opera's *première* was to have coincided with the opening of the Canal, at which the Empress Eugénie (cousin of the Vicomte de Lesseps, builder of the waterway) would be present. But Napoleon's defeat at Sedan and Eugénie's flight from the burning Tuileries to a shelter in England had put an end to such picturesque plans. Instead, the Khedive Ismail Pasha proposed that *Aïda* be used

for the inauguration of a new Italian theater in the shadow of
the Pyramids. This too was a great honor, and a financially
profitable one, for Verdi. But the disappointment about Suez
left him resentful of all things German, a mood that also colored
his attitude toward Wagner.

Repeatedly there had been opportunities for the two composers to meet, yet each sensed hostility in the other and so
avoided a confrontation. When, early in 1876, an opening date
for the Bayreuth Festspiel Haus began to be talked about,
Verdi was traveling in Germany. Curiosity prompted him to
consider a detour through Bavaria, but he repressed the impulse. He had just visited Cologne to attend a performance of
Schiller's *Fiesco,* a play on which his own unsuccessful opera,
Simon Boccanegra, had been loosely based. The experience
had left him fretful and dissatisfied, hardly of a mind to applaud another German's luck.

By midsummer a date for the inauguration of Wagner's Festival Theater was set, with the composer's magnum opus, *Der
Ring des Nibelungen,* scheduled for a world *première.* Four
days would be required for the cycle, from August 13 through
17. The cast was chosen from a roster of leading singers, among
them Georg Unger (Siegfried), Amalia Materna (Brünnhilde),
Franz Betz (Wotan), Karl Hill (Alberich), Karl Schlosser
(Mime), Mathilde Weckerlin (Gutrune), Gustav Siehr (Hagen), Luise Jaide (Erda), and two inexperienced young ladies
named Lilli and Marie Lehmann in the roles of Rhine Maidens.

The conductor for the performance was the thirty-three-
year-old Hans Richter, a future luminary in the Bayreuth firma-
ment. The time was coming when the podium of the Festspiel
Haus would lend its occupant a cachet equal to that furnished
by La Scala in Milan.

CHAPTER 7

REHEARSALS for the greatest tour de force in operatic history began on June 3, with Wagner taking a firm hand in the proceedings. Day and night he spent coaching singers and set designers, and driving costumers and wig makers to distraction. The hubbub backstage was indescribable, as artists were not given time to go to their lodgings for meals. Lunch trays were served at an improvised table amid Valkyrie rocks and Gibichung scenery, with Cosima expertly in charge.

Matters not relevant to Wotan's world of gods and semimortals received attention on some of these occasions. It was observed, for instance, that Fräulein Jaide (who sang Erda and also doubled as the warrior maid Waltraute) had atrocious table manners. Summarily Cosima took the offender to task.

"You may be a fine mezzo," she scolded, "but I'll not have you sitting here with a knife in your mouth!"

A different problem came up with Herr Hill (Alberich), a high-strung basso from Schwerin. Unlike the fierce fellow he was to portray, this sensitive artist quavered before the demands of his actually very short and secondary role. So tense did Herr Hill's nerves become that he could neither eat nor sing unless braced by a stout dosage of champagne.

"I don't think Alberich is worth all that expense," Cosima commented. But Richard pointed out that there was less wear and tear in ordering a case of sparkling wine than in auditioning a batch of possible or impossible replacements.

As for the leading voices, they were of excellent caliber. The tenor Georg Unger (Siegfried) was a handsome giant who had studied theology in Leipzig before turning to music for a career. Franz Betz (Wotan and Wanderer) had won acclaim throughout Europe with his ringing baritone voice; "an admirable singer," Saint-Saëns had called him. Then there was Gustav Siehr, the Wiesbaden basso, who had learned his difficult role (Hagen) in two weeks, owing to a string of conflicting concert commitments. Lastly, a young niece of Richard Wagner, Johanna Jachmann, acquitted herself nobly in testing for the mezzo part of the First Norn.

Midway through the rehearsal period a strange visitor arrived to seat himself far back in the shadows of the great auditorium. No one save Wagner knew the tall, cloaked figure to be Ludwig II of Bavaria. The King had not been seen in public during recent years, nor had photographs appeared, disclosing the changes wrought by illness and obesity. He was not recognized during this brief escape from the guarded asylum that was his palace.

Now completely at odds with his ministers, Ludwig was more than ever haunted by neuroses. But he had clear moments when his mind eagerly absorbed such news as came to him from the outside world. The widely publicized events at Bayreuth proved irresistible. He knew he could never attend *The Ring's* gala opening. Even if his medical custodians had permitted such a step, Ludwig abhorred crowds and found surcease only in solitude. But to see the mirage of Bayreuth transformed into reality, and to hear Wagner's titanic tetralogy in its final completion—this he would not deny himself.

As he sat there under cover of darkness, the full witchery of the Nibelungen epos now unfolded before the monarch's eyes. There, in a mystic shimmer, was *Das Rheingold,* the simple and naïve fairy tale of a river's treasure guarded by water nymphs against a covetous dwarf, black Alberich. To the beholder with even a shred of his childhood imagination intact the acceptance of this lovely fable brought purest magic for reward. *Die Walküre* and *Siegfried* moved on to more symbolic spheres, depicting the struggle of gods trying to live like men and thereby faring rather worse than men might do as gods. Finally *Götterdämmerung,* a kind of Apocalypse of Norse Paganism, pointed up the eternal moral of retribution for error, whether committed knowingly as by Wotan or in Siegfried's innocent ignorance.

To Ludwig these meanings were, of course, no longer clear. He reveled only in the visual delight of changing scenes and the even greater ecstasy of sounds such as had never before reached his ear. Two tryout performances had been held under his sponsorship in Munich, of *Rheingold* and *Walküre*, in 1869 and 1870, which must be counted world *premières*. But their sonority and power gained immeasurably through the acoustics and the impressive proscenium height of the Bayreuth stage.

The King's absence from Munich was soon discovered. Dr. Gudden and his colleagues were called on the carpet by the Ministry, while an immediate search was instituted. The royal fugitive was not hard to find. Where else could he have gone but to Bayreuth? A discreet deputation waited outside the Festspiel Haus. As the last chords of *Götterdämmerung* died away, Ludwig emerged and was taken into custody.

Special measures were meanwhile being pushed at the Munich *Residenz*, so as to prevent a repetition of such royal excursions. Iron bars were placed on bedroom windows and reinforced locks put on doors. For a time palace servants, loyal to their master, removed all such devices as fast as they appeared. But presently these culprits were replaced by more trustworthy male nurses under whose watchful eyes the lonely captive undertook no further flights.

Ludwig had yet a number of years to live. As his dementia progressed he was removed to his former childhood home, Castle Berg, under still stricter supervision. An uncle of the sick monarch, Prince Luitpold of Wittelsbach, was proclaimed Regent of Bavaria. At Berg, eventually, the tragic epilogue played itself out. After a period of seeming tractability Ludwig managed to foil his captors one last time; he lured Dr. Gudden for a stroll along the shore of Starnberg Lake and succeeded in drowning both the doctor and himself. The date was June 13, 1886.

Long before that, at Bayreuth, Richard Wagner lived through the breath-taking climax of his career: the inauguration of the Festival Theater. During the final construction stages, as the roof was being laid on the great building, the composer had written a long poem in praise of all who had helped the project along. Hodcarriers, stonemasons, bricklayers, carpenters—all were mentioned. King Ludwig's bounty, the architect's vision, the benevolent support of Bayreuth's burgomaster and the townspeople themselves who had consented to the sale of the building site—Richard gave praise to each. But in conclusion he added a stanza, patterned in Hans Sachs measure, and to be read aloud—not by himself or some pompous official but by a humble laborer. It ran:

> *Nun setzen wir aufs Haus das Dach;*
> *bewahr' es Gott vor Sturz and Krach!*
> *Lass' ich jetzt den Bauherrn leben,*
> *welch' Namen soll ich ihm geben?*
> *Ob Wagner, oder seine Patrone,*
> *oder gar der im Lande trägt die Krone? . . .*
> *Der sich als den besten Bauherrn erweist,*
> *es lebe, so ruf' ich, der deutsche Geist!*

(Now on this house we place the roof:
Pray God, it be strong and damage proof!
Then, would we praise the master mason,
Whom shall we name for that high station?
Is it Wagner, or all those friends—
Including a king—who helped his ends?
No . . . There's no builder of greater merit
Than, praise to thee, the German spirit!)

Here was the oriflamme Wagner would hold aloft for future generations to salute. Here the ultimate exposition of his message. He had the above strophe repeated when the moment arrived for throwing open the theater's doors.

The festive days went by in a rhapsodic trance. Celebrities from the world of art, society and politics converged on tiny Bayreuth, creating a crisis among rooming-house proprietors and the town's single hotel. To alleviate the congestion, private homes took in guests, as did farm settlements and villages within a radius of some fifty miles.

The performance itself, extending over four unforgettably

glorious days, brought Wagner face to face with a new set of responsibilities. He had conceived his music-festival idea in terms of cultural uplift, not only for the privileged few but for the masses. The business angle, characteristically, had not occurred to him. The inaugural performance of *The Ring* cycle had been an invitational affair, to be followed in future by state-supported operatic productions, admission free, for the benefit of all lovers of art. For himself Wagner wished only a sustaining salary sufficient to permit a regulated continuance of his work as composer and stage manager. All administrative duties were to be taken over by a local committee made up of leading Bayreuth citizens.

There were several flaws in this attractive plan, which the sponsoring committee, headed by the burgomaster, quickly pointed out. After congratulating Richard on the resounding critical success earned by the opening Festival venture the burgomaster raised a primary issue. Philanthropy was highly laudable but it had no place in a project of this sort. Operation of the Festspiel Haus must be put on a sound business basis.

"But that is not what I wanted at all!" Wagner protested. "I wished to open an art center, financed by the state and by such private contributions as might voluntarily be offered. But no ticket sales. People from every corner of the world are to be made welcome and admitted free."

"Such a plan is manifestly impossible!"

"Why?" The look in Wagner's eyes was naïve. He truly was devoid of sense where money was concerned.

The burgomaster spread out a file of papers. "Because there's already an accumulation of bills awaiting payment. Stage sets, orchestra equipment, a fire curtain, not to mention a first mortgage that became necessary when the building fund ran out."

"Oh." Richard fell to brooding, but he soon came up with a bright thought. "I am at work on a new composition, gentlemen, a semireligious drama entitled *Parsifal*." He rummaged through his desk and held up pages of scattered manuscript. "Here! The proceeds from this may solve all our problems."

"Hardly." The burgomaster was diffident but firm. "You do

not understand, Master. The matter involves running expenses and permanent upkeep. If the Festival Theater is to endure into the future, it will take more than the . . . er . . . conjectural earnings of one opera, that is not even finished as yet, to keep it going. As for depending on charity—" there was a general shaking of heads—"that is out of the question."

"I see. Then what do you propose for a solution?"

One of the committee members stepped forward with a large document which the burgomaster unfolded. "We have here the listing of a tentative board of directors and an administrative body trained in business procedure. The plan calls only for your signature."

Wagner hesitated before reading the document. Then, obediently, he signed. His expression was one of confused surrender. "You are right, gentlemen. I do not understand these things very well." He laid down the pen. "I only know my music was not written to remain unheard."

The burgomaster accepted the signed paper and bowed his thanks. One by one the committee members shook Wagner's hand and then filed down the steps of Villa Wahnfried. The continuity of the Bayreuth Theater was assured.

Prospects for *Parsifal* were to be less sanguine. Shortly after disclosing that he was at work on this theme Richard completed the poetic text. It took from January through April of 1877 to write. During May of that year he was offered eight concert engagements at London's Albert Hall, a financially rewarding opportunity he could not refuse. This put off all musical composition till summer and early fall.

News of the projected opera and its mystic nature made conversation meanwhile in theatrical and journalistic circles. It also caught the attention of the Catholic Church. At Munich a solemn conference took place between a learned ecclesiastic, Father Cyprian, and his superior, Bishop Stollenberg. The Church, it appeared, had reason to keep a wary eye on the demoniac Bayreuth composer whose attitude toward questions of dogma was unconventional, to say the least. Father Cyprian had heard reports of goings-on at Wahnfried that disquieted him. He lost no time in transmitting his alarms.

"I have it on good authority that this heretic, Richard Wagner, is contemplating a theatrical piece that employs the Sacrament of the Holy Eucharist for a dramatic device."

The Bishop was outraged. "Blasphemy!" he cried. "What is the name of this—this act of heresy?"

Father Cyprian made a gesture of distaste. "Something called *Parsifal*, a word of Arabic or Hindu origin, I venture."

The Bishop's erudition was more profound, and he could not resist the human temptation to parade it. "The *Parsees*, my friend, were Persian fire worshipers and followers of Zoroaster, who believed in purification by flame. The word *fal* is of Iranian origin and means 'fool.' This *Parsifal*, therefore is the purest and most unmitigated of fools!" His Reverence burst into uncontrolled mirth at so pithy a bit of speculation.

Father Cyprian smiled respectfully before channeling the colloquy back to its original issue. "Aside from making a travesty of the ceremony of Communion," he emphasized, "this sinful opera is said to wind up with a sequence called the Good Friday Music, an out-and-out offense against Mother Church!"

The revelation was poison and gall to the episcopal ears. "We shall take steps," declared Stollenberg. "That villainous Wagner must be excommunicated."

"Such a measure would disturb him not at all," Father Cyprian reminded carefully. "He already lives in Lutheran error. Yet he falls short of even what *that* misguided creed demands."

"Hmm, is that so?"

"By his standards there was nothing wrong in breaking up another man's home and living in sin with that woman, Cosima."

A sudden gleam of inspiration lighted up Bishop Stollenberg's face. "Frau von Bülow, she was Cosima Liszt, was she not? Her father, the great pianist, some years ago saw the evil of his worldly ways and did penance by taking the cloth."

The younger cleric nodded. "He is one of our most devout votaries, no doubt in atonement also for his daughter's guilt."

"I am very fond of the Abbé Liszt," mused the Bishop. "He should be useful to us in keeping the sacrilegious *Parsifal* from ever appearing on the boards."

"Amen!" said Cyprian.

"I shall send Liszt to Bayreuth with orders from . . ." The Bishop paused to ponder the most efficacious measure at his disposal.

"The Holy See?" suggested Cyprian.

"Excellent!" Stollenberg made a mental note regarding the priest's qualifications for advancement.

"Shall I make contact with the Abbé? He has returned to Italy again after a visit to his home in Weimar."

"*Dominus tecum*," intoned His Reverence. "I am depending on you."

CHAPTER 8

A FEW days later Franz Liszt, now a decorous, white-haired figure of benign abstraction, sat meditating in the monastery garden of the Roman order to which he was pledged. From the near-by colonnade a monk approached in company of a cleric in hat and travel cloak.

"Brother Francesco, there is a visitor to see you." Introductions followed. "Monsignor Cyprian—the Abbé Liszt."

During the exchange of greetings the monk departed on soft-soled sandals.

"I have been sent here by my superior, Bishop Stollenberg of Munich," Cyprian began without needless verbiage.

Liszt had risen. "Yes? I trust there is some way I may be of service?"

"There is."

As the stranger looked about for privacy, Liszt led the way to an arbor. "We shall be undisturbed here."

"Good. Let me come quickly to the point. You are the father of one Cosima Wagner, are you not?"

The answer came after uneasy hesitation. "Yes."

"A deplorable matter, that." Cyprian sniffed with unconcealed disapproval. "Divorce, immorality. Our Mother Church frowns on such flagrant depravities."

Liszt remained unfailingly courteous. "So do I, Monsignor."

"Ah! Of course." There was a pause. "I regret to say that a new and even more shocking offense threatens from . . . er . . . that quarter."

The white head jerked forward with alarm. "Again?"

"It has come to the Bishop's ears that the man, whose marriage to your daughter we do not recognize, is composing an opera that violates Vatican prerogatives."

426

"No!"

"We make no idle accusations, my dear Abbé. You mean to say you have heard nothing regarding this newest plot of the devil?"

"I have been out of touch. I know nothing."

"No matter." Cyprian's tone grew authoritative as he explained further the nature of his mission. "Now that you have been told, the Bishop wishes me to transmit an urgent . . . request."

"By all means."

"You are to leave at once for Bayreuth. This profane opera *Parsifal* must be prevented from appearing, at all costs."

Liszt hesitated, then spoke softly. "I shall do what I can."

Both men rose and walked from the arbor. With a slight nod Cyprian donned his hat and cloak, then departed quickly through the winding cloister.

That same week the Abbé sat in a speeding train that made its way across the Dolomites and the Tyrol to the scenic valleys of Bavaria. Beyond Munich, Nürnberg and Erlangen the wooded hills of Bayreuth at last came into view, with the great silhouette of the Festspiel Haus outlined against a sunset sky. Liszt leaned out of a window to observe it intently, his long white hair blowing in the breeze.

On arrival at the small railroad station he took a carriage and asked to be driven straight to his daughter's home. Wahn-fried, he discovered, was located on a street called Wagner-strasse. The town itself seemed to be steeped in Nibelungen nomenclature. There were avenues marked Rheingold, Lohen-grin, Siegfried and Walkürenstrasse, though a number of thoroughfares deferred to such memorable personages as Hegel, Beethoven and Goethe. Judging from appearances, Bayreuth had gone to some length in fostering a rampant Wagner cult.

At the gate of Villa Wahnfried the Abbé dismissed the carriage. He walked through the flowering garden and up the front steps. The door was unlocked.

On the threshold Liszt paused to collect himself. He had broken years ago with his daughter over her scandalous behavior, even though mindful of the shocking example he himself had set his children in his own younger days. He was a man of religion now, whose fingers had grown too stiff for public concertizing, whose mind was too withdrawn for the composer's task. His purpose today was straightforward and uncompromising. He had been charged with an earnest mission, to lay down the law of God's Vicar, chapter and verse, to the pagan genius dwelling in this house.

From an upper floor came the sound of someone pacing. Ah, then Richard's studio must be upstairs. But the acoustics of Wahnfried were deceptive, for Liszt found himself presently only a step removed from the music room. He entered without knocking, to see Wagner, pen in hand, striding back and forth beside a littered desk.

Several seconds passed before the absorbed composer looked up and beheld the silent visitor. He dropped his pen now and rushed forward with a cry.

"Franz!"

Liszt said nothing. His steel-blue eyes observed that Wagner too had grayed, but his movements were those of a boy.

Now Richard halted in mock hesitation. "Father-confessor or father-in-law—I don't know exactly which to call you." He held out his hand. "But there is no one I've longed more to see!"

"That is fortunate," Liszt said with cool severity, "because I have come to talk to you on an important matter."

Richard pulled up a chair. "Splendid! To you and me the most important matter in the world was always love, translated into music. True?"

For the briefest second Liszt consented to unbend. "True. But it is time that we concerned ourselves with our immortal souls." He drew himself up very erect, fingering the buttons of his black cassock. "I am told that you are working on a new theme which deals with religion in an . . . er . . . unorthodox and daring way." As he spoke, his gaze took in the high-vaulted study with its music shelves and polished grand piano. Broad settees and arm chairs stood about, with coffee tables beside them, but nowhere an ash tray, as at Wahnfried no one smoked.

Wagner's voice rang with enthusiasm. "Yes, think of it! I

am using the greatest of the Arthurian Legends, *Parsifal.*" He hopped to the piano. "Listen to this. It's the Grail motif."

For several minutes he played a passage that imitated the sonorous peal of cathedral chimes. Liszt frowned forbiddingly, his face averted, though he could not quite keep from cocking a furtive ear.

Wagner played on, carried away by some inner vision. "I borrowed this from the *Amen* sung years ago by the choir boys in the court chapel at Dresden." He gestured with both arms, swinging an imaginary bell rope. "These are the carillons of Monsalvat, hailing the young Parsifal to the holy community."

Liszt leaned forward, the better to listen. But now a pang of conscience shot through him and he drew himself upright. His lean frame seemed to shake as he cleared his throat with a basso bark.

"My dear Richard, aren't you touching on sacred matters that lie quite outside the layman's reach?" His brows met in a frown. "The Church guards its mysteries in reverent trust."

"Of course." Wagner's enthusiasm was not to be dimmed. "And how wonderful those mysteries are! I am trying to take what is best in Christianity, Buddhism and all other enlightened faiths to point up their common path to salvation, namely through the four stages of suffering, compassion, service and renunciation."

"But that is antiscriptural, to mingle true revelation with false fancies! The Vatican strictly forbids it!"

At the keyboard Wagner was completely wrapped up in his music. "Here is the Temptation theme, in the evil Klingsor's garden, where Parsifal, like Tannhäuser in the Venus Grotto, must resist all manner of seductions."

The melody poured forth and swelled magnificently until the room quivered with sound. Liszt was beginning to succumb, despite all efforts to the contrary. Gradually he relaxed into an almost voluptuous mellowness, entranced by the sheer witchery that smote his ear. There was a brief instant when duty fought one last battle against the demon in his soul. Then the surrender was deliciously complete. "Ah," he cried out with passion, "that is splendid—the noblest thing you have done!"

As soon as he had spoken these words the pious Abbé crossed himself. He had come, a servant of Rome, well rehearsed in anathema to hurl at Wagner's head. His duty was to chide and catechize, not to enjoy. But the old magician Klingsor (how melodic and onomatopoetic a name!) had taken possession of his senses. Entranced, Liszt rushed forward to the piano and replaced Wagner at the keyboard. In his superlative virtuoso style he played from the manuscript before him, not like a retired instrumentalist but with the verve and fire of an artist at his peak.

Then, as suddenly, he broke off. Pointing to his churchman's hat and canonicals, he burst out, "How masterfully you have exposed me to myself! I am a priest in costume only. Even after the long silence of professional retirement I've remained first and always a strolling piano player." He flexed his beautiful long fingers, smiling. "And a show-off, too!"

At this moment the double doors to the music room opened, both wings swinging wide, as Cosima appeared on the threshold. She stood there, gaunt like her father and with his majestic bearing. Her hair, parted severely in the center, showed traces of gray, though she was only forty-five years old as against her husband's sixty-nine.

A long silence reigned while the bitter words spoken at Triebschen seemed to hover in the air. Then Liszt ran toward his daughter. They embraced. Watching this reconciliation scene, Richard folded up his music. Already a blessing seemed to have issued from the *Parsifal* score, for Liszt's crabbed heart had melted. Cosima had been forgiven.

Now Richard closed the piano. "Suffering, compassion, service, renunciation," he repeated, as if to himself. "They sum up what I have learned of life. This is my last opera. It shall be my spiritual bequest."

Liszt turned around with a quizzical look. "Well, at my age I've little left but gout, compassion and prayers. Renunciation is no longer a problem." He pursed his lips meditatively.

Cosima looked from one to the other. "You are a pair of rascals, you two," she said, grinning. "You expound a typical old-age philosophy: after the fun of a dissipated youth you recommend virtue and continence!"

The men exchanged sheepish nods. There was a twinkle in Wagner's eyes. "In any case, my dear Franz, the *Parsifal* formula ought to be a perfect fit."

Liszt agreed. "It is, Richard, it is." Suddenly an expression of dismay came over his face as he snatched his cloak and hat. "But what am I going to tell the Bishop?"

In a ticklish theological quandary the Abbé departed. He would return soon thereafter, however, for the world *première,* on July 26, 1882, of his son-in-law's final opus. A golden midsummer spread its glory over Bayreuth as a long stream of carriages moved up the great Nibelungen Avenue to the Festival Theater on the hill. Landau tops were down, so that foreign ticket holders and local gentry could get a good view of one another. There was a sprinkling of exotic costumes—a fez from Egypt, saris and turbans from Bengal—mingled with bemedalled dignitaries from every corner of Europe, a delegation from America and even a royal personage or two. From the front portico roof of the Festspiel Haus four trumpeters sounded a fanfare (the horn flourish from *Siegfried,* which was to become traditional) announcing the start of the performance.

As people settled in their seats and the theater lights were dimmed, many binoculars remained fixed on the Wagner family group, in a roped off section at the back. For most observers this was the first view of the sensational pair, Richard and Cosima, whose love affair had been the scandal of the era. How imperceptibly the passing years erased the tarnish of transgression! There the celebrated lovers sat, domesticated, comfortably aging, surrounded by their growing brood—for all the world like Mr. and Mrs. Ordinary Citizen on a Sunday outing with the children. To complete the cozy tableau Papa Liszt, in somber cleric's frock, lent respectability to the scene.

A few thoughtful minds in that vast assemblage might have speculated on the transitoriness of human obloquy and its peculiar direction. Was it not odd how condemnation mounted in exact ratio to the youthfulness (whether in actual years or in capacity for enjoyment) of those condemned? No one made much of a to-do over wickedness in old age, though its depravity and degradation could far exceed the derelictions of life's spring. But how inexorable the punishment inflicted on the young! Did this not contingently unveil the fierce impulse of envy in the breast of fervid moralists? It was easy indeed to overlook sin in the old, since the accumulation of years aroused only revulsion and pity. But who would not trade everything for a return to the morning or noon of living? And who, knowing that the clock cannot be set back, is able to look with equanimity on joys untasted and pleasures irrevocably missed?

In the days of the Triebschen idyl, when public disapprobation was at its peak, Richard Wagner served as a target for more than purely moral reasons. Apart from a very human resentment against lechery in others, the average mind abominates that which is not average. Compensation is sometimes found in the discovery that intellectual endowments may be accompanied by a corresponding erotic indifference. "Ah," gloats the common clay, "he may have genius, but me—I've got sex!" Only when, as in Wagner, both endowments—the cerebral and the carnal—were of maximum caliber did they become unbearable to the beholder. Sin, by itself, could be forgiven. So could, by itself, genius. But both, at one and the same time, were not to be tolerated.

The passing years fortunately had brought about a shifting of balance. The Wagner now under public scrutiny was more nearly King Marke than Tristan, brain rather than brawn, spirit grown mighty at the expense of withering flesh. Now, though there was something indeed to envy, there remained also that for which to grieve: the loss of youth. This placated that most implacable enemy—convention. They who sat in judgment could applaud now, for the imbalance wrought by age left something in their favor once again. Stellar magnitude on one plane, rather than two, was far more allowable.

Another factor governing the public's attitude toward Wagner on this particular occasion was the choice of conductor for the *Parsifal première*. Over the years, in writings and verbal utterances, the composer had gained a reputation for anti-Semitism. Unquestionably a stubborn prejudice had taken root at one time in Richard's breast when he felt himself mocked and intimidated by the scornful Meyerbeer. But that formidable ogre had died long ago, and his widely touted works were fading into obscurity. The day was fast approaching when even such noteworthy successes as *Les Huguenots, Le Prophète* and *L'Africaine* would not be heard on any stage. In this respect the prediction once hurled in Meyerbeer's face by the immature and certainly uninformed Wagner was coming true.

The bitterness, of course, had long faded. Richard counted today many outstanding Jews among his friends. In testimony to this fact he now went out of his way to offer the baton, for the world's first performance of *Parsifal,* to a brilliant Jewish conductor, Hermann Levi.

The choice was perhaps more than a mere demonstrative gesture. Richard must have had the *première's* outcome equally in mind. For Levi was a musical prodigy who practically guaranteed the superlative in orchestral production.

CHAPTER 9

THE curtains parted as the Prelude to *Parsifal* drew to a close. A wild mountain scene, supposedly somewhere in the Spanish Pyrenees and almost identifiable with Monserrat in Catalonia (though Wagner never confirmed this), brought the beholder into the hallowed region of Monsalvat. Here, rising above a dense forest, the Temple-Fortress of the Holy Grail stood hidden in the clouds. It was built by a pious knight, Titurel, as a shrine for the vessel or cup from which, according to Arthurian and Provençal legends, the Saviour drank at the Last Supper. Through Joseph of Arimathea, who in it had gathered the blood dripping from Christ's wounds, the Grail had been salvaged and miraculously brought to the West, to be guarded by a brotherhood of holy fighters who pledged themselves to a life of purity and prayer.

Among the Knights Templar of the Grail was a renegade, Klingsor, who fought with Titurel for kingship over Monsalvat and was cast out. Klingsor thereafter turned to black magic. He conjured up an enchanted garden peopled with voluptuous dancing girls through whom he enticed other knights away from virtue and into his service.

Sometime before the opening of the opera, Titurel, grown old, surrendered the throne to his son Amfortas and armed him with the Sacred Spear, said to be the one that pierced Christ's side. Amfortas, however, soon fell victim to Klingsor's most dangerous temptress, Kundry—a strange creature able to transform herself from loveliest Venus to revolting witch or humble penitent. The new king escaped from the enchanted garden, but not until Klingsor inflicted a terrible wound and robbed him of the Sacred Spear. As a symbol of unhappy humanity, the ailing Amfortas must await the coming of a pure and innocent being (in Klingsor's eyes, a "guileless fool") to recover the stolen spear before the wound could close.

PARSIFAL

ACT I

SCENE 1: At the start of the play, Gurnemanz, an aging Knight of the Grail, wakes two sleeping guards to tell them that Amfortas is about to be brought down from the castle, "weak from pain past bearing," for his daily bath in a forest pool, the waters of which are said to relieve his agony. To taunt the suffering King, who has just arrived in his litter, the wicked Kundry appears, this time in virtuous guise, clad in rough skins, and protesting repentance. She offers a balsam, which Amfortas accepts, though with little confidence. His hope is pinned on the promised redeemer, whom he has seen in a vision.

As Amfortas is borne away, some guards bring on the youth Parsifal. Hunting in the forest, with bow and arrow, the boy has killed one of the wild swans within the bird sanctuary of Monsalvat. Gurnemanz rebukes Parsifal, who responds in all candor, "I knew not it was wrong." The simplicity of these words, the accompanying lack of fear and unconsciousness of evil, impress the listeners. Kundry, gifted with prophecy, now steps forward to tell the lad that his mother, Herzeleide, widow of the noble lord Gamuret, has died. Pained by this news, Parsifal clutches the witch by the throat. But he grows faint, unable to harm her. Observing this, Gurnemanz suspects that here indeed may be the "Innocent One," incapable of evil, for whom Amfortas is waiting. He asks the lad to accompany him to the Grail Temple, where the ceremony of the Eucharist is about to take place.

SCENE 2: The stage set changes to a shallow woodland path, leading over rocks to the heights of Monsalvat. Gurnemanz and the boy walk on as the music pattern shifts from the gentle leitmotiv of Parsifal the "Guileless Fool" to Parsifal the "Deliverer." Soon bells begin to toll, in the rising sixths of the *Amen* learned by Wagner in his choirboy days at Dresden. And now the wanderers enter a door carved into the side of a hill, which leads into the sacred precincts.

SCENE 3: Twilight reigns in the interior of the great Temple.

From the lofty dome comes the chanting of a chorale, as the
Knights of the Grail file in to a martial theme. The voice of
Amfortas next is heard, pleading with his father to be released
from the burden of leadership. But Titurel is old and himself
near death; he orders Amfortas to bow to duty. "Serve thou,
and so thy guilt atone! Uncover the Grail!"

Amfortas obeys. In the exact manner of the Christian Communion Service, with the Elevation of the Host, the Holy Cup
is held aloft. It glows mysteriously in the sudden darkness that
has fallen on the Temple. Then, as daylight returns, the thrilling
glow vanishes. But all who have looked upon it are blessed.

The Knights, who have knelt during the ceremony, now take
their seats at prepared tables and drink from goblets filled with
wine. They also partake of bread that unseen hands have put
before them. Amfortas is too ill to share in the repast. Nor
does Parsifal take part, though he has been invited. The lad
stands motionless, only once laying a hand on his own heart as
he hears Amfortas groan with pain.

As the ceremony ends and the Grail company departs, Gurnemanz asks Parsifal if he understands what he has seen. The
boy shakes his head in denial. At this the old Knight is in-
furiated. "You are not simple," he cries, "but a simpleton! Get
out of here, and in future do not hunt among swans. Go looking, gander, for a goose!"

Act II

Scene 1: Cast out, Parsifal heads unwittingly for the abode
of the magician, Klingsor. The inner keep of a mighty castle
appears on stage, with Kundry asleep in the shadows. Klingsor
rouses her with news that Parsifal, who embodies virtue and
must therefore be destroyed, is headed this way. In invoking
the temptress, he calls her the "Eternal Female, Luciferess,
Herodias, Rose of Hell," whom the forces of Satan have used
through the ages for man's downfall. Half willing, half reluctant, Kundry obeys the summons and prepares—this time
in ravishing guise—to seduce the approaching youth. Darkness
descends over the castle tower and its occupants.

Scene 2: The set has changed to Kingsor's Enchanted Garden, filled with sunshine and luxuriant blooms. A band of
diaphanously clad maidens rushes in, lamenting at first that

a stranger has dispersed and overcome their lovers, but then turning on him—Parsifal—with amorous desire. Kundry joins them, in her loveliest and most irresistible form. The youth resists all advances, but Kundry manages to throw her arms about him and to kiss his lips, giving him a first taste of passion. A fiery flash sweeps through him. At the same instant, however, he feels in memory the wound of Amfortas, as though opening in his own breast. The warning flings him to his knees, in prayer to God. Kundry renews her wooing, but he is proof against it. He urges her to repent and return with him to Monsalvat. In desperation the temptress calls on Klingsor, who materializes with the stolen Spear, which he now hurls at Parsifal. A miracle occurs: the Sacred Spear halts in mid-air. The "Guileless Fool" calmly reaches for it and with the weapon makes the sign of the Cross. At this, Klingsor is annihilated and the castle crumbles into ruin, while the garden turns into a withered wilderness. Before rushing off, Parsifal reminds Kundry: "You know where you shall find me. . . ."

ACT III

SCENE 1: A spring landscape on the slopes of Monsalvat. It is Good Friday. Some years have elapsed since the destruction of Klingsor's power. Parsifal has wandered far over the world before finding his way back to the Holy Brotherhood. Kundry has arrived there ahead of him, in beggar's garb, a sincere penitent. She is received by the now ancient Gurnemanz, who permits her to do servant work for the Knights. While they talk, a figure in black armor and carrying a mighty spear approaches.

Gurnemanz warns angrily that no one in warrior dress is allowed on this hallowed ground. But now his old eyes recognize Parsifal and the Sacred Spear. He helps Kundry take off the wanderer's armor. The woman fetches water to bathe his feet, then dries them with her hair. Deeply moved, Parsifal baptizes the pagan creature, while the Good Friday Spell weaves musically about them. Soon this blends with the familiar bells of Monsalvat, calling the faithful to worship. Gurnemanz now goes to fetch the coat of mail and mantle of a Grail Knight, with which he attires Parsifal, bidding him then to follow the path to the Temple.

SCENE 2: Again the great hall of worship is seen, this time in deeper gloom and without spread tables. The bells toll gravely as the procession of knights files in, decked with signs of mourning, for old Titurel has died and a special service is to be held over his body. Amfortas also is brought in on his litter, too ill to lift up the Grail in blessing of the living and the dead. Consternation grips the Brotherhood, just as Parsifal enters unperceived. Slowly he advances and with the Sacred Spear touches the still-gaping wound of Amfortas, which instantly heals. At the saving touch, the face of Amfortas lights up with rapture and his hands are lifted to welcome Parsifal as the community's new king. The Grail bearers now unveil the shrine, whereupon the holy vessel glows in mystic red brilliance. Titurel miraculously revives to be given extreme unction by Parsifal, who has taken the Grail in his hands and waves it to and fro. From the majestic dome a white dove descends slowly, hovering above the new king's throne in token of divine favor. A choir of boys' voices rings forth, proclaiming the consummation of Parsifal's mission and the lasting sanctity of the Grail.

In the first Bayreuth production of this religious allegory the leading roles were filled by singers already familiar with Wagnerian style. Amalia Materna was Kundry; Hermann Winckelman, Parsifal; Theodor Reichmann, Amfortas; Emil Scaria, Gurnemanz. But due to the opera's great length and the taxing nature of the music, relief voices were brought in to alternate throughout the season. Among these were Marianne Brandt, Therese Malten, Heinrich Gudehus, Wilhelm Jäger and Gustav Siehr. The practice was to become traditional, in years to come, wherever the opera found acceptance, just as Holy Week—and, if possible, Good Friday—would be given preference as a presentation date.

CHAPTER 10

A S THE curtain closed on the transporting climax of *Parsifal*, that midsummer night of 1882, a hushed audience sat motionless. No applause was heard, so overpowering had been the impact of the drama. This too would set a pattern at Bayreuth, where future audiences, held captive in an almost worshipful mood, would thenceforth file in silence from the theater.

A conspicuous example was set, unwittingly, on the *première* night by an unheralded visitor. He sat alone, far to one side of the auditorium, a little man with thick gray hair and sharply expressive features. At the opera's end he rose quickly and was seen bowing in the direction of Richard Wagner, before donning a slouch hat and losing himself in the crowd that began leaving the building.

"Who was that?" Richard asked, raising his binoculars.

Franz Liszt's keen eyes narrowed intently. "Giuseppe Verdi," he replied without hesitation. "I've read that he has been on tour."

Wagner jumped to his feet. "Verdi! Come. We must catch him!" He ran down the foyer, followed by Cosima. But, every few steps, they were halted by people who recognized Wagner and swamped him with demands for autographs. Seeing himself obstructed, he gave up in dejection. Cosima caught up with him at last. She steered him toward a side exit whence they managed to escape the mob.

Outside, Richard gave vent to his disappointment. "The one man I have wanted to know all these years, the single Italian whose work bears a relation to mine—we've let him slip into Bayreuth anonymously, without honor, without a fitting salute!"

"Don't worry, Richard," Cosima comforted him. "We start

for Italy next month. You can let Signor Verdi know. I'm sure a letter to his publishers will reach him."

"That's right!" As in youth, Richard's despair turned to exuberance. He kissed her, there in the street. "We must write him to meet us in Venice at the Teatro La Fenice, as our guest."

"To hear your C-Major Symphony, of course!"

Richard grew doubtful again. "Ah, there's the difficulty. Will he take offense at finding no work of his included in the program?"

"Venice is honoring *you*," Cosima pointed out firmly. "It's to be a jubilee, isn't it?"

He nodded. "Fifty years, since my first and only symphonic effort. I never managed another." He looked up a trifle sheepishly. "I didn't do so well, did I? Verdi will not be overwhelmed."

She took his arm. To her it would never matter what Giuseppe Verdi thought. They walked back toward the carriage stand, to rejoin Liszt and the children.

A few weeks later they were packed and ready for the Italian journey. It was early September and the La Fenice celebration had been set for the Christmas season. That left two months for rehearsals with the local orchestra, which had no experience in Wagnerian verve and style. The program had been expanded, meanwhile, to include not only the "Youth Symphony" but a symposium of the composer's operatic works.

Since the occasion could be combined with a family holiday, the children had been taken along. Living quarters were found along the Canale Grande, where Wagner had spent an earlier and most miserable Venetian sojourn. This time, instead of a shabby room, he was able to rent an entire three-storied villa, the Palazzo Vendramin, for his comfort and pleasure.

The weeks passed in a hubbub of sight-seeing, rehearsals and daily bouts with the Italian language. Not until the concert date was almost on them did Richard and Cosima realize that there had been no news of Verdi. Perhaps he would be at the theater, they told themselves. Signor Giuseppe most likely wished to surprise them.

The great evening arrived. The boat terrace of the Teatro

La Fenice was brightly lighted to receive the many guests who came by the water route. A variety of gondolas was to be seen, public and private, the former guided by picturesquely garbed *gondolieri* while the latter featured attendants in fine livery and gold braid. The audience inside the theater presented a corresponding mixture, from simple citizens in plain street clothes to titled *grandezza* wrapped in silk and galloon.

In the official box, usually reserved for visiting royalty, the Wagner family sat surrounded by Venice dignitaries. Applause greeted Richard's appearance, and he spent considerable time bowing his thanks to left and right. Before the house lights went down he whispered anxiously to his wife, "No sign of Verdi? No message from him at the box office?"

"Nothing. We must have had the wrong address, or else he is still abroad."

"Probably." Richard sighed his resignation. "In any case, it's much too late. I don't think we shall ever meet. Not in *this* life, anyway."

"Nonsense." Cosima touched his hand. "Ssh—they're beginning!"

The lights had been dimmed. Richard leaned closer to her ear and finished his thought. "Verdi is seventy, the same as I. And if we couldn't manage it in all those years . . ."

Cosima shrugged off that word *seventy* by holding up the printed program for him to see. He barely made out the text:

GALA PERFORMANCE IN HONOR OF
THE FIFTIETH ANNIVERSARY OF
RICHARD WAGNER'S
YOUTH SYMPHONY IN C MAJOR

A smile was on Cosima's face as her fingers moved across the page and came to rest under the word *youth*. He responded, also with a smile, then turned toward the stage. The music had begun.

While the concert progressed behind closed portals, the waves of sound issued through open skylights into the warmish Adriatic night. On the wide theater terrace a motley crowd of passers-by, beggars and boat attendants gathered to listen. Some lolled about under the shadowy portico. Others carried on a desultory conversation, while less musical elements huddled in the glow of a lantern to engage in a fast gambling session of *morra*.

Some distance apart a single gondola was moored to a bright post. A cloaked figure, gray-haired and in a slouch hat, sat in the cabin, while the boatman stood on shore and looked bored. The man in the gondola was Giuseppe Verdi, too discerningly honorable to push himself forward on this day that belonged to the genius of Bayreuth. In his breast pocket Verdi carried Wagner's letter. He had all but committed it to memory, assuring himself that his presence was truly desired by his German colleague. Yet at the last moment, on the very steps of the theater, Verdi's diffidence held him back.

Here would surely be the last chance for the two musical giants, each of whom was the cynosure and glory of his own country, to meet. Both were artists of the first magnitude; both, national heroes who had suffered in patriotic causes. Each spoke only a smattering of the other's language, but they were brothers under the skin. Yet the nimbus of greatness that surrounded their names contrived somehow to keep them apart. On visits to Germany the Italian idol repeatedly came within greeting distance of his reputed rival, while Richard, when at Milan or Bologna on concert tours, had reflected that he was in Verdi's country and a courtesy call on the great Giuseppe might be the perfect *beau geste*. But neither had ever got beyond such elevated contemplations, for, like two small boys, each dreaded meeting with rebuff.

On the day of the Youth Symphony performance Verdi had arrived early on the Rome Express. Long before dark he chartered a small gondola and began circling the Fenice Theater. The boatman, Angelo (his name was painted on the prow), showed signs of weariness by the time the music poured forth across the waters.

"What is it, Angelo?" the eccentric passenger asked. "You do not like the concert?"

"No one *sings* in there." Angelo jerked a contemptuous

thumb toward the vast building. "What is music, *signore,* when you do not have a song?"

"Ah, that is because they are playing a symphony concert tonight, not an opera."

Angelo was scornful. "*Calamittà!* I like it better with the big arias." He inhaled deeply and broke out with an ambitious bar from *Celeste Aïda.*

In the shadows Verdi bowed, secretly flattered. Then he waved a silencing hand. "Ssh—listen!"

From the direction of the theater a muffled echo of applause could be heard, followed by a pause. Angelo beamed hopefully. "They have finished?"

A burst of brasses poured forth in answer. Verdi leaned forward to listen, then nodded his head in recognition.

"The second part of the program has started," he explained to the listless boatman. "Now come portions of Signor Wagner's dramatic works." He waited, then cried out exultantly, "Ah—that is the 'Ride of the Valkyries!' "

"Holy Madonna—the *what?*" Angelo shook his head in awed puzzlement.

"Valkyries are goddesses on horseback, who carry fallen heroes off to a place called Valhalla." Verdi smiled futilely, aware that he wasn't making himself very clear. "I suppose . . er . . . one really must be German to understand that." He broke off.

Just then the gondolier gave a sign of sudden perception. "*D'avvero, signor,* that is true," he cried. "Clop, clop, clop— the horses, I hear them now!" In his excitement he beat time with his foot against the edge of the shaky craft, almost upsetting his passenger into the water.

"Whoa!" exclaimed Verdi. "You are not in the cavalry yourself, my friend."

All the while, from the theater, the Galloping theme of *Die Walküre* mounted to a thunderous crescendo that was followed by a storm of applause. A moment later the *Siegfried Idyl* began.

Verdi leaned back on the gondola's worn cushions. "What you hear now, Angelo," he continued elucidating, "are the sounds of the forest. Of course, perhaps you have never been in a forest."

"No." With a great splash the boatman pushed an oar into the water. The lagoons of Venice obviously were all he knew or cared about in nature.

"Listen! Those are the voices of birds, speaking to a young lad named Siegfried."

For a moment Angelo brightened. "Like the birds of Francesco d'Assisi?" He thought better of it and shook his head wisely. "Francesco, he was a saint. But the birds, they do not speak to one who is not a saint." He seemed to be searching his memory, without success. "In church I never hear of a Saint Sigfrido!"

Bored, his interest in the concert was fading. He continued dawdling with his oar, while Verdi fell silent. The sounds issuing from the theater wove ever-new patterns of magic, ending at last in a vivid climax. In the mingling of human outcries and enthusiastic hand clapping that followed, it was difficult to discern when the music actually came to a stop.

Now the heavy portals were thrown open and the audience poured into the starry night. As the crowd scrambled for the waiting gondolas a cordon of theater attendants cleared a narrow avenue for the Wagner family and accompanying dignitaries to pass through to the official barge. At this point Verdi, rising in his gondola, set one foot ashore. His eyes lighted up as they fixed on a proudly erect, gray-haired, frock-coated man followed by a lady in stiff silks and three half-grown children. From Verdi's throat issued a cry, "Riccardo Wagner! *Bravo, bravissimo!*"

Angelo stared at his fare in surprise. "The *signori* know each other?"

"No. But I must reach him and shake his hand." Resolutely Verdi leaped ashore and ran up the stone steps. He headed for the opposite end of the piazza, where the Wagner party was just entering the official barge manned by a stalwart crew of eight. The passage through the crowd had closed again as people scrambled for their own boats. Verdi's impulse had come too late. He rushed back to his gondola, urging Angelo to make haste.

"An extra piece of silver for you if you catch up with them—in the red-and-gold barge up there, with the flag of the city's *comendadore!*"

Angelo pocketed the coin. *"Ecco, ecco."* He slipped the little gondola from its moorings and pushed it deftly through the maze of water traffic. With quick strokes he steered his craft in the choppy wake of other oarsmen, heading toward the main stream. The flag of the *comendadore* fluttered far ahead. It was growing smaller.

"They cannot be going very far." Verdi dug up more cash and handed it to Angelo. "They must be headed for one of the hotels or perhaps the Governor's Palace."

"Look, *signor,* the Rialto."

"Ah!" Verdi brightened. "That is where they will disembark and cross the bridge on foot. Hurry. Pull up alongside!"

He was mistaken, however, for the official gondola sped on without halting. What the pursuers could not know was that Wagner, elated by the evening's eulogies and the beauty of the mellow starlit night, had asked to be taken on a cruise of the Lagoon City. It had been many years since his last visit here. Also, Cosima and the children were pleading to be shown the sights. Thus the eight oarsmen set to with vigorous strokes, turning off just beyond the Rialto Bridge and leaving the Canalazzo to enter the network of tributary waterways that interlaced the exotic town.

Far in the rear Verdi and his boatman were confounded. Angelo was the first to grasp the situation. "They are making the *viaggio intero,* the whole circuit for sight-seeing, like all the *turisti,*" he pointed out. His tone implied that he would not be able to continue the now expanded chase without additional recompense.

Verdi agreed, but he was running out of change. While he extracted his billfold from an inner pocket his eyes observed Angelo resting on the oars, letting the small gondola's pace slacken to a mere crawl. A substantial persuader changed hands. With an ostentatious mopping of brow Angelo put away the folding money and displayed a new spurt of energy.

The chase continued, moving from the main stream into narrower byways where traffic became congested and the race assumed an almost grotesque character. For a time the Verdi craft, being more maneuverable, gained several lengths. Up ahead the blond Siegfried Wagner, a tall lad of thirteen, could be seen towing paper serpentines over the water. A long-buried sorrow cut deep into Giuseppe Verdi's heart.

"I too had children," he mused aloud, though this information could not be of the slightest concern to the mercenary (and unmarried) Angelo. "They were taken from me, with their mother, by a plague." He broke off, aware that it was time to dredge up more cash, for the little gondola was again falling behind. Angelo's delaying tactics were blackmail, of course, and the rascally fellow knew it, but his keyed-up passenger had no choice.

Up ahead the Wagner party, unaware that its sleek luxury craft was engaged in a race, now struck an open stretch and gained an impressive lead. Soon identification became doubtful and finally impossible. Hopelessly the frantic Verdi urged his boatman on, going through coat, vest and trousers for a last remnant of currency. It was no use. One more time the cunning Angelo fell to dawdling, but he had tried the trick just once too often.

"I am sorry, my friend," said Verdi, spreading empty hands. "I have run out of bribes."

CHAPTER 11

IT WAS past midnight when Richard Wagner's nocturnal boat tour of Venice ended. The official gondola deposited its happy guests at the mooring loggia of the Palazzo Vendramin, then headed back to the center of town.

In the foyer of the Palazzo the children dropped their wraps, kissed their parents and ran upstairs, while Richard stopped to check his watch against a mantel clock which struck 1:00 A.M. From the first stair landing the boy Siegfried called down, "It's thirteen steps up to here, Papa, and another thirteen to the next landing."

"It's long past bedtime, young man." Richard cut short that bit of procrastination. "Save your statistics for another day."

As the children disappeared along an upper corridor Wagner smiled at Cosima and put an arm around her shoulders. Slowly they too started upstairs. On the first landing Cosima now halted. She knew what Siegfried had meant.

"The number thirteen has had a curious and recurring significance in your life. Your name has thirteen letters. You were born in 1813, one plus eight plus one plus three. You entered Leipzig Conservatory in 1831, the digits making the same total. And you've written thirteen operas. Surely it's your lucky number!"

"Lucky? That *Tannhäuser* scandal happened on a March thirteenth."

"But August thirteenth makes up for it. Your Bayreuth opening date for the first cycle of *The Ring* . . . remember?"

Yes, he remembered. Cosima caught the faraway look in his eyes before she turned down the gas lantern on the newel post and followed him the rest of the way up.

Her mention of Bayreuth kept him awake a long time. How

447

could he forget? More than an international music center and
a symbol of success, Bayreuth had become for Richard Wagner
a personal justification, a monument to his unswerving faith in
himself. Cosima's obsession with calendar dates amused him,
to be sure. He could not realize, lying there in the dark, that
one more thirteenth day would punctuate the score—the date
of his own dying.

It came that same week, in December of 1883, as Wagner
sat near an open balcony and gazed out at the brilliant Italian
afternoon sky. The sun was pouring in oblique rays over a small
flower market near the Palazzo Vendramin. A well-dressed
man accompanied by a young and extremely pretty woman
stopped at one of the stands to select a few blooms. Wagner
could not distinguish their faces nor could he guess that he
was the subject of their conversation, for the strangers were
Monsieur and Madame Catulle Mendès from Paris, in Italy on
holiday. Madame Mendès, Judith Gautier before her marriage,
was the daughter of the novelist Théophile Gautier and, like
her father, a Wagner worshiper.

While her husband paid for the flowers, Judith took an en-
graved card from her purse and wrote a few words on it. Monsieur Mendès studied the greeting critically, then added his
name as well. He turned to the flower vendor, a gay, fat peasant woman.

"You are to send this bouquet to Signor Wagner at—" he
paused to verify the address in an article on the music page of
a newspaper—"the Palazzo Vendramin, on the Canale Grande."

At this moment Judith was seized with a sudden impulse.
She reached for the flowers. "Oh, let's take them there ourselves!"

Her husband stared gravely through his pince-nez. "You're
serious, my dear?"

"Of course I am." She clung to his arm. "I do so want to see
that man of miracles and tell him what his music means to me.
I want to look into his face and touch his hand."

Mendès shook his head toward the flower vendor. "My wife
is in love with a seventy-year-old musician, and I have to buy
him posies. What do you think of that?"

"*Per Bacco, signor!* Love is like the good Calabrian wine."
The peasant woman made a slurping sound. "It improves with
age, eh?" She laughed joyfully, uproariously.

Not quite so happy, Mendès separated Judith from the bouquet and led her quickly away. As they rounded the next corner the gurgling guffaws of the flower vendor could still be
heard, relishing her own salty retort.

A short while later Cosima held the greeting card in hand.
She had just arranged the Mendès blooms in a vase at Richard's
elbow, and she now allowed her thoughts to dwell on the
senders. She knew Judith Gautier, for the young woman appeared to follow Wagner's trail wherever he went; Cosima had
observed her in Bayreuth, at the *première* of *Parsifal* and here
in Venice at the Jubilee concert. It was becoming obvious,
thought the alert wife, that Madame Mendès was infatuated
with the aging master, as once the adolescent Cosima had been.
Moreover, unlike the latter, Judith was attractive and full of
Gallic sparkle. Judith's father had launched the maxim *l'art
pour l'art* ("art for art's sake"), and her husband Catulle ranked
high among nineteenth-century French intellectuals; hence she
came naturally by a heritage of *esprit*. For Wagner, in any
case, as for the old Goethe, it was a benison to be thus warmed
again—even if only metaphorically—by the fresh fires of youth.

Cosima understood this. But she did not have to *like* it.
Turning from the flowers to Richard, she pulled the wool cover-
let up higher across his knees. Despite the in-pouring rays of
the sun, he appeared drawn and ailing.

She handed him the card, unable to resist a comment. "That
Madame Mendès, she is ridiculously young, isn't she?"

"Nineteen." He glanced at the writing, then smiled. "You
were younger than that when we first met. Remember?"

The expression on Cosima's face indicated that this was not
all she remembered. She appeared to be speculating on the
possibility of the adoring Judith coming to call in the completely proper company of Monsieur Mendès, just as Cosima
had done with Bülow at Zürich, much to the mortification of
poor Minna.

There was in this a lesson for the possessive "high priestess" and one that Cosima's quick mind learned without flinching. She could do nothing to drown out this evening glow. Richard did not belong to her, despite her delusion that she, Cosima, had won him from all others. He belonged to no one, only to the ages.

Richard was imperturbably calm to the struggle fought out in Cosima's heart. The past did not matter very much any more. It seemed to grow blurred as he mused aloud in broken snatches of thought: "Judith's father, yes, Théophile. I saw him at Meyerbeer's apartment in Paris—or was it at Princess Metternich's?" His head shook softly. "That is a long way back."

Cosima heard the words, but she had no key to his ultimate thoughts. This only did she know: for him the realm of emotion had always been unequivocal and supreme, not to be clouded by restraints or inhibitions. He had given rhapsodic voice to this belief in the closing lines from Brünnhilde's Immolation scene, in the last act of *Götterdämmerung*:

> *Nicht Gut, nicht Gold*
> *noch göttliche Pracht,*
> *noch herrischer Prunk;*
> *nicht trüber Verträge*
> *trügender Bund*
> *noch heuchelnder Sitte*
> *hartes Gesetz—*
> *selig in Lust und Leid*
> *lasset die Liebe nur sein!"*

> (Not goods nor gold,
> nor show of godliness;
> not house nor manor,
> nor haughty display;
> not traitorous pledge
> to doubtful pacts,
> nor cruel decrees
> by custom staled—
> no, not these. . . .
> In joy and sorrow
> be ruled only by love!)

And so he was ruled.

To understand him, more was required than critical acumen or intellectual affinity—more, even, than a sensitive ear for music. The heart speaks only to the heart.

As he sat near the balcony of his Venetian palazzo the limpid sunlight poured across the waters, and on its glittering rays danced a prism of images out of his past creations: the classic-ballet scene from *Rienzi;* the homesick sailors from *The Flying Dutchman,* joining in their chant; the Dove's Descent from Monsalvat, in *Lohengrin;* the Venus Grotto Bacchanal, in *Tann-häuser;* the Love Tryst of *Tristan und Isolde;* the balladeer contest in *Meistersinger;* the vast symphonic panorama of *The Ring;* and the final exaltation of the Good Friday Spell, in *Parsifal.* . . .

Somewhere in this apotheosis of creation the finger of death descended softly, like Lohengrin's Dove, and touched the Promethean heart. Aloft thundered the steeds of the Valkyries, galloping toward Valhalla. This time that thunder rang for his ears alone as, on the wave of grandeur that is his music, Richard Wagner was carried off.

And there, in its grandeur, he lingers still.

Cosima looked at the calendar on the table. The date was December 13, 1883. She turned her back on the balcony and the overpowering radiance of the Venetian sunset.